D1583350

ENGINEERING FUNDAMENTALS FOR
PROFESSIONAL ENGINEERS' EXAMINATIONS

Engineering Fundamentals for Professional Engineers' Examinations

LLOYD M. POLENTZ, P. E.

Consulting Engineer
Instructor, Engineering Fundamentals
University of California Extension Division

McGRAW-HILL BOOK COMPANY, INC.

New York   Toronto   London

1961

ENGINEERING FUNDAMENTALS FOR
PROFESSIONAL ENGINEERS' EXAMINATIONS

Copyright © 1961 and 1960 by Lloyd M. Polentz. Printed in the United States of America. All rights reserved. This book, or parts thereof, may not be reproduced in any form without permission of the publishers. *Library of Congress Catalog Card Number:* 60-15863

VIII

50376

THE MAPLE PRESS COMPANY, YORK, PA.

To my parents

Gustav E. Polentz
Ethel M. Polentz

Preface

This book is the outgrowth of some ten years of teaching a course in engineering fundamentals for the Engineering Extension Division of the University of California. The purpose of the course was to aid practicing engineers review their engineering. The majority of these engineers were reviewing in preparation for taking the fundamentals portion of the professional engineering examination. A surprisingly large percentage, however, were reviewing, not for the specific purpose of taking an examination, but to gain a better grasp of the engineering fundamentals to aid them in their professional activities as practicing engineers. Fortunately, both these goals can be achieved in the same fashion, because there is no better guide to a review of engineering fundamentals than the material covered in the fundamentals portion of the professional engineering examinations as offered by the different states and territories.

Over the past few years, through cooperation between the states and the activities of the National Council of State Boards of Engineering Examiners, the fundamentals portions of the different state examinations have become remarkably similar in character. Indeed, similar problems are frequently encountered in different examinations, and occasionally the same problem will appear in two or more different examinations. The emphasis in all examinations has been on the application of the fundamental engineering principles, and this application has been stressed throughout the writing of this book. Memorization of formulas has served to get many a college student through a given course with a passing grade. Such a procedure is not practicable, however, for a comprehensive type of examination such as an engineer-in-training examination or the fundamentals portion of a professional engineering examination.

This is also true in the solution of problems which confront an engineer in the practice of his profession. There are too many different cases and too many different types of problems to permit memorization of a formula for each case. It is actually easier, and certainly much more satisfactory, to learn how to apply the fundamental principles of engineering and from them develop a formula to fit the case at hand.

In working with engineers, helping them review their engineering fundamentals throughout the past decade, the author has found the most effective method of teaching to consist essentially of three steps:

1. Explain the engineering principle.

2. Illustrate the application of this principle by means of an appropriate problem or problems.

3. Supply problems for individual practice and review.

This three-step sequence—explain, illustrate, practice—is the pattern followed in this book. The principles are first discussed, then illustrated through the solution of sample problems selected from past examinations. A group of sample problems is given at the end of each chapter for the reader to solve for practice.

These sample problems have all been selected from past examinations as given by the various states and territories. Except for minor editing, they have been copied as given, and some of them, like some of the problems used for illustration, contain errors such as incomplete or incorrect data. An attempt has been made here to give a good cross section of the type and complexity of the problems the examinee may expect to be confronted with. In addition, the number of the problems collected at the ends of the chapters is an indication of the frequency with which problems in that category appear in individual examinations. That is, if there are 100 sample problems at the end of one subject chapter and only 50 sample problems at the end of another subject chapter, the examinee may expect roughly twice as many problems in the first subject. This is a general observation, however, and indicates an average, which may not always be faithfully reflected in individual examinations. In the case of apparent errors in problems, the author suggests that the examinee ask for clarification. If none is forthcoming, the suggestion is to treat the problem as examples have been treated in the text, carefully explaining every step and every assumption.

The fundamentals portions of the professional engineering examinations include problems falling in the main into the eight engineering categories covered in the chapters of this book. Some of the different states also include a few miscellaneous problems largely concerning the general subject of physics. This is such a broad subject and such a small over-all percentage of problems falls into this category that no separate chapter has been included covering it. Principles of physics have, however, been covered as they apply to the different subjects discussed. For instance, Chap. 2, Mechanics, covers a goodly amount of physics, and Chap. 3, Fluid Mechanics, also covers many of the elementary physical principles as applied to fluids. Chapter 4, Thermodynamics, and Chap. 6, Electricity and Electronics, also include discussions of the fundamental physical relationships of these subjects. Study of these portions of the different chapters will adequately prepare the examinee for the majority of questions he may expect on general physics.

Fundamentals examinations are given both open book and closed book. Contact your own state board to determine which policy is followed in your state. The degree of difficulty of the problems given seems to be the same regardless of whether references are permitted or not. It would also be a good idea to ask your state board if they would supply you with a sample copy of a recent past examination so that you might familiarize yourself with the type of problems used by your particular state. Some states make past examination copies available in public libraries, and some supply copies of "sample questions" which may or may not bear a close resemblance to actual examination problems. The author's experience has been that few state boards make available copies of past examinations for study. For this reason numerous problems selected from past examinations have been included at the end of each chapter. Answers to these problems are given in the back of the book. The answers have been obtained with a slide rule except where greater accuracy was specified in the problem. In these few cases seven-place log tables ("Baron Von Vega's Logarithmic

Tables," D. Van Nostrand Company, Inc.) were used.   A word of caution is in order here.   Even though great care was exercised in the working of these problems, it is probable that a few errors have crept in.   The important thing to consider in working these problems is not just to obtain the correct answer but to understand how to arrive at it.   Method is probably of more importance in most state examinations than numerical answers alone.   Learn how to work the problems, not just how to get the answers.

This brings us to a discussion of how one should complete an examination most effectively.   There are always two persons to consider in any examination—yourself and the reader.   Every effort should be made to utilize your own abilities as effectively as possible; it is almost as important to keep in mind that the demands upon the reader should be kept to a minimum.   After all, it is not how well you think you know the subject that counts but how well you can apply your knowledge, and this must be determined by the reader.   At best, the reader's job is a difficult one; if you keep his difficulties in mind as you do your examination you will write a better paper.   This is particularly true when you make an assumption.   Write down your assumption and give your reasons for it. Explanations will not hurt you and they may quite possibly help, by clarifying your reasoning in your own mind and in the reader's.

The first thing to do when you sit for an examination is to read the instructions *carefully*.   When you have these in mind, read through the examination problems, checking those you are sure you can do as you go through.   Then go back and do these easiest ones first.   Then do the more difficult ones and those you think you can do.   Then check your work and spend the rest of the time on the really difficult problems—the ones you are doubtful about being able to do.   Doing the easy ones first is important.   Too many people have fallen into the trap of becoming intrigued with a very difficult (for them) problem and have spent the major part of an examination period trying to solve it because of the challenge it presented.   You can easily flunk an examination in this way.

When you work a problem, the author recommends drawing a figure whenever possible and labeling this figure completely.   This will be of considerable help in solving the problem.   The figure should be drawn to scale and constructed neatly.   It will then provide a rough graphical check of your solution.   You should take scale, straight edge, compass, and protractor to the examination for this purpose.   When you write your solution it should be put in a logical sequence of steps, with all steps written down.   This will make it easy for you to check and easy for the reader to follow. Few things are quite so disconcerting to a reader (or to an engineer trying to explain his solution to a colleague some months later) as trying to guess at the mental gymnastics involved in bridging a large gap in the calculational sequence.

This book has been written to help engineers review subjects with which they are already reasonably familiar.   It has not been written to serve as an introduction.   If you find that it goes too rapidly or if you are very rusty, it is recommended that you avail yourself of a text devoted exclusively to the subject causing you difficulty.   In most cases your college texts will be adequate as references.   If such are not available or if you find them inadequate, at the end of each chapter there is a list of texts with which the author is familiar and which he recommends for further study.   These lists do not contain all the available texts nor do they even, necessarily, contain the best texts on the particular subject.   They merely list texts that the author has found useful and understandable.

The emphasis in this book is on technical material and on the coverage of the fundamentals portions of the various state examinations.   No information has been included on registration procedures or requirements.   This type of information has been well covered in the following books: La Londe, William S.: "Professional Engineer's Examination Questions and Answers," McGraw-Hill Book Company, Inc., New York, 1956; Constance, John: "How to Become a Professional Engineer," McGraw-Hill Book Company, Inc., New York, 1958.   The reader who is interested in becoming a registered professional engineer is advised to write to the board in charge of registration in the state or territory in which he wishes to become registered.   He is further advised to contact the board as far in advance of the time he wishes to become registered as possible, because it sometimes takes an appreciable length of time to satisfy all the necessary requirements.   The state board of registration is the only official source and the only completely reliable source of information regarding registration.   Contact it early.

There are, of course, many people who have been helpful in the preparation of this book.   In particular, thanks are due to J. C. Dillon of the University of California, without whose confidence and cooperation it could not have been written, and to my wife Rose, without whose assistance such a task would have been impossible. Thanks are also due the many engineers who have offered suggestions and criticisms, especially those groups who wrote letters containing comments and recommendations concerning the course content and method of presentation.   Grateful acknowledgment is given to the many boards of registration for professional engineers in the different states and territories who were kind enough to send copies of their past examinations and sample questions indicating the coverage of their examinations.

Lloyd M. Polentz

Contents

Mathematics

Introduction. One of the most difficult and certainly one of the most important factors in any review of mathematics is the "bounding" of the material to be covered. Engineers interested in such a review unfortunately have a great diversity of backgrounds. Some have used little or no mathematics since graduation from college; others have made more or less continual use of one branch or another of mathematics. The term "review of mathematics" can then be inferred by some to mean a review of algebra, trigonometry, etc., stopping just short of the calculus, and the inference by others may be that of a review starting with the elementary calculus and progressing from there. As you can see, "bounding" the subject matter to be reviewed is a considerable problem. As a guide to the material to be covered a study was made of fundamentals examinations given during the past 5 years. These examinations included problems in mathematics alone and problems in engineering subjects which required mathematics for their solution. Study of these various examinations indicated that the examinee can expect problems requiring a knowledge of algebra with particular emphasis on exponents and logarithms, trigonometry, perhaps some analytic geometry, differential calculus, and a small amount of integral calculus.

Because of the varied mathematics backgrounds of the engineers who may be interested in this review, it will start with a discussion of algebra and then take up each of the other subjects in turn.

1-1. Algebra. The basic algebra requirement includes factoring and solution of quadratic equations. All engineers will recall the second-order-binomial expansion—$(a \pm b)^2 = a^2 \pm 2ab + b^2$—and the other common special product—$(a + b)(a - b) = a^2 - b^2$.

The engineer should be able to recognize these from either end, i.e., he should be able to perform the multiplication or the factoring without difficulty. It is more difficult to recognize the higher-order polynomials, and if one is not factoring them or using them with fair regularity it is senseless to try to commit to memory a great number of them just to pass an examination. Factoring can be accomplished almost as quickly by trial division, and long division of polynomials is a process with which any engineer should be familiar.

1-2. Factoring. As an example of this process, suppose it is required to factor the polynomial $x^4 - 6x^3y + x^2y^2 + 24xy^3 - 20y^4$. If there is a linear factor it will be of the form $x \pm ny$, where n must be a factor of 20. Since the sign of the last term is minus, there must be both a minus n term and a plus n term, if the polynomial is factorable. As a first trial let us see if the polynomial is divisible by $x + y$.

If it is divisible by $x + y$, then $x = -y$ would be a solution to the equation resulting from setting the polynomial equal to zero. If $x + y$ is a factor, then substituting $-y$ for x in the polynomial would give zero for the value of the polynomial. Performing this substitution gives us

$$y^4 + 6y^4 + y^4 - 24y^4 - 20y^4 = -36y^4$$

which does not equal zero.

Next let us try $x - y$ as a factor. If $x = y$, the polynomial would equal $y^4 - 6y^4 + y^4 + 24y^4 - 20y^4$, which does equal zero, so $x - y$ is a factor.

The next step is to divide the polynomial by $x - y$.

$$
\begin{array}{r}
x^3 - 5x^2y - 4xy^2 + 20y^3 \\
x - y\overline{\smash{)}\,x^4 - 6x^3y + x^2y^2 + 24xy^3 - 20y^4} \\
\underline{x^4 - x^3y} \\
-5x^3y + x^2y^2 \\
\underline{-5x^3y + 5x^2y^2} \\
-4x^2y^2 + 24xy^3 \\
\underline{-4x^2y^2 + 4xy^3} \\
20xy^3 - 20y^4 \\
\underline{20xy^3 - 20y^4}
\end{array}
$$

The procedure is as follows: The x^4 term can be divided by the x of the $x - y$ term and gives a quotient of x^3. The divisor is then multiplied by x^3 and the resulting product $x^4 - x^3y$ is then subtracted from the dividend and the next term in descending power sequence is brought down. If there is no such term a zero is brought down in its place. This gives the subpolynomial $(-5x^3y + x^2y^2)$. The first term $-5x^3y$ is divided by the first term of the divisor, the quotient $-5x^2y$ is placed on top, and the process is repeated. When the process has been completed we find a remainder of zero, so $x - y$ is a factor (which we already know). The quotient is found to be $x^3 - 5x^2y - 4xy^2 + 20y^3$. If new trials are made with the resulting polynomial factor (the quotient), it will be found that $x + 2y$ is a factor and the quotient remaining is $x^2 - 7xy + 10y^2$. This can be factored in the same manner as before or it can be factored by observation, giving as a final result

$$x^4 - 6x^3y + x^2y^2 + 24xy^3 - 20y^4$$
$$= (x - y)(x + 2y)(x - 2y)(x - 5y)$$

The trials which have been indicated but not performed are left as exercises for the reader.

A past examination problem asked:

- If 4 is a root of the equation $x^3 - 5x^2 - 2x + 24 = 0$, find the remaining roots.

If 4 is a root of the equation, then $x - 4$ will be a factor of the polynomial. We can find the other factor by long division.

$$
\begin{array}{r}
x^2 - x - 6 \\
x - 4\overline{)x^3 - 5x^2 - 2x + 24} \\
\underline{x^3 - 4x^2} \\
-x^2 - 2x \\
\underline{-x^2 - 4x} \\
-6x + 24 \\
\underline{-6x + 24}
\end{array}
$$

The quotient $x^2 - x - 6$ can be further factored by inspection into $(x - 3)(x + 2)$. We then have that
$$(x - 4)(x - 3)(x + 2) = 0$$
and the roots are 4, 3, and -2

1-3. Quadratic Equations.   Quadratic equations can frequently be solved by factoring.   However, only the general form of the quadratic equation will be discussed here and the solution derived. This general solution can then be used for all special cases as well. The general form of the quadratic equation may be written as $ax^2 + bx + c = 0$, where a, b, and c are constants.   A solution to this equation may be obtained by completing the square.   The procedure is as follows:

Transfer the constant term c to the right-hand side of the equation and divide through by the constant of the x^2 term, a.   This gives $x^2 + (b/a)x = -c/a$.   The left side of this equation can be made a perfect square by adding to it a constant equal to the square of one-half the constant part of the x term, which amount would equal $(\tfrac{1}{2}b/a)^2$.   This gives the equation

$$x^2 + \frac{b}{a}x + \frac{b^2}{4a^2} = -\frac{c}{a} + \frac{b^2}{4a^2}$$

The left side is now a perfect square, and if we combine the terms on the right-hand side of the equation and take the square roots of both sides, the result is $x + (b/2a) = \pm \sqrt{b^2 - 4ac}/2a$; it should be remembered that a square root may be either positive or negative. Transferring the constant on the left side to the right side gives the familiar general solution to a quadratic equation

$$x = \frac{-b \pm \sqrt{b^2 - 4ac}}{2a}$$

The reader is urged to run through the algebraic manipulations required for this derivation a few times by himself for the practice they will give in reviewing some of the fundamentals of algebra and also to familiarize himself with the derivation so that when he needs to solve a quadratic equation there will be no doubt in his mind as to the correct form, or if there should be a doubt, he will be able quickly to dispel it by deriving the necessary relationship.

As an example to illustrate the use of this equation, assume that a problem reduces to the relationship $17x^2 + 41x - 74 = 19$.   This becomes

$$17x^2 + 41x - 93 = 0$$

where $a = 17$
$\quad\quad b = 41$
$\quad\quad c = -93$

Then $\quad\quad x = \dfrac{-41 \pm \sqrt{41^2 - 4 \times 17 \times (-93)}}{2 \times 17}$

$\quad\quad\quad\quad\quad = -1.21 \pm 2.63$

$\quad\quad\quad\quad\quad = -3.84 \quad$ or $\quad 1.42$

Note that both roots found in this case are real, but if the term $b^2 - 4ac$ is less than zero both roots will be imaginary.

1-4. Logarithms and Exponents. A review of the principles of exponents and logarithms is important to any engineer interested in taking a "fundamentals" examination, and the author has found that many practicing engineers have only a vague knowledge of this subject. The rules of exponents are few and not at all complicated. When these rules are applied to the study of logarithms, however, considerable difficulty often ensues.

The fundamental principles are that multiplication is performed by adding exponents, division by subtracting exponents, and raising to powers and extraction of roots are achieved by multiplying exponents.

$$x^a \cdot x^b = x^{(a+b)} \quad\quad (x^a)^2 = x^{2a}$$
$$x^a \div x^b = x^{(a-b)} \quad\quad (x^a)^{1/5} = x^{a/5}$$

These principles are readily applied to logarithms and form the basis of the theory of logarithms, with the x's used in the examples being replaced by the base of the logarithmic system used.

There are two systems of logarithms in use: the common, or Briggsian, logarithms, which have the base 10, and the natural, or Naperian, logarithms, which have the base e. The same principles of operation apply to both systems, since both are merely applications of the theory of exponents. A logarithm to the base 10 will be abbreviated "log," and a natural logarithm will be abbreviated "ln" throughout this work. We have then, by definition, that if $a = \log B$, $10^a = B$; and if $m = \ln P$, $e^m = P$. Expanding a little further, the problem $[(A \cdot B)/C)]^m$ can be rewritten, using logs and letting the answer be represented by W,

$$\log W = (\log A + \log B - \log C)m$$

or $10^w = (10^a \cdot 10^b \div 10^c)^m = 10^{(a+b-c)m}$, giving $w = (a + b - c)m$, where $10^w = W$, $10^a = A$, etc., or $w = \log W$, $a = \log A$, $b = \log B$, etc.

A few examples may help here.

- In a past examination it was necessary to find the value of x from the relationship $x = \ln e + 2 \log 100 + 1/\ln e^2$.

The logarithm of any number is the power to which the base must be raised to equal that number. This being the case, $\ln e = 1$, since $e^1 = e$. Similarly $\ln e^2 = 2$, since $e^2 = e^2$. The

$$\log 100 = \log 10^2 = 2$$

since $10^2 = 100$. We then find that $x = 1 + 2 \times 2 + \frac{1}{2} = 5\frac{1}{2}$. Another example taken from a past examination is:

- *Given:* $R = re^{\tan\alpha}$
  Find: $\tan \alpha$.

If the ln's of both sides are taken, $\ln R = \ln r + \ln (e^{\tan\alpha})$; but $\ln e^{\tan\alpha} = \tan \alpha$, so $\tan \alpha = \ln R - \ln r$, or $\tan \alpha = \ln (R/r)$.

Another problem asked:

- What is the logarithm of 243 to the base 3? What is the number whose logarithm is 5 to the base 1?

For the first part, we have $\log_3 243 = A$; then $3^A = 243$, and $A \log 3 = \log 243$, giving $A = \log 243/\log 3 = 2.386/0.477 = 5$, or $3^5 = 243$, and the answer is 5. For the second part, $\log_1 B = 5$, $B = 1^5$, $B = 1$.

If you have difficulty remembering the correct sequence you can always use the relationship $\log_{10} 100 = 2$ and $10^2 = 100$ to check.

Another problem asked:

- Find M if $\log_5 M = \log_{25} 4$

Restating, we have $\log M$ to the base 5 $= \log 4$ to the base 25. Let $\log_5 M = A$; then, by definition, $5^A = M$; $\log_{25} 4 = A$, and, by definition, $25^A = 4$. Taking the logs of this last relationship, we get $A \log 25 = \log 4$, or $A = \log 4/\log 25 = 0.602/1.398 = 0.431$. Then, from the other relationships, $M = 5^A = 5^{0.431} = 2$, which is the required answer. Or, since $25^A = 4$,

$$(5^2)^A = 5^{2A} = (5^A)^2 = 4 = 2^2$$

giving $5^A = 2$. Since $5^A = M$, $M = 2$.

The use of logarithms to raise numbers, particularly numbers less than 1, to powers is one facet of logarithmic manipulation which frequently causes considerable difficulty. If the procedure is broken down into the basic steps, however, it becomes quite simple and the problems are easily handled. First, let us review a few more of the fundamentals of common logarithms. A log consists of two parts, the whole number, or characteristic, and the mantissa, or decimal part. As an example, the log of $2{,}310 = 3.3636$, and the log of $0.00231 = \bar{3}.3636$, or $7.3636 - 10$, or -2.6364. The first example, $\log 2{,}310 = 3.3636$, has a characteristic of 3 and a mantissa of 0.3636. This follows directly from the reasoning that $2{,}310 = 2.310 \times 10^3$ and

$$\log (2.310 \times 10^3) = \log 2.310 + \log 10^3 = 0.3636 + 3 = 3.3636$$

The rule for obtaining the characteristic of a number greater than 1 can be stated, "The characteristic of the common log equals the number of integral figures in the number minus 1," which is a description of the method of obtaining results in the system utilized in the above example. In other words, the actual procedure is to divide the number into two factors, one containing a single integer to the left of the decimal point and the other composed of 10 to the necessary power, as in the example, $2{,}310 = 2.310 \times 10^3$. The characteristic is then the power of 10 required, and the mantissa is the power to which 10 must be raised to equal the number remaining. The log of the number is the sum of these two powers of 10.

For a number less than 1 the same reasoning applies. For this case the memorized, or rote, rule may be stated as, "For numbers less than 1, the characteristic equals 9 minus the number of zeros between the decimal point and the first significant figure, minus 10 (the 10 being written after the mantissa)." The occasional user of logs will save himself much worry and many mistakes if he will actually determine the value of the log by the application of the fundamentals instead of by rote using memorized rules. This may be demonstrated by means of the example given above. $0.00231 = 2.31 \times 10^{-3}$, or

$$\log (0.00231) = \log (2.31 \times 10^{-3}) = \log 2.31 - 3 = -2.6364$$

which means that $10^{-2.6364} = 0.00231$. Another way of demonstrating this is $0.00231 = 1/432.9$ and

$$\log \frac{1}{432.9} = \log 1 - \log 432.9 = 0 - 2.6364 = -2.6364$$

Other ways of writing this are $\bar{3}.3636$, which means $0.3636 - 3$, or $7.3636 - 10$. Either method will reduce to the log as found above: -2.6364.

Examples from past examinations show the usefulness of these fundamental principles:

• In $x^{0.55} = 0.8/0.23y$ find x for $y = 9$. Use no tables, only a slide rule.

$$x^{0.55} = 0.386 \qquad x = 0.386^{1/0.55} = 0.386^{1.82} = \left(\frac{3.86}{10}\right)^{1.82}$$

which can be solved by logs using an ordinary slide rule.

$$\log \left(\frac{3.86}{10}\right)^{1.82} = (\log 3.86)1.82 - (\log 10)1.82$$

$$= (0.586 \times 1.82) - 1.82 = -0.754$$

$$-0.754 = 0 - 0.754 = \log 1 - \log 5.68 = \log \frac{1}{5.68} = \log 0.176$$

Then $x = 0.176$.

The problem can, of course, be solved more quickly by means of the log-log scales of a slide rule, but log-log scales are not necessary and if a person has not already developed an aptitude for using them there is no reason to do so for a single examination. An additional word might be appropriate, however, about the use of log-log scales. Some slide rules do not carry the log-log scales below 1 and even if a rule has log-log scales for numbers less than 1 they are frequently confusing to the occasional user. Unless a person has had considerable practice using the scales for numbers less than 1 it is probably better not to use them at all, since the same results can be obtained by forming fractions. For example:

$$0.784^{0.382} = \left(\frac{1}{1.275}\right)^{0.382}$$
$$= \frac{1}{1.097}$$
$$= 0.912$$

Another example may help to illustrate further the above discussion.

• Find x from $x^{1.21} = 5y^{4.15}$ when $y = 9$.

$$\log 9 = 0.954 \qquad \log y^{4.15} = 3.96$$
$$3.96 = \log 10^3 + \log 9.12 = \log 9,120$$
$$x = (5 \times 9,120)^{1/1.121} = 45,600^{0.826}$$
$$\log x = (4 + 0.659) \times 0.826 = 3.85 = \log 7,080$$
$$x = 7,080$$

One other facet of the subject of logarithms which should be discussed here is the method of obtaining the logarithm of a number which is close to 1.

The series for calculating the natural logarithm of a number close to 1 is $\ln(1 + x) = x - (x^2/2) + (x^3/3) - (x^4/4) + \cdots$. When x is very small the natural logarithm of $1 + x$ (or $1 - x$) is very nearly equal to x. This can also be noted on a log-log slide rule, where the ln of $1.0025 = 0.0025$ and other ln's are found similarly for the rest of the numbers smaller than 1.0025.

An example of the use of such small logarithms is found in a problem from a past fundamentals examination:

• Carbon in living matter contains a definite proportion of radiocarbon—C^{14}. Upon death of this living matter, the radiocarbon decreases at the rate of 1 part in 8,000 per year. Derive an equation where A is the original amount of C^{14} at the death of the living matter and y is the amount of C^{14} left at any time t in years measured from the death of the living matter.

 Charcoal from a tree killed by the eruption of the volcano which formed Crater Lake assayed at 44.5 per cent radiocarbon. How many years ago did the eruption occur?

For the first part of the problem, there would remain

$$\left(1 - \frac{1}{8,000}\right) \times A = A_1$$

at the end of the first year, $A_1[1 - (1/8,000)] = A_2$ at the end of the second year, $A_2[1 - (1/8,000)] = A_3$ at the end of the third year, etc. At the end of the t'th year there would remain

$$A\left(1 - \frac{1}{8,000}\right)^t = y \text{ radioactive carbon}$$

and this is the answer to the first part of the problem

$$y = A\left(1 - \frac{1}{8,000}\right)^t$$

which may be recognized as an example of the compound interest law. (See Chap. 8.)

To solve the second part of the problem we must first assume that the amount of the carbon present in the charcoal right after the eruption was radioactive and was equal to A. At the end of t years, y equalled $0.445 \times A$. The equation to be solved is, then, $0.445A = [1 - (1/8,000)]^t A$, or $0.445 = [1 - (1/8,000)]^t$. This can be most easily solved by taking the logarithms of both sides, which gives $\ln 0.445 = t \ln [1 - (1/8,000)]$.

$$\ln 0.445 = \ln \frac{1}{2.247} = 0 - 0.810$$

and $\ln [1 - (1/8,000)] = -0.000125$. Then

$$t = \frac{-0.810}{-0.000125} = 6,480 \text{ years}$$

Unfortunately there is no simple series or easy method of calculating the Briggsian or common logarithm of $1 + x$ directly, but it can easily be determined by utilizing one further relationship; then the above problem can be solved quite easily with an ordinary slide rule.

We know that if $A = \ln B$, then $e^A = B$, and if $D = \log B$, then $10^D = B$. We then have that $e^A = 10^D$, and if we take the natural logarithms of both sides we get $A = D \ln 10$, or $A = 2.3026 \times D$, or the natural logarithm of $B = 2.3026$ times the common logarithm of B. Conversely $\log B = (1/2.3026) \ln B$. Returning to the example $0.445 = [1 - (1/8{,}000)]^t$ and this time taking the logs of both sides, $\log 0.445 = t \log [1 - (1/8{,}000)]$,

$$\log 0.445 = \log \frac{1}{2.247} = -0.351$$

$$\log \left(1 - \frac{1}{8{,}000}\right) = 0.434 \ln \left(1 - \frac{1}{8{,}000}\right)$$
$$= 0.434 \times (-0.000125) = -0.000542$$

Then $t = -0.351/-0.0000542 = 6{,}480$ years.

1-5. Trigonometry. The examinee should review his trigonometry rather thoroughly if he is at all rusty. Some of the more basic things with which he should be particularly familiar are the signs of the functions in the various quadrants, the definitions of the various functions and their relationships to one another, the law of sines, the law of cosines, double-angle relationships, and the basic right triangles.

The various functions can be explained by means of the unit circle.

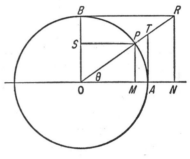

Fig. 1-1

Referring to Fig. 1-1, OP is the radius and is equal to 1;

$\sin \theta = PM$ = opposite side divided by the hypotenuse

$\cos \theta = OM$ = adjacent side divided by the hypotenuse

$$\tan \theta = \frac{\sin \theta}{\cos \theta} = \frac{PM}{OM}$$

By proportion $PM/OM = TA/OA = TA$; so $\tan \theta = TA$.

Also by proportion $OA/TA = BR/OB$, or $1/TA = BR$. The cotangent is equal to 1/tangent, so $BR = \cot \theta$.

Similarly, $OM/OP = OA/OT$, or $OM = 1/OT$, giving $\sec \theta = OT$

and $PM/OP = RN/OR = OB/OR$, or $PM = 1/OR$, giving

$$\csc \theta = OR$$

Summarizing, we have:

$$\sin \theta = PM \qquad\qquad \sec \theta = 1/\cos \theta = OT$$
$$\cos \theta = OM \qquad\qquad \csc \theta = 1/\sin \theta = OR$$
$$\tan \theta = \sin \theta/\cos \theta = TA \qquad \cot \theta = 1/\tan \theta = BR$$

It might also be noticed that the relationship $\sin^2 \theta + \cos^2 \theta = 1$ is apparent from the diagram.

Fig. 1-2   Fig. 1-3

The signs of the functions in the various quadrants can be determined easily by means of the unit circle, as can also the relationships of the functions of second-, third-, and fourth-quadrant angles to the functions of first-quadrant angles.

Second-quadrant angles, as shown in Fig. 1-2, will possess the following features:

$$\sin \theta = PM \text{ positive} \qquad \sin (180° - \theta) = \sin \theta$$
$$\cos \theta = SP \text{ negative} \qquad \cos \theta = -\cos (180° - \theta)$$
$$\tan \theta = \sin \theta/\cos \theta \text{ negative} \qquad \tan \theta = -\tan (180° - \theta)$$

Third- and fourth-quadrant angles may be analyzed similarly (see Fig. 1-3).

$$\sin \theta = MP \text{ negative} \qquad \sin \theta = -\sin (\theta - 180°)$$
$$\cos \theta = SP \text{ negative} \qquad \cos \theta = -\cos (\theta - 180°)$$
$$\tan \theta = \sin \theta/\cos \theta \text{ positive} \qquad \tan \theta = \tan (\theta - 180°)$$

From Fig. 1-4:

$$\sin \theta = MP \text{ negative} \qquad \sin \theta = -\sin (360° - \theta)$$
$$\cos \theta = SP \text{ positive} \qquad \cos \theta = \cos (360° - \theta)$$
$$\tan \theta = \sin \theta/\cos \theta \text{ negative} \qquad \tan \theta = -\tan (360° - \theta)$$

From these figures it can also be seen that $\sin(-\theta) = -\sin\theta$, $\cos(-\theta) = \cos\theta$, and $\tan(-\theta) = -\tan\theta$. In addition it can be noted that $\sin\theta = \cos(90-\theta)$ and $\tan\theta = \cot(90-\theta)$, or $\tan\theta = 1/[\tan(90-\theta)]$.

Three types of right triangles which should be reviewed are the 30-60° right triangle, the 45° right triangle, and the 3-4-5 right triangle.

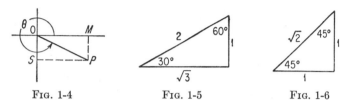

FIG. 1-4   FIG. 1-5   FIG. 1-6

The 30-60° right triangle (Fig. 1-5) gives the functions of 30° and 60° angles. From the triangle it can be seen that

$$\sin 30° = \cos 60° = \tfrac{1}{2} = 0.500$$
$$\cos 30° = \sin 60° = \sqrt{3}/2 = 0.866$$
$$\tan 30° = \cot 60° = 1/\sqrt{3} = 0.577$$

The 45° right triangle (Fig. 1-6) is the isosceles right triangle, and the functions are:

$$\sin 45° = \cos 45° = \sqrt{2}/2 = 0.707$$
$$\tan 45° = \cot 45° = 1.000$$

The 3-4-5 right triangle (Fig. 1-7) is met quite commonly in mechanics and is a standard method for laying out right angles.

FIG. 1-7   FIG. 1-8

The interior angles are almost 37° and 53°. Another common form of right triangle is the 5-12-13 right triangle.

The law of sines, which holds for any triangle (Fig. 1-8), is easily remembered and need only be stated. It is:

$$\frac{\sin A}{a} = \frac{\sin B}{b} = \frac{\sin C}{c}$$

1-6. Law of Cosines. The law of cosines is more difficult to remember and, in accordance with the previously stated philosophy, will be derived (Fig. 1-9).

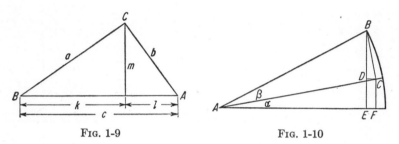

FIG. 1-9   FIG. 1-10

Given: Triangle ABC with the values of sides b and c and angle A known.

Find: The length of side a.

Solution: First construct line m from the vertex C perpendicular to base c.

$$a^2 = m^2 + k^2 \qquad k = c - l \qquad l = b \cos A$$
$$k^2 = c^2 - 2bc \cos A + b^2 \cos^2 A$$
$$m^2 = b^2 - l^2 = b^2 - b^2 \cos^2 A$$
$$a^2 = (b^2 - b^2 \cos^2 A) + (c^2 - 2bc \cos A + b^2 \cos^2 A)$$

which gives

$$a^2 = b^2 + c^2 - 2bc \cos A$$

This is the law of cosines. Care should be exercised to select the right sign for the cosine of angle A, since, as shown previously, the cosine of an obtuse angle is negative. This means that if the known angle is greater than 90°, the third term of the right side of the equation is positive.

1-7. Double Angles. Functions of double angles are also somewhat difficult to remember exactly when one uses them only occasionally, and the derivation is a short exercise in trigonometry which will aid in reviewing other trigonometric fundamentals.

Figure 1-10 shows the double angle $\alpha + \beta$. AB is equal to unity, the sin $(\alpha + \beta) = BE$, and cos $(\alpha + \beta) = AE$. The values of these two functions can be determined in terms of the functions of the individual angles α and β, as follows:

Construct $BC \perp AC$, $BE \perp AF$, $CF \perp AF$, $CD \perp BE$.

$$BC = \sin \beta$$

and from right triangle BCD, $BD = \sin \beta \cos \alpha$. $AC = \cos \beta$, and from right triangle ACF, $CF = \cos \beta \sin \alpha$.

$$\sin (\alpha + \beta) = BE = BD + DE = BD + CF$$
$$= \sin \beta \cos \alpha + \cos \beta \sin \alpha$$

Similarly, cos $(\alpha + \beta) = AF - EF = AF - CD$.

From right triangle BCD, $CD = \sin \beta \sin \alpha$; and from right triangle ACF, $AF = \cos \beta \cos \alpha$; then

$$\cos (\alpha + \beta) = \cos \beta \cos \alpha - \sin \beta \sin \alpha$$

The same relationships will hold for the difference of two angles. If we replace β with $-\beta$, we get

$$\sin (\alpha - \beta) = \sin \alpha \cos \beta - \cos \alpha \sin \beta$$
$$\cos (\alpha - \beta) = \cos \alpha \cos \beta + \sin \alpha \sin \beta$$

since $\sin (-\beta) = -\sin \beta$ and $\cos (-\beta) = \cos \beta$

The trigonometry requirement also includes manipulation of the various functions algebraically with their various equivalents. No general set of rules can be laid down to cover all cases; the reader is urged to go over the preceding derivations to familiarize himself with the more important equalities and different methods of substitution.

This algebraic manipulation of functions can be demonstrated through solution of a past examination problem:

• What is sec $\theta \sin^3 \theta \cot \theta$ equal to?

Substitution gives $1/(\cos \theta) \times \sin^3 \theta \times \cos \theta / \sin \theta = \sin^2 \theta$, which also equals $1 - \cos^2 \theta$.

Another example is:

- Simplify $1 - \tan^2 \theta \cos^2 \theta$.

Substitution gives $1 - (\sin^2 \theta / \cos^2 \theta) \times \cos^2 \theta = \cos^2 \theta$.

One other phase of trigonometry covered in past examinations is that of calculations involving angles concerned with surveying problems. An example of this is furnished by the following question taken

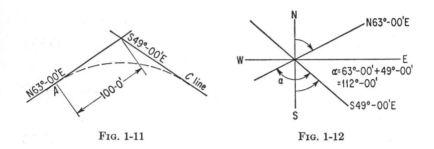

Fig. 1-11   Fig. 1-12

from a past engineer-in-training examination:

- Lay out curve tangent at point A and tangent to line C (Fig. 1-11).
  a. What is the radius of the curve?
  b. What is the length of the curve? (Graphical solution not permitted.)

Whenever possible, the first step in such a problem is to construct the figure to scale. This gives a clearer picture of the problem (sometimes sketches are just enough out of scale to mislead the observer) and also provides a rough graphical check.

First determine the angle between lines B and C. This can be done easily from the figure by including the north-south line (Fig. 1-12). The center of the arc of the circle forming the curve will lie on the bisector of the angle (Fig. 1-13). This gives a right triangle, since a line drawn from the center of a circle to the point of tangency of a line tangent to that circle is perpendicular to the tangent line. With one leg 100 ft in length and the adjacent angle equal to $11\frac{2}{2} = 56°$, the other leg, which is the radius of the circle, must equal $100 \tan 56° = 100 \times 1.483 = 148.3$ ft. The length of the curve will equal 68°/360° × circumference, or

$$\frac{68}{360} \times 2\pi \times 148.3 = 176 \text{ ft}$$

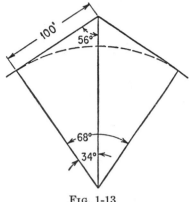

The reader should also remember that the sum of the internal angles of a polygon is equal to $(n - 2) \times 180$, where n is the number of sides of the polygon. This relationship is important in determining the error of closure of a polygonal survey. A problem selected from a past examination will serve to illustrate this.

FIG. 1-13

• Survey as shown in Fig. 1-14. What does the sum of the internal angles equal if there is no error of closure?

Since there are five sides to the figure, the sum of the internal angles should equal $(5 - 2) \times 180 = 540°$. The sum of the five angles

FIG. 1-14

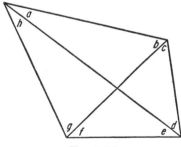

FIG. 1-15

given equals 594°92' or 595°32'. There is an error of 55°32' in the recorded internal angles.

Another similar problem taken from a different examination is:

• A surveyor measures the following angles on the property as shown in Fig. 1-15. However, when he gets back to the office he finds that his work does not check. Check the data as shown below and show which two angles do not check.

$$a = 21°47'10'' \qquad e = 36°17'41''$$
$$b = 40°43'40'' \qquad f = 26°13'09''$$
$$c = 71°10'30'' \qquad g = 87°36'40''$$
$$d = 46°18'50'' \qquad h = 29°52'30''$$

From Fig. 1-15 we see that the property can be broken into triangles. Adding the angles of the individual triangles we have:

$$a + b + g + h = 180°$$
$$c + d + e + f = 180°0'10''$$
$$a + b + c + d = 180°0'10''$$
$$e + f + g + h = 180°$$

Since the sum of the interior angles of a triangle must equal 180°, two of these are in error. Since angles c and d are both in the two incorrect triangles and are not in any of the correct sums, while a, b, e, f, g, and h all appear in triangles adding exactly to 180°, the two angles which do not check are c and d.

1-8. Functions of Angles Close to Zero. Just as we have discussed a method of determining the values of logarithms close to zero, so we should discuss a method of determining the values of the sine and the cosine of an angle when they are close to zero. For angles which are close to zero an examination of Fig. 1-1 shows that the tangent of the angle will be very close in value to the sine of the angle. In fact, for angles less than 2°30' the difference between the values of the tangent and the sine occurs in the fifth place ($\tan 2°30' = 0.04366$, $\sin 2°30' = 0.04362$); the difference is approximately 0.1 per cent. The error of considering the tangent as equal to the sine does not exceed 1 per cent until the angle exceeds 8°. In addition, the tangent and the sine of small angles are very nearly equal to the angle itself measured in radians. The number of radians in any angle given in degrees can easily be determined if one remembers that there are 2π radians in a circle. Then 2π radians equal 360°, and one radian equals $360/2\pi = 57.296°$. The error obtained by considering sine $\alpha = \alpha$ is a little less than the error obtained by considering sine $\alpha = \tan \alpha$. A 0.1 per cent error occurs at about 5° (5° = 0.08727 radians, $\sin 5° = 0.08716$) and 1 per cent error occurs at an angle of approximately 14° (14° = 0.24435 radians, $\sin 14° = 0.24192$). We can, then, for ordinary slide-rule calculations, assume that for angles less than 8° the sine equals the tangent and both are equal to the angle.

An example of the usefulness of this relationship is given by a problem taken from a past examination:

- The surveyor wishes to determine the distance AC in Fig. 1-16. How many minutes or seconds of arc would cause an error of 1.0 ft in the distance AC?

FIG. 1-16

$AC = 100.000/\tan \theta$, and $AC + \Delta AC = 100.000/[\tan (\theta - \Delta\theta)]$; but ΔAC is $AC/2,000$, so $AC + \Delta AC = 1.0005\ AC$, and we have $100.000/[\tan (\theta - \Delta\theta)] = 1.0005(100.000/\tan \theta)$.

We know that for angles of the size being considered, $\tan \theta$ is very nearly equal to θ, so we can safely substitute the angles for their tangents. This gives us $100.000/(\theta - \Delta\theta) = 100.05/\theta$, which reduces to $0.05\theta = 100.05\Delta\theta$, or $\Delta\theta = 0.0005\theta$, where θ and $\Delta\theta$ must be in the same units.

$$\theta = 2 \times 60 \times 60 + 52 \times 60 = 10,320''$$

The number of seconds of arc which would cause an error of ± 1.0 ft in the distance AC would equal $0.0005 \times 10,300 = 5.15''$ or $5''$ of arc.

1-9. Analytic Geometry. A few of the fundamentals of analytic geometry should be reviewed, primarily those pertaining to straight lines and circles. Not infrequently we are confronted by problems in which we have given information which consists of two lines and it is desired to find the point of intersection of those two lines. Another fairly common case is the intersection of two fields of force or the intersection of two circles. Both these cases can be handled easily by means of analytic geometry.

FIG. 1-17

1-10. Equation of a Straight Line. The equation of a straight line through the origin (Fig. 1-17) can be written as

$$\frac{y}{x} = \text{constant} = \tan \theta, \quad \text{or} \quad y = mx$$

Alternatively, using points x and y, $y = (y_1/x_1)x$. The more general case is one in which the line does not pass through the origin. The line may then be specified by one point and the angle or by two points (Fig. 1-18).

FIG. 1-18   FIG. 1-19

If two points are given, the slope equals $(y_2 - y_1)/(x_2 - x_1) = m$, or $m = (y - y_1)/(x - x_1)$, so the equation of the line is

$$\frac{y_2 - y_1}{x_2 - x_1} = \frac{y - y_1}{x - x_1}$$

or $y = y_1 + [(y_2 - y_1)/(x_2 - x_1)](x - x_1)$, which is of the form $y = mx + c$.

If one point and the slope of the line are given, the equation of the line is $y - y_1 = m(x - x_1)$. The special cases where one intercept or more is given will be seen to fit easily one of the cases discussed.

The slope of a perpendicular to a line can be seen to equal the negative reciprocal of the slope of the line (Fig. 1-19).

We know that $\tan \beta = - \tan (180 - \beta)$. From Fig. 1-19 we see that $180 - \beta = 90 - \alpha$ and the tangent of $(90 - \alpha) = 1/\tan \alpha$. Combining these gives us $\tan \beta = - (1/\tan \alpha)$, or the slope of a perpendicular to a line equals the negative reciprocal of the slope of the line.

1-11. Equation of a Circle. The equations of circles are as easily derived as those of a straight line. Given a circle with its center at the origin, the equation will be $x^2 + y^2 = r^2$, which can readily be seen from Fig. 1-20. If the center is not at the origin, the equation changes to $(x - a)^2 + (y - b)^2 = r^2$. This relationship follows readily from Fig. 1-21.

An example of the application of some of these relationships is afforded by a problem which asked:

- 1. Find the points of intersection of:
    a. $x - 7y + 25 = 0$
    b. $x^2 + y^2 - 25$
  2. Write the equation of a tangent to the circle (*b*), whose slope is $-\frac{3}{4}$.

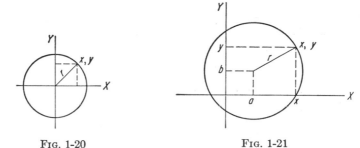

FIG. 1-20   FIG. 1-21

Equation (*a*) is that of a straight line and Eq. (*b*) is that of a circle. If the line crosses the circle then the two points of intersection will satisfy both equations. If we solve them simultaneously we can find both points.

$$x = 7y - 25$$

$$\begin{array}{r} x^2 = 49y^2 - 350y + 625 \\ x^2 = -y^2 \qquad\qquad + 25 \\ \hline 0 = 50y^2 - 350y + 600 \end{array}$$

$$0 = y^2 - 7y + 12$$
$$(y - 4)(y - 3) = 0 \qquad y = 4 \qquad y = 3$$
$$y = 4 \qquad x = 28 - 25 = 3$$
$$y = 3 \qquad x = 21 - 25 = -4$$

The two points are $x = 3$, $y = 4$; and $x = -4$, $y = 3$.

The given circle has its center at the origin, and the required tangent will be perpendicular to the diameter whose slope is the negative reciprocal of the slope of the tangent. The slope of the diameter would then be $4/3$, and the equation of the diameter would be $y = 4/3x$, since the diameter line would go through the origin.

The diameter line would intersect the circle at two points.

$$y^2 = 25 - x^2 \qquad y^2 = (16/9)x^2$$
$$(16/9)x^2 = 25 - x^2$$
$$x = \pm 3$$

The two points of intersection would be $x = 3$, $y = 4$; and $x = -3$, $y = -4$.

The tangent line selected would then go through point 3, 4, or point -3, -4 and have a slope of $-3/4$. Since the slope of a line also equals $(y - y_1)/(x - x_1)$, the equation of the required tangent is $(y - 4)/(x - 3) = -3/4$, or $(y + 4)/(y + 3) = -3/4$, which reduce to $4y + 3x = 25$ and $4y + 3x = -25$.

Other examples will be given after some of the calculus relations have been reviewed.

1-12. Calculus. The mere mention of the word "calculus" seems to erect a mental block in many engineers. This is unfortunate because the use of a moderate amount of calculus can be of a considerable help in solving many engineering problems, and in its simpler forms calculus is not difficult. True, calculus in its entirety is a very broad subject, and considerable study (or a bit of genius) is required to apply it in all its ramifications. In the simpler forms, however, calculus is not complicated and it can be extremely helpful in the practice of engineering as well as in passing examinations.

Basically, calculus is the study or science of infinitesimals; much of the engineer's use of calculus is devoted to determining the area under a curve by dividing the area into many thin slices and then adding the areas of all those little slices to obtain the total area. Another important phase of calculus is the determination of the maximum and/or the minimum point of a function. Both these processes will be discussed later, but first we shall need to review some of the mechanics of calculus which are necessary to perform the desired calculations.

1-13. Derivatives. A few of the commoner derivatives should be recalled to memory. These include:

$$d\ ax = a\ dx \qquad a \text{ is a constant}$$
$$d\ (u + v) = du + dv \qquad u \text{ and } v \text{ are variable}$$
$$d\ (uv) = u\ dv + v\ du \qquad u \text{ and } v \text{ are variable}$$
$$d\ x^n = nx^{(n-1)}\ dx$$
$$d\ e^x - e^x\ dx$$
$$d\ \sin x = \cos x\ dx$$
$$d\ \cos x = -\sin x\ dx$$
$$d\ \ln x = dx/x$$

This list is a minimum that should be remembered. From these we can derive a few more important relationships; the derivations will obviate memorizing and will also provide drill in manipulating some of the listed derivatives.

The derivative of u/v is also important. $u/v = uv^{-1}$.

$$d\ (uv^{-1}) = ud(v^{-1}) + v^{-1}\ du$$
$$= u(-v^{-2}\ dv) + v^{-1}\ du$$
$$= -\frac{u\ dv}{v^2} + \frac{du}{v}$$

Combining terms gives $d\ (u/v) = (v\ du - u\ dv)/v^2$.

The derivative of $\tan x$ can be determined using this relationship.

$$\tan x = \frac{\sin x}{\cos x}$$
$$d\ \tan x = \frac{\cos x\ (\cos x\ dx) - \sin x\ (-\sin x\ dx)}{\cos^2 x}$$
$$= \frac{(\cos^2 x + \sin^2 x)\ dx}{\cos^2 x} = \frac{dx}{\cos^2 x} = \sec^2 x\ dx$$

1-14. Integration. Integration is the opposite of differentiation; thus we have:

$$\int a\ dx = ax + c \qquad \text{where } c = \text{the constant of integration}$$
$$\int x^n\ dx = (1/n + 1)x^{(n+1)} + c \qquad (\text{except for } n = -1)$$
$$\int dx/x = \ln x + c$$
$$\int e^x\ dx = e^x + c$$
$$\int \sin x\ dx = -\cos x + c$$
$$\int \cos x\ dx = \sin x + c$$

One more important integral which should be remembered is $\int u\, dv = uv - \int v\, du$, where u and v are both functions of the same variable.

An illustration of the usefulness of this relationship is provided by the examination problem which asked:

• *Find:* $\int x \cos x\, dx$

Let $u = x$; then $du = dx$. $dv = \cos x\, dx$; then $v = \sin x$; $uv - \int v\, du = x \sin x - \int \sin x\, dx = x \sin x + \cos x + c$. To check, $d\, (x \sin x + \cos x) = \sin x\, dx + x \cos x\, dx - \sin x\, dx$, or

$$d\,(x \sin x - \cos x) = x \cos x\, dx$$

which checks.

It might be worthwhile here to discuss briefly the solution of some of the simpler types of differential equations—those which can easily be solved by separation of variables. As an example, let us look at a problem given in one of the early examinations:

• *Solve:* $\dfrac{dy}{dx} + \dfrac{1}{x}\, y = xy^2$

By multiplying by $x\, dx$ this can be rearranged to give

$$x\, dy + y\, dx = x^2 y^2\, dx$$

Here we recognize that $x\, dy + y\, dx$ is the derivative of xy, so further rearranging gives

$$\frac{x\, dy + y\, dx}{(xy)^2} = dx$$

or

$$(xy)^{-2}\, d\,(xy) = dx$$

which gives

$$-(xy)^{-1} = x + c$$

or

$$y = -\frac{1}{x^2 + cx}$$

Another example from a past engineer-in-training example is the problem:

• What is the derivative with respect to x of $(3x^2 + x)^{1/2}$?

This is of the form

$$du^{1/2} = \tfrac{1}{2}\, du^{-1/2}\, du$$

where

$$u = 3x^2 + x$$

Then du equals $6x + 1$, and the answer becomes

$$\frac{d}{dx}\,(3x^2 + x)^{1/2} = \frac{1}{2}(3x^2 + x)^{-1/2}(6x + 1)$$

which could also be written $(6x + 1)/[2(3x^2 + x)^{1/2}]$. The term d/dx means "derivative of with respect to x."

Whenever we have an equation which gives y as a function of x [abbreviated $y = f(x)$], it can be represented by a curve [We shall assume that the function $y = f(x)$ is continuous and differentiable throughout the area in which we are interested.] when a series of

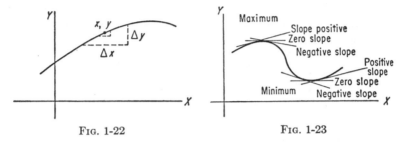

FIG. 1-22   FIG. 1-23

points is plotted on a graph (Fig. 1-22). The derivative dy/dx is the limit of the fraction $\Delta y/\Delta x$ as Δx approaches zero.

1-15. Maximum and Minimum. As can be seen from Fig. 1-22, the quotient of $\Delta y/\Delta x$ is the slope of the hypotenuse of the indicated triangle or the tangent of the angle the hypotenuse makes with the abscissa. As Δx becomes smaller and smaller (approaches zero) the triangle also becomes smaller and smaller until, finally, it vanishes at the point x, y. At the point of extinction, the hypotenuse coincides with the tangent to the curve at the point x, y, and the slope of the tangent is given by the derivative of the function at that particular point. As we can see from Fig. 1-23, whenever the curve becomes a maximum or a minimum, the slope of the curve at the particular point of maximum or minimum is horizontal. In other words, the tangent to the curve at the particular point where the curve is either a maximum or a minimum will be parallel with the x axis and will, therefore, have a slope of zero, since the tangent of $0°$ (and of $180°$) is zero. This means that at any point of maximum or minimum of the function $y = f(x)$ the derivative at that point,

dy/dx, will equal zero. Conversely it can be shown that wherever $dy/dx = 0$, the tangent of the curve of the function $y = f(x)$ is parallel to the abscissa. In all but a few special cases this parallelism will indicate either a maximum or a minimum.

There are three methods whereby we may determine whether the point at which $dy/dx = 0$ is a maximum or a minimum. The first is to take the second derivative of the function at the particular point; if d^2y/dx^2 is positive, the point is a minimum; if d^2y/dx^2 is negative, the point is a maximum. This can be proved in a rigorous fashion by means of the theorems of mean value, or it can be reasoned by applying a slightly different approach. If we call on our training in mechanics we can imagine that y of $y = f(x)$ corresponds to the displacement at the particular time x. This means that dy/dx corresponds to the rate of change of y with change in x, another way of stating that for $dy/dx = 0$ there is no change of y with x or that y is either a maximum or a minimum. d^2y/dx^2 will then correspond to a rate of change of dy/dx with x (acceleration); if dy/dx (velocity) is a maximum, this rate of change (or acceleration) must be negative or decreasing at that point; and if dy/dx is a minimum (velocity a minimum), then the only possible way in which dy/dx can change is in an increasing fashion and d^2y/dx^2 will be positive. Another method of showing this is to solve for dy/dx at a point just before the point of minimum or maximum under investigation ($x_1 < x$) and at a point just beyond the point of investigation ($x_2 > x$). If the point being investigated is a maximum, the slope just before this point will be positive ($dy/dx > 0$ at $x = x_1$), indicating an increasing y, and the slope of the curve just beyond this point will be negative ($dy/dx < 0$ at $x = x_2$), indicating a decreasing y. Similarly $f(x)$ is a minimum if $f'(x) = 0$ and $f'(x)$ changes sign from negative to positive (Fig. 1-23).

The third method of determining whether $f(x)$ for $f'(x) = 0$ is a maximum or a minimum is to calculate the value of $f(x)$ a short distance on either side of the point of interest. If these values calculated for $f(x + \Delta x)$ and $f(x - \Delta x)$ are larger than the value calculated for $f(x)$, then $f(x)$ is a minimum. If they are smaller, then $f(x)$ is a maximum. Points on both sides are recommended to provide a check.

An example, selected from a past examination, is found in the problem:

• Find y_{max} for the relationship $y = -3x^2 + 6x + 5$.

$dy/dx = -6x + 6$, giving $x = 1$ for $dy/dx = 0$. Since this is the only solution to the equation $dy/dx = 0$, the curve has either a maximum or a minimum but not both. $d^2y/dx^2 = -6$, which is negative, so the point $x = 1$, $y = 8$ is a maximum. Also the slope of the curve can be seen to be positive for x less than 1 and negative for x greater than 1.

1-16. Limit of an Indeterminate Fraction. In a past examination one of the problems was to determine the limit of the fraction $(6x^2 - 2x - 2)/[(2x + 1)3x]$ as x approaches infinity. If we merely substitute the value of infinity for x we get the indeterminate fraction ∞/∞, which is not a solution to the problem. In the actual case the numerator may approach its limit more rapidly than the denominator, or vice versa.

In such an event the answer would be a fraction. If both numerator and denominator approach their limits simultaneously the limit of the fraction will be 1. In this case we can expand the fraction to $(6x^2 - 2x - 2)/(6x^2 + 3x)$, and then if we divide the numerator by the denominator by the method described previously (long division of a polynomial) we shall obtain as our quotient 1 with a remainder of $(-5x - 2)/(6x^2 + 3x)$. If we divide the numerator and the denominator of this remainder by x we obtain $[-5 + (2/x)]/(6x + 3)$. The limit of the remainder as x approaches infinity is zero, since it becomes $-5/\infty$, which is zero. The limit of the original fraction, as x approaches infinity, is then 1.

Sometimes the method of dividing and reducing a fraction to its simplest terms will not provide the desired answer. An example of such an instance is provided by a problem given in another past examination in which it was asked to find the limit of $(5x^3 - \cos x + e^x)/(x^2 + 2x)$ as x approaches zero. This cannot be handled in the same way as the preceding example. To solve this problem it is easiest to employ the rule of L'Hospital. This rule may be stated as follows: if $f(a) = \varphi(a) = 0$, and if the ratio $f'(x)/\varphi'(x)$ approaches a limit as $x \to a$, then $f(x)/\varphi(x)$ approaches the same limit. The same rule will hold if $f(a)$ and $\varphi(a)$ both approach infinity as $x \to a$. To apply this rule to the example given, since both numerator and denominator equal zero for $x = 0$, we differentiate both numerator and denominator to obtain $(15x^2 + \sin x + e^x)/(2x + 2)$, which equals $\frac{1}{2}$ for $x = 0$. If the first differentiation results in another indeterminate fraction, then differentiate numerator and denominator again, and again if necessary. As soon as a determinate fraction is obtained, however, the process must be discontinued; further differentiation will give an erroneous result.

1-17. Parametric Equations. A word about parametric equations may also be in order, since questions on past examinations have occasionally referred to them. An example is the question

- Given the parametric equations $x = a(\theta - \sin \theta)$ and $y = a(1 - \cos \theta)$, find the maximum value of y.

The coordinates x and y of a point on a curve are often expressed as functions of a third variable, or *parameter*—hence the term "parametric equations." In the example given, the maximum value of y can be determined as previously discussed. $dy/d\theta = a(\sin \theta) = 0$; $\theta = \pi, 3\pi \cdots$ for y a maximum, so $y_{max} = a(1 + 1) = 2a$. The corresponding value of $x = a\pi, 3\pi a$, etc.

1-18. Double Integration. A word about double integration should also be included. It was required to find A from the relationship $A = \int_0^\pi \int_0^R r \, d\theta \, dr$ in a past fundamentals examination. The only point to remember here is that one variable must be considered constant while we integrate with respect to the other. The example can be rewritten as

$$\int_0^\pi d\theta \int_0^R r \, dr$$

which equals

$$\int_0^\pi d\theta \left[\frac{r^2}{2} \right]_0^R$$

or

$$\int_0^\pi \frac{R^2}{2} \, d\theta$$

which equals $(\pi R^2)/2$; this, incidentally, may be recognized as the area of a semicircle.

1-19. Approximate Value of an Integral. Integration, in its physical sense, is the determination of an area. The integral sign is actually a replacement of the summation sign as Δx gets very small or "approaches zero." The summation of all the products of $y \, \Delta x$ from 0 to B would equal the area under the curve $y = f(x)$ between the bounding lines $x = 0$ and $x = B$. As Δx approaches zero (gets smaller and smaller) the sum of the quantities $y \, \Delta x$ gets closer and closer to the true area under the curve (Fig. 1-24) until

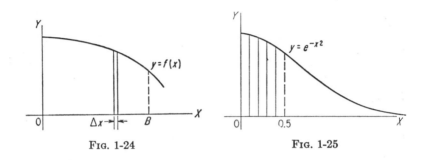

FIG. 1-24   FIG. 1-25

just before Δx becomes so small as to vanish altogether, we get area (under the curve between lines $x = 0$ and $x = B$) $= \int_0^B y \, dx$.

Generally, this relationship is used to determine the area under a curve between given limits. It can, however, be reversed to give an approximation for the value of an integral. As an example, a problem in one fundamentals examination was to find an approximate value of the integral $\int e^{-x^2} \, dx$ between the limits 0.5 and 0. This can be calculated by expanding e^{-x^2} in the form of a series, integrating each part, and then adding the parts. It can also be calculated (approximately) by plotting the curve $y = e^{-x^2}$ and measuring the area in the portion bounded by the lines $x = 0$ and $x = 0.5$. For the example given, let $y = e^{-x^2}$ and divide the portion of the curve between $x = 0$ and $x = 0.50$ into a series of equal-width cells. Then find the area of each cell and add these individual areas to give the total area, which will equal, approximately, the integral of $e^{-x^2} \, dx$ between the limits of 0.5 and 0 (Fig. 1-25).

1-20. Approximate Solution of an Equation.　Occasionally it is necessary to solve an equation for which it is difficult to find an analytic solution.　An example of such an equation is the relationship $\cos x - x^2 = 0$.　This particular example may be solved by use of the series for $\cos x$,

$$\cos x = 1 - \frac{x^2}{2!} + \frac{x^4}{4!} - \frac{x^6}{6!} + \cdots$$

but even the series relationship does not simplify this particular example very much.　A general method of obtaining solutions of

FIG. 1-26

problems of this type is to solve them graphically.　In the example given, we have $x^2 = \cos x$.　We can rewrite this as two equations: $A = x^2$ and $B = \cos x$.　We then plot A and B vs. x, and the crossing of the two curves is the answer we are seeking.　The method is illustrated in Fig. 1-26.　Note that after we have obtained the first approximate answer we can expand the scales of the x and y axes and solve again; in this manner we may get whatever degree of accuracy we desire.

1-21. Additional Examples and Solutions.　A few more problems selected from past fundamentals examinations are included with their solutions to help illustrate the principles discussed above.

1. A box is to be constructed from a thin sheet of copper 10 in. square by cutting equal squares out of each corner and turning up the remaining parts of the sheet copper to form the four sides of the box.　Since *this is a problem in mathematics, use calculus* and determine the *largest-volume* box that can be made from this material by the method described.

First, draw a figure (Fig. 1-27) illustrating the problem.　Next, write an equation for the volume of the finished box in terms of the size of the cutout x.

$$\text{Volume} = \text{height} \times \text{area of base} = x \times (10 - 2x)^2$$

which gives $V = 100x - 40x^2 + 4x^3$.   Now that we have $V = f(x)$, we must differentiate V with respect to x and set $dV/dx = 0$ to find V_{max}. $dV/dx = 100 - 80x + 12x^2 = 0$.   This may be factorable but can be solved easily by means of the general solution of a quadratic equation given above under Quadratic Equations.

$$x = \frac{80 \pm \sqrt{6,400 - 4,800}}{24} = \frac{80 \pm 40}{24}$$

$$= 5 \text{ or } 1\tfrac{2}{3}$$

$x = 5$ is obviously a minimum, since this value for x would give a volume of zero.   For illustration, however, let us take the second

FIG. 1-27   FIG. 1-28

derivative of V with respect to x. $d^2V/dx^2 = -80 + 24x$; d^2V/dx^2 for $x = \tfrac{5}{3}$ equals -40, for $x = 5$ equals $+40$; so $x = 5$ gives V_{min} and $x = \tfrac{5}{3}$ gives V_{max}.   The maximum volume would then equal 74.1 cu in.

2. Find the entire area between the curve $y = x/(1 + x^2)^2$ and its asymptote.

First sketch the curve (Fig. 1-28).   We see that the asymptote is $y = 0$.   The area will then be equal to

$$A = \int_{x = -\infty}^{x = \infty} y \, dx = 2 \int_0^\infty \frac{x}{(1 + x^2)^2} \, dx$$

since the curve is symmetrical about both x and y axes.   The derivative of $(1 + x^2)$ is $2x$; so if we let $(1 + x^2) = B$, we can rewrite the integral as

$$A = \int_{x=0}^{x = \infty} B^{-2} \, dB$$

which equals

$$-B^{-1} \Big|_{x=0}^{x=\infty}$$

or

$$A = -\left(\frac{1}{1 + \infty^2} - \frac{1}{1 + 0}\right) = 1.0$$

which is the entire area between the curve and its asymptote.

3. Determine the equations of the tangent and the normal to the circle $(x - 4)^2 + (y + 3)^2 = 25$ at the point $(7,1)$.

The tangent to the curve equals dy/dx, and we can solve for this by differentiating the above equation and then solving for dy/dx. Differentiation gives $2(x - 4)\, dx + 2(y + 3)\, dy = 0$, and

$$\frac{dy}{dx} = -\frac{x - 4}{y + 3}$$

The slope of the tangent line at the point $(7,1)$ is $-\tfrac{3}{4}$, and the slope of the normal line at the point $(7,1)$ is $\tfrac{4}{3}$. Recalling the discussion of analytic geometry, we know that the equation will be of the form $y = mx + b$ and that the equation of the tangent line must have the slope $m = -\tfrac{3}{4}$ and pass through the point $(7,1)$; so we have $1 = -\tfrac{3}{4}(7) + b$; $b = {}^{25}\!/_4$, and the equation of the tangent line is $y = -\tfrac{3}{4}x + {}^{25}\!/_4$, or $4y = -3x + 25$. Similarly, the equation of the normal line is found to be $3y = 4x - 25$.

4. The equation of a parabola is $y^2 = 16x$. Find the equation of a chord through the points in the curve whose abscissas are 1 and 4 and whose ordinates are positive.

The two points will be $y = 4\sqrt{x}$ or $\begin{cases} y = 4 \\ x = 1 \end{cases}$ and $\begin{cases} y = 8 \\ x = 4 \end{cases}$. Required is the equation of the line which passes through two points. The slope of the line will be

$$\frac{y_2 - y_1}{x_2 - x_1} = \frac{8 - 4}{4 - 1} = \frac{4}{3}$$

The line will be of the form $y = mx + b$, and b can be determined by substituting the coordinates of either point. Using $(1,4)$, $b = \tfrac{8}{3}$, and the required equation of the line is $3y = 4x + 8$.

5. Two points P and Q on opposite sides of a stream are not intervisible because of an island. A straight line AB is run through

Q, and the following measurements are made: $AQ = 824$ ft, $QB = 662$ ft, $QAP = 42.57°$, $QBP = 57.75°$. Calculate the distance PQ.

Fig. 1-29

First draw and label the figure (Fig. 1-29). We can find the distances AP and BP by means of the law of sines.

$$(\alpha + \beta) = 180 - (42.57 + 57.75) = 79.68°$$
$$PB = (AQ + QB)\frac{\sin 42.57°}{\sin 79.68°} = 1,022'$$

$AP = (AQ + QB)(\sin 57.75°/\sin 79.68°) = 1,278'$. Now, having two sides and the included angle of the triangles APQ and BPQ, we can find PQ in two ways, using the law of cosines.

$$(PQ)^2 = (PB)^2 + (QB)^2 - 2QB \cdot PB \cos 57.75° = (872 \text{ ft})^2$$
or $\quad (PQ)^2 = (AP)^2 + (AQ)^2 - 2 \cdot AP \cdot AQ \cos 42.57°$

which also gives $PQ = 872$ ft.

6. *a.* $\log_2 65 = x$; find x.
   b. $\log_e 753.6 = x$; find x.
   c. $\cos^2 x - 2\tan^2 x = \sec^2 x$; find the principal values of x.

For part (*a*), by definition $2^x = 65$ and

$$x = \frac{\log 65}{\log 2} = \frac{1.813}{0.301} = 6.02$$

For part (*b*), by definition $e^x = 753.6$;

$$x = \frac{\log 753.6}{\log 2.72} = \frac{2.877}{0.434} = 6.62$$

or x can be found directly using natural logs on the slide rule.   For part (c), substitute the equivalent values and simplify the resulting equation.

$\cos^2 x - 2(\sin^2 x/\cos^2 x) = 1/\cos^2 x$ gives $\cos^4 x - 2\sin^2 x = 1$. $\sin^2 x = 1 - \cos^2 x$ gives $\cos^4 x - 2 + 2\cos^2 x = 1$.   Combining terms and rearranging gives $\cos^4 x + 2\cos^2 x - 3 = 0$, which can be factored into $(\cos^2 x + 3)(\cos^2 x - 1) = 0$.

The factors are $\pm i\sqrt{3}$ and $\pm\sqrt{1}$.   The principal values of x are, then, $x = \cos^{-1}(1) = 0°$ and $x = \cos^{-1}(-1) = \pi$.

7. Find the coordinates of the point of intersection of the two tangents to the curve $y = x^2 + 4$ at the points (1,5) and (2,8). The slope of the tangent to a curve equals dy/dx, and for this curve $dy/dx = 2x$.   The first line will then have a slope equal to 2, and the second a slope equal to 4.   Both lines will be of the form $y = mx + b$ and must pass through their respective points.   For the first line $5 = 2 \times 1 + b$; $b = 3$, and the equation of the first line is $y = 2x + 3$.   Similarly, the equation of the second line will be $y = 4x$.   The intersection of these two lines will be at a point which will satisfy both these equations, and we can find that point by solving the two equations simultaneously.

$$y = 2x + 3$$
$$y = 4x$$

These two equations form one equation, $4x = 2x + 3$, which gives the answer, $x = 1\frac{1}{2}$ and $y = 6$.

8. Determine the points of intersection and the angle between the curve $(x - 2)^2 + y^2 = 49$ and the line $2x - 3y = 6$.   To find the points common to the curve and the line, solve the two equations simultaneously, $y = (2x - 6)/3$ (from $2x - 3y = 6$), so

$$y^2 = \frac{(2x - 6)^2}{9}$$

and $(x - 2)^2 + [(2x - 6)^2/9] = 49$, which reduces to

$$13x^2 - 60x - 363 = 0$$

This can be solved by means of the general solution of a quadratic equation: $x = (-b \pm \sqrt{b^2 - 4ac})/2a$, giving $x = 8.08$ and

$x = -3.46$, with the corresponding values of $y = +3.39$ and $y = -4.31$. The angle desired is probably the angle between the line and the tangent at the point of intersection. (This would give two angles, but only one will be determined; the other would be determined in the same fashion.) The slope of the tangent equals dy/dx, which can be found by differentiating the equation

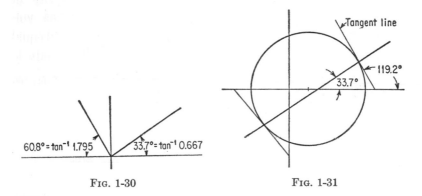

FIG. 1-30   FIG. 1-31

$2(x - 2)\, dx + 2y\, dy = 0.$ $dy/dx = (2 - x)/y.$ The slope of the tangent at the point $(8.08, -3.39)$ then equals

$$\frac{-6.08}{+3.39} = -1.795$$

The slope of the line equals

$$\frac{y_2 - y_1}{x_2 - x_1} = \frac{-4.31 - 3.39}{-3.46 - 8.08} = 0.667$$

To find the angle between these two lines, first draw a figure (Fig. 1-30). The slope of the tangent is negative, so it is a second-quadrant angle, but the slope of the line is positive, so it is a first-quadrant angle. The angle between the two lines is

$$180 - (60.8 + 33.7) = 85.5°$$

A good check of this work is to draw the figure and make a rough graphical check (Fig. 1-31).

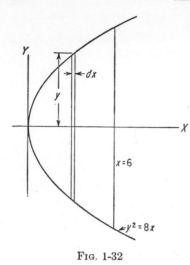

Fɪɢ. 1-32

9. Determine the volume generated by the rotation about the x axis of the area bounded by the segment of the parabola $y^2 = 8x$ between the origin of the x axis and the ordinate $x = 6$.

First, draw the picture (Fig. 1-32). Since the volume to be determined is due to the rotation of a section of the parabola about the x axis, we can treat it as the volume occupied by a series of disks of thickness dx. The volume of each of these disks will equal $\pi r^2 \, dx$, where r = the ordinate y.

We have, then, $V = \int_0^6 \pi y^2 \, dx$, or, substituting the equivalent value for y^2,

$$V = \int_0^6 \pi 8x \, dx = 8\pi \, (x^2/2) \,\Big|_0^6$$

$V = 8\pi(\tfrac{36}{2}) = 453$ cubic units.

10. Given: $y = wlx/2 - wx^2/2$. Determine the area between this curve and the x axis for values of x between $x = 0$ and $x = 1$. The area will equal $\int_{x=0}^{x=1} y \, dx$, so we write

$$A = \int_0^1 \left(\frac{wlx}{2} - \frac{wx^2}{2}\right) dx = \frac{w}{2} \int_0^1 (lx - x^2) \, dx = \frac{w}{2} \left(\frac{lx^2}{2} - \frac{x^3}{3}\right)\Big|_0^1$$

$$A = \frac{w}{2} \left(\frac{l}{2} - \frac{1}{3}\right) = \frac{wl}{4} - \frac{w}{6}$$

11. A roofer wishes to make an open gutter of maximum cross section whose bottom and sides are each 4 in. wide and whose sides have the same slope. What will be the width across the top?

To solve this problem we need an equation which will give the area as a function of the top dimension or of some other variable upon which the top dimension depends. If we draw a figure

(Fig. 1-33), top dimension D is a function of the angle α. The area of the cross section can be equated as follows:

$$A = (4 \times 4 \sin \alpha) + (4 \cos \alpha \times 4 \sin \alpha)$$
$$= 16 \sin \alpha + 16 \cos \alpha \sin \alpha$$

Next, find $dA/d\alpha$, set it equal to zero, and solve for α.

$$\frac{dA}{d\alpha} = 16 \cos \alpha + 16 \cos^2 \alpha - 16 \sin^2 \alpha = 0$$

Remembering that $\sin^2 \alpha = 1 - \cos^2 \alpha$, we obtain

$$2 \cos^2 \alpha + \cos \alpha - 1 = 0$$

Factoring gives $(2 \cos \alpha - 1)(\cos \alpha + 1) = 0$; $\cos \alpha = -1$ and $\cos \alpha = \frac{1}{2}$. These values give $\alpha = 180°$ and $\alpha = 60°$. For

FIG. 1-33

$\alpha = 180°$ the area would equal zero, so $\alpha = 60°$ is a maximum. The width of the top D equals $4 + 2 \times 4 \cos \alpha = 8$ in.

REFERENCES

A good general review book for mathematics covering algebra, trigonometry, logarithms, analytic geometry, quadratic equations, and the elements of differential and integral calculus is:

Andres, P. G., H. J. Miser, and H. Reingold: "Basic Mathematics," John Wiley & Sons, Inc., New York, 1955.

Plane trigonometry and logarithms are covered in

Sparks, F. W., and P. K. Rees: "Plane Trigonometry," Prentice-Hall, Inc., Englewood Cliffs, N.J., 1952.

Calculus is well explained in

Bacon, H. M.: "Differential and Integral Calculus," 2d ed., McGraw-Hill Book Company, Inc., New York, 1955.

Granville, W. A., P. F. Smith, and W. R. Longly: "Elements of Calculus," Ginn & Company, Boston, 1946.

Sherwood, G. E. F., and A. E. Taylor: "Calculus," Prentice-Hall, Inc., Englewood Cliffs, N.J., 1954.

SAMPLE PROBLEMS SELECTED FROM PAST EXAMINATIONS

1-1. A bombardier is sighting on a target on the ground directly ahead. If the bomber is flying 2 miles above the ground at 240 mph, how fast must the sighting instrument be turning when the angle between the path of the bomber and the line of sight is 30°?

1-2. A transformer core is to be built up of sheet-steel laminations, using two different strip widths, x and y, so that the resultant symmetrical cross

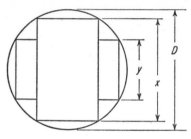

Fig. 1-P-2

section will fit within a circle of diameter D. Compute the values of x and y in terms of D so that the cross section of the core will have maximum value (see Fig. 1-P-2).

1-3. It is desired to measure the width of a river. A base line 1,000 ft long is laid out along one bank. An object on the other bank opposite the base line is sighted on from one end of the base line and found to make an angle with it of 60°. The same object is sighted on from the other end of the base line and found to make an angle with it of 30°. Calculate width of the river.

1-4. Find the equation of the parabola in the form $y = f(x)$ which passes through the points (1,2), (3,20), and (4,35).

1-5. The base and altitude of a rectangle are 5 and 4 in., respectively. At a certain instant they are increasing continuously at the rate of 2 and 1 ips, respectively. At what rate is the area of the rectangle increasing at that instant? (Solve by calculus.)

1-6. Write the equation of the straight line that passes through the point (0,6) and the point $(-3,-8)$.

1-7. A roll of tape is unrolled on a plane surface at the rate of 6 fps of length. Assuming a true circular roll, if the tape is ⅛ in. thick, at what rate is the radius of the roll decreasing when the radius is 1 ft? (Solve by calculus.)

1-8. A tract of land 400 by 300 ft is to be crossed diagonally (see Fig. 1-P-8) by a road 100 ft wide. What area is comprised in the right of way?

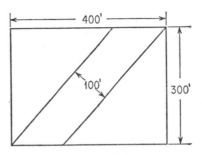

FIG. 1-P-8

1-9. $\sec^{-1} 1.40 = ?$

1-10. A gasoline tank consists of a horizontal closed cylinder 1 ft in diameter and 5 ft long. Determine the number of gallons in the tank when a gauge rod in the plane of the vertical diameter shows a depth of 4 in. in the tank. One gallon equals 231 cu in.

1-11. $\int_{\pi/2}^{\pi} \cos x \, dx = ?$

1-12. One ship A is sailing due south at 15 mph, and a second ship B 32 miles south of A is sailing due east at 12 mph.

a. At what rate are they approaching or separating at the end of 1 hr?

b. At the end of 2 hr?

c. When do they cease to approach each other, and how far apart are they at that time?

1-13. Given: $y = wlx/2 - wx^2/2$. Determine the area between this curve and the x axis for values of x between $x = 0$ and $x = 1$.

1-14. Integrate: $\int_0^L \dfrac{dx}{\sqrt{7 - 6x - x^2}}$

1-15. *a.* Determine the points of intersection and the angle between the curve $(x - 2)^2 + y^2 = 49$ and the line $2x - 3y = 6$.

b. Simplify: $\cos x/(1 - \sin x) - (1 - \sin x)/\cos x$.

1-16. From one corner of a pasture, one bears due east and the other bears S62°E. The owner wishes to build a new fence diagonally across the corner starting at a point 800 ft due east of it. If he has only 1,200 ft of fencing, where will the new fence intersect the one that runs southeast?

1-17. The equation of a parabola is $y^2 = 16x$. Find the equation of a chord through the points on the curve whose abscissas are 1 and 4 and whose ordinates are positive.

1-18. The equation of a curve is $4a^2y = (x^3/3) - 2ax^2 + 5a^2$.

a. Determine the slope for $x = 0$ and $x = 2a$.

b. Determine the points where the curve is parallel to the x axis.

c. Find the points at which the slope is 1.

1-19. Determine the volume generated by the rotation about the x axis of the area bounded by the segment of the parabola $y^2 = 8x$ between the origin of the x axis and the ordinate $x = 6$.

1-20. A rectangular plot of ground has two adjacent sides along Highways 20 and 32. In the plot is a small lake, one end of which is 256 ft west from Highway 20 and 108 ft north from Highway 32.

Find the length of the *shortest* straight path which cuts across the plot from one highway to the other and passes by, i.e., is just tangent to or touches, the end of the lake.

1-21. A man is buying two square lots of unequal size which lie adjacent to each other. Together the lots have a total area of 12,500 sq ft. To embrace the two lots in a single enclosure would require 500 ft of fence. Determine:

a. Dimensions of each lot

b. Area of each lot in square feet

1-22. Prove that $\sec^2 \theta = 1 + \tan^2 \theta$.

1-23. Evaluate the following definite integral:

$$\int_0^{\pi/2} \frac{\cos \theta \, d\theta}{1 + \sin^2 \theta}$$

1-24. Determine the length of the catenary from $x = 0$ to $x = x_1$, using the exponential equation $y = \frac{1}{2}a(e^{x/a} + e^{-x/a})$.

1-25. Along the bank of a stream of water two points A and B are laid out 100 yd apart. A tree is visible from points A and B across the stream and very near to the opposite bank of the stream. The angle at A subtended by the distance from B to the tree is found to be 30°, and the angle at B subtended by the distance from A to the tree is 105°. With these data calculate:

a. Angle at the tree subtended by the distance AB

b. Width of the stream

1-26. Water is flowing into a conical reservoir 20 ft deep and 10 ft across the top, at the rate of 15 cfm. Find how fast the surface is rising when the water is 8 ft deep.

1-27. In the expression $R = re^{\tan x}$, where r is a constant and e is the natural logarithm base,

a. What value of x will give $R = r$?

b. What value of X will give $R = 0$?

1-28. Two ships leave the same port at the same time, one sailing due northeast, at a rate of 6 mph, and the other sailing due north at a rate of 10 mph. Find the distance between the two ships after 3 hr of sailing.

1-29. The equation of a parabola is $x^2 = (b^2/a)y$, where b is the limit of x and a is the limit of y. Show by calculus that the area B equals $\frac{1}{3}ab$, and that the area C equals $\frac{2}{3}ab$ (Fig. 1-P-29).

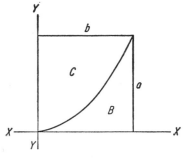

Fig. 1-P-29

1-30. How would you determine logarithmic functions of an angle greater than 90°?

1-31. Simplify the following mathematical expressions:

a. $\dfrac{3}{5x^{-2}} + \dfrac{5}{3x^{-2}}$

b. $(8y^6 Z^9)^{-\frac{2}{3}}$

c. $\dfrac{a^{-1} x^{-1}}{a^{-1} + x^{-1}}$

d. $\dfrac{\sqrt{10}}{\sqrt[3]{20}}$

e. Solve for x: $\log_4 3 + \log_4 [x - (5/3)] = 2$

1-32. Two sides of a triangle are 84 and 48 ft. The angle opposite the 84-ft side is 35°20′. Find the other two interior angles and the third side.

1-33. A trapezoidal trough has a bottom twice as wide as the slant length of a side. What angle does the side make with the bottom for maximum capacity of the trough?

1-34. Solve for x by logarithms and *show each step:* $x = 5.29(0.896)^{0.435}$.

1-35. The half-life of a radioactive element is the time required for half a given quantity of that element to disintegrate into a new element. For example, it takes 1,600 years for half a given quantity of radium to change into radon. In another 1,600 years, half the remainder will have disintegrated, leaving one-quarter of the original amount. The half-life of radium is therefore said to be 1,600 years. If the rate of disintegration of a radioactive material is 35 parts per 100 every hour, what is the half-life of this material?

1-36. Find the coordinates of the maximum ordinate on the curve

$$y - 10 = 3x^2 - 2x$$

1-37. *a.* Plot the curve $y = x^3/100 - 5x/4$ for the interval $x = 0$ to $x = 9$.
b. Write the equation of the tangent to the curve at $x = 5$.
c. Calculate the area between the tangent defined in (*b*), the x axis, and the line $x = 5$.

1-38. A cylindrical tank having a flat top and bottom is to have a capacity of 10,000 cu ft. What should be its diameter and length if the surface area is to be a minimum?

1-39. A surveyor runs a line $AC = 380.00$ ft. With 0 as the mid-point on the line AC, he lays out a 20° curve CB. What is the distance between A and B? (See Fig. 1-P-39.)

FIG. 1-P-39

1-40. If x approaches zero in the expression $y = (5x^3 - \cos x + e^x)/(x^2 + 2x)$, then what does y approach as a limit?

1-41. Find the value of $\int_0^{\pi/2} \sin \theta \cos \theta \, d\theta$.

Mechanics

Mechanics is the most basic of all the different subjects which combine to make up the composite of engineering. Many of the other subjects are essentially expansions of the fundamentals of mechanics, and a satisfactory handling of them is dependent upon a good grasp of these fundamentals. This is particularly true of fluid mechanics, thermodynamics, and mechanics of materials. To a lesser degree most of the other phases of engineering also require a firm foundation in mechanics for a satisfactory understanding of their principles. For this reason many of the fundamentals examinations place more emphasis on mechanics than on any of the other subjects.

Conventionally the subject of mechanics is divided into two parts, statics and dynamics. That is the division which will be used here, with the addition of a short discussion of friction, which will be treated as a separate subdivision because of the difficulty this particular phase of the subject seems to cause many engineers. There will be no attempt to treat the subject exhaustively, and only the high points will be reviewed, with particular emphasis on those portions of the subject which have been important in past fundamentals examinations.

2-1. Statics. The subject of statics can be summarized by the statement of Newton's first law of motion. "When a body is at rest or moving with constant speed in a straight line, the resultant of all of the forces exerted on the body is zero." Mathematically this can be written as:

$$\Sigma F_x = 0 \qquad \Sigma F_z = 0$$
$$\Sigma F_y = 0 \qquad \Sigma M = 0$$

or the summation of all the forces in the X, Y, and Z planes must equal zero and the summation of all moments must also equal zero. These conditions are both necessary and sufficient.

The study of statics consists merely of the development of different methods of satisfying the above four equations, which reduce to three equations for the two-dimensional case.

2-2. Vectors. Perhaps the best place to start is to review the subject of vectors. Forces are vectors, and both the magnitude of the force and its direction of application must be given before the force is completely defined. A vector quantity is one which has both magnitude and direction. If only the magnitude is given the quantity is not a vector but a scalar quantity. A vector quantity can be represented graphically by an arrow of the correct length, pointed in the proper direction. Vector quantities can be added vectorially graphically by moving the vector to be added parallel to itself until the tail or starting point of the vector to be added (the second vector) just touches the head or ending point of the vector to which it is to be added (the first vector). The vector sum will then be a vector starting from the tail of the first vector and ending at the head of the second vector. This process can be repeated for any number of vectors; the tail of the third vector should just touch the head of the second, etc. The final sum of all the vectors will be the vector starting at the tail (or beginning) of the first vector and ending at the head (or ending) of the last vector. This is shown graphically in Fig. 2-1. Note that we have added only the vector forces and have ignored any moments that may be present. These must be handled separately and will be discussed later.

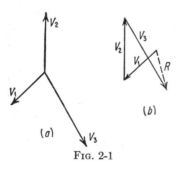

Fig. 2-1

The described method, when two forces are considered, is sometimes termed the "triangle law," which may be stated as follows: "The resultant of two concurrent forces is represented in magnitude and in direction by the third side of a triangle, the other two sides of which represent the two forces in magnitude and direction."

A slightly different method of describing the same thing is by the "parallelogram law," which can be stated as: "The resultant of two forces which act on a rigid body is represented in magnitude and in direction by the diagonal of a parallelogram, the sides of which represent the magnitudes and directions of the two forces." These are illustrated in Fig. 2-2.

All the above methods are essentially the same, and any number of vectors can be added by either

Fig. 2-2

method by first adding vector 1 to vector 2, getting resultant 1, and then adding R_1 and V_3, getting R_2, which is equal to $V_1 + V_2 + V_3$, etc. (Fig. 2-1).

If two vectors can be added to equal a third vector, then it should also be possible to divide any single vector into two smaller vectors; this can be done. Any vector can be divided into two or more

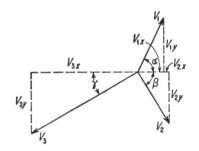

Fig. 2-3

$$\Sigma F_x = V_{1x} + V_{2x} + V_{3x} = V_1 \cos \alpha + V_2 \cos \beta - V_3 \cos \gamma$$
$$\Sigma F_y = V_{1y} + V_{2y} + V_{3y} = V_1 \sin \alpha - V_2 \sin \beta - V_3 \sin \gamma$$

Total angles, measured from 0 to 360°, may be used, but it is usually easier to sketch the problem and use angles of 90° or less.

components. For mathematical calculations it is usually convenient to divide the vector into its components in the X and Y directions for two-dimensional problems and into its X, Y, and Z components for three-dimensional problems. The two-dimensional case is illustrated in Fig. 2-3. Here we see that each of the individual

vectors is broken down into its X and Y components, and then all
the X components and all the Y components are added. The
resultant component forces obtained are the X and Y components
of the resultant of these three forces and are easily calculated as
shown, with $R = \sqrt{R_x{}^2 + R_y{}^2}$ and the angle equal to $\tan^{-1}(R_y/R_x)$.

Often the summation of the component forces alone will not be
sufficient to give the required answer. In such an event it will be
necessary to use the summation of the moments as well. An
example is shown in Fig. 2-4. Here we have a beam loaded as

FIG. 2-4

$$\Sigma F_y = 0 = R_1 + R_2 - 7 - 10 - 4$$
$$\Sigma M_A = 0 = -3 \times 7 - 7 \times 10 - 10 \times 4 \mid 12R_2$$
$$R_2 = \frac{21 + 70 + 40}{12} = 10.9 \text{ lb}$$
$$R_1 = 21 - 10.9 = 10.1 \text{ lb}$$

Check by taking $\Sigma M_B = 0 = 2 \times 4 + 5 \times 10 + 9 \times 7 - 12R_1$.

$$R_1 = \frac{8 + 50 + 63}{12} = 10.1 \text{ lb}$$

shown. There is no component in the X direction, and there are
two unknown quantities R_1 and R_2. Two equations are required
to determine the two unknowns; these equations result from the two
relationships that the summation of the forces in the Y direction
must equal zero and the summation of moments about any point in
the system must also equal zero for the system to be in equilibrium.

2-3. Coplanar Forces. All determinate statics problems can be
solved by the application of the two requirements that the summation of all forces and the summation of all moments must equal zero.
A considerable saving in time and effort can often be made, however,
by a variation in the method of application of these requirements.
An important simplification can often be made, for instance, by the
application of the principle that if three forces are in equilibrium

the forces must be coplanar and must also be either parallel or concurrent. This means that if we have three forces acting in a static condition, either these three forces must be parallel or else the lines of action of these three forces, when extended, must intersect at a single point. This principle can be extended to include the case of four coplanar forces by obtaining the resultant of two of the four forces, which then gives us three forces. The cases of five or more coplanar forces can also be treated similarly by the method of combining two or more forces into a single resultant. Examples of the

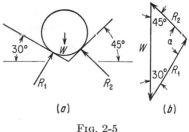

Fig. 2-5

application of this principle are shown in Fig. 2-5, where it is required to find the reactions of the planes on a 100-lb sphere held as shown.

This problem can be solved graphically by constructing the force triangle as shown, since we know both the magnitude and the direction of the weight force W, and the directions of the forces R_1 and R_2. The mathematical solution follows directly from the figure by the application of the law of sines.

$$\frac{W}{\sin \alpha} = \frac{R_1}{\sin 45°} = \frac{R_2}{\sin 30°} \qquad \alpha = 180 - (30 - 45) = 105°$$

$$R_1 = \frac{\sin 45°}{\sin 105°} \times W = \frac{0.707}{0.966} \times 100 = 73.2 \text{ lb}$$

$$R_2 = \frac{\sin 30°}{\sin 105°} \times W = \frac{0.500}{0.966} \times 100 = 51.8 \text{ lb}$$

2-4. Free-body Diagrams. Another of the methods of attacking statics problems which should be reviewed here is the concept of the "free-body diagram." When working a problem concerning the equilibrium of a body or a juncture of forces, it is necessary to consider *all* the forces acting on the particular body or point under investigation. It is just as important to omit any force which does not act on the body being investigated, since one force too many or one force too few would destroy the conditions of equilibrium. The first step in attacking a problem in statics should then be the determination of just which forces are acting upon the body or juncture under investigation. The diagram of all these forces is called a free-body diagram. First a decision must be made as to what constitutes the body to be used. The writer then finds it convenient to draw a line around that part of the system to be considered as the free body. This serves to give a somewhat clearer picture and isolates the body from the ground or from any other body. All known external forces acting on the free body should then be clearly shown on the diagram with their correct magnitudes and directions. The known external forces generally include the forces applied to the body and the weight of the body. The weight of a body will act as if it were concentrated at the center of mass of the body. The reactions to be solved for are exerted at the points where the free body is supported or connected to other bodies. The points of application of these unknown reactions will be known, but the directions of the forces may or may not be known, and each force may or may not be accompanied by a couple. Some samples of free-body diagrams are shown in Fig. 2-6. The unknown forces should be labeled and the senses of these unknown forces assumed. If the assumed sense of an unknown force is incorrect, subsequent calculations will show the correct direction. All the internal forces in a free-body diagram will be balanced within the free body and will have no effect on any of the external forces acting.

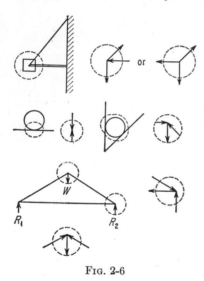

FIG. 2-6

2-5. Method of Joints. Figure 2-7 is an example of a statics problem taken from a past engineer-in-training examination and serves to illustrate some of the above points. Here it is required to determine the reactions at A and G and the forces in the various members of the truss.

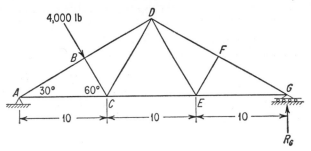

Fig. 2-7

The three external forces acting on the framework are the reactions R_A and R_G and the applied force of 4,000 lb. The vertical force at G, R_G, may be found by taking moments about point A.

$$\Sigma M_A = 0 = -4,000 \times 10 \cos 30° + 30 R_G$$
$$R_G = \frac{34,600}{30} = 1,156 \text{ lb}$$

From $\Sigma F_y = 0$,

$$A_y + 1,153 - 4,000 \cos 30° = 0$$
$$A_y = 2,308 \text{ lb}$$
$$A_x = 4,000 \sin 30° = 2,000 \text{ lb}$$

Construct a free-body diagram about point A (Fig. 2-8). Here we have two unknowns, the forces in AB and AC. These can be

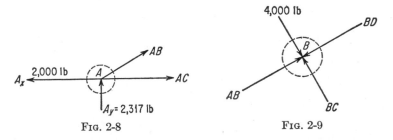

Fig. 2-8   Fig. 2-9

determined by satisfying the two equilibrium relationships: $\Sigma F_x = 0$ and $\Sigma F_y = 0$.

$$\Sigma F_x = 0 = -2,000 + AC + AB \cos 30°$$
$$\Sigma F_y = 0 = 2,308 + AB \sin 30°$$

$AB = -2,308/\sin 30° = -4,616$ lb, so the assumed direction of action of the force in member AB was incorrect, and AB is in compression, not in tension as tentatively expected.

$AC = 2,000 - AB \cos 30° = 6,000$ lb tension. We now have two unknown forces meeting at point B and three unknown forces meeting at point C. Since we have only two equations at our disposal ($\Sigma F_x = 0$ and $\Sigma F_y = 0$), we next solve for the forces acting at point B (Fig. 2-9).

B is taken as a pin joint, so it can withstand no torque. Therefore, the applied force of 4,000 lb must be resisted entirely by member BC. The force in BC will then equal 4,000 lb compression. Similarly, the force in BD will equal 4,616 lb compression.

FIG. 2-10   FIG. 2-11

There are now three unknown forces at point D and two at point C, so the forces acting at point C can now be determined (Fig. 2-10).

$$\Sigma F_x = 0 = -6,000 + 4,000 \cos 60° + CD \cos 60° + CE$$
$$\Sigma F_y = 0 = -4,000 \sin 60° + CD \sin 60°$$

which gives $CD = 4,000$ lb tension. Then

$$CE + 6,000 - 2,000 - 2,000 = 2,000 \text{ lb tension}$$

Now two of the four forces acting at point D are known and the remaining two unknown forces may be solved for (Fig. 2-11).

$$\Sigma F_x = 0 = BD \cos 30° - CD \cos 60° + DE \cos 60° - DF \cos 30°$$
$$\Sigma F_y = 0 = BD \sin 30° - CD \sin 60° - DE \sin 60° + DF \sin 30°$$

Solution of these two equations gives $DE = 0$ and $DF = 2,310$ lb. Examination of the forces at point F indicates that since F is a pin joint, the force in EF must equal zero and $FG = DF = 2,310$ lb compression.

Examination of the forces acting at point E (Fig. 2-12) shows that $EG = CE = 2,000$ lb tension.

FIG. 2-12   FIG. 2-13

The forces acting at point G must total to zero if the analysis is correct (Fig. 2-13).

$$\Sigma F_x = 2,310 \cos 30° - 2,000 = 0$$
$$2,000 - 2,000 = 0$$
$$\Sigma F_y = 1,156 - 2,310 \sin 30° = 0$$
$$1,156 - 1,155 = 1 \text{ (slide-rule discrepancy)}$$

The check indicates that the calculations are correct.

The method used in determining the forces in the members of the truss is termed the "method of joints."

Another selected example is shown in Fig. 2-14. The problem is to determine:

- *a.* The vertical components of the reactions at M and G
  b. The horizontal components of the reactions at M and G
  c. The stress in member DH

Since point G is on rollers, it can withstand no horizontal force. All the horizontal force must, then, be resisted at point M. The 50-kip load must first be resolved into its x and y components. Call the 50-kip load P. Then

$$\tan^{-1} (20/75) = \tan^{-1} 0.267 = 15°$$
$$P_x = 50 \text{ kips} \sin 15° = 12.9 \text{ kips}$$
$$P_y = 50 \text{ kips} \cos 15° = 48.3 \text{ kips}$$

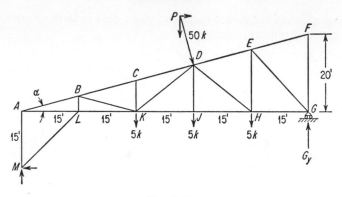

FIG. 2-14

Taking moments about point M gives $DJ = \frac{3}{5} \times 20 = 12$ ft.

$$\Sigma M_M = 0 = -30 \times 5 \text{ kips} - 45 \times 5 \text{ kips} - 60 \times 5 \text{ kips} - 45$$
$$\times 48.3 \text{ kips} - (12 + 15) \times 12.9 \text{ kips} + 75G_y$$
$$G_y = \frac{3,198}{75} = 42.6 \text{ kips}$$

From $\Sigma F_y = 0$,

$$M_y = 5 \text{ kips} + 5 \text{ kips} + 5 \text{ kips} + 48.3 \text{ kips} - G_y = 20.7 \text{ kips}$$

This can be checked by taking moments about point G.

$$\Sigma M_G = 0 = 15 \times 5 \text{ kips} + 30 \times 5 \text{ kips} + 45 \times 5 \text{ kips} + 30$$
$$\times 48.3 \text{ kips} - 12 \times 12.9 \text{ kips} - 75 \, M_y - 15M_z$$
$$M_y = \frac{1,551}{75} = 20.7 \text{ kips}$$

which checks. To complete this check we must know M_z, which equals P_x since $G_x = 0$.

$$M_x = 12.9 \text{ kips}$$

acting to the left from $\Sigma F_x = 0$. The answers to parts (a) and (b) are, then,

a. $M_y = 20.7$ kips $G_y = 42.6$ kips
b. $M_x = -12.9$ kips (or 12.9 kips to the left) $G_z = 0$

2-6. Method of Sections. We can determine the force (the word "stress" should actually be "force," since stress is force divided by area and the cross-sectional area of member DH is not given) in member DH by the method of joints as illustrated in the previous example, starting at either point M or point G. A quicker way is the method of sections. First, cut a section through members DE, DH, and JH, and draw the resulting free-body diagram, showing the actions of all the external forces (Fig. 2-15).

FIG. 2-15   FIG. 2-16

The directions of the forces in members DE, DH, and JH are assumed; if these directions are later found to be in error, this will be shown by the signs of the answers. There are three unknown quantities; thus, three equations are necessary. Since the conditions of $\Sigma F_x = 0$, $\Sigma F_y = 0$, and $\Sigma M = 0$ must all be met for equilibrium to exist, three equations can be written.

First, the angle between DH and the horizontal must be determined (Fig. 2-16).

$$\beta = \tan^{-1}(12/15) = 38.7° \qquad \sin \beta = 0.625$$
$$\cos \beta = 0.781$$
$$\alpha = \tan^{-1}(20/75) = 15° \qquad \sin \alpha = 0.258$$
$$\cos \alpha = 0.966$$

$$\Sigma F_x = 0 = -M_x + P_x + DE \cos \alpha + JH - DH \cos \beta$$
$$0 = 0.966DE - 0.781DH + JH$$
$$\Sigma F_y = 0 = M_y - 5 \text{ kips} - 5 \text{ kips} - P_y + DH \sin \beta - DE \sin \alpha$$
$$37.6 = 0.625DH - 0.258DE$$
$$\Sigma M_M = 0 = -30 \times 5 \text{ kips} - 5 \text{ kips} \times 45 - 45P - 27P_x - DE$$
$$\times 15 \cos \alpha - 15JH + 45DH \sin \beta - 27DH \cos \beta$$
$$2{,}896 = 49.2DH - 15JH - 14.5DE$$

Simultaneous solution of these three equations gives $DH = 77.2$ kips. Note that the direction of the force in DE was incorrectly

FIG. 2-17

assumed and that this member is actually in compression instead of in tension as initially assumed.

The same result can be obtained more easily by taking the section on the right end of the truss (Fig. 2-17).

$$\Sigma F_x = -DE \cos \alpha - JH + DH \cos \beta = 0$$
$$- 0.966DE - JH + 0.781DH = 0$$
$$\Sigma F_y = 42.6 \text{ kips} - 5 - DH \sin \beta - DE \sin \alpha$$
$$37.6 \text{ kips} = 0.625DH + 0.258DE$$
$$\Sigma M_G = 0 = 5 \text{ kips} \times 15 + 20 \cos \alpha \times DE - 15 \sin \beta \times DH$$
$$75 \text{ kips} = -19.3DE - 9.38DH$$

Simultaneous solution of these three equations also gives $DH = 77.1$ kips, which checks.

2-7. Center of Gravity. The location of the center of gravity of a body or of a system is sometimes important because, as previously noted, the weight of the body or system acts at its center of gravity. Later, when we review the subject of dynamics, the location of the center of gravity will again prove important because the inertia of a body acts at the center of gravity (or the center of mass). By definition, the sum of all the moments due to the weight (or mass) of a body about its center of gravity must equal zero, which gives the mathematical expression $\Sigma r \, \Delta W = 0$, where r is the distance to the infinitesimal weight ΔW, and the summation of all the ΔW's equals the total weight.

2-8. Centroid. For a plane surface, which has no weight, the term center of gravity is replaced by the "centroid of the area," which gives the mathematical expression $\Sigma r \,\Delta A = 0$. Since we know that the weight of a body or system will act as if it were concentrated at the center of gravity, the moment of a body or system about any point 0 will equal WS, where S is the horizontal distance from point 0 to the center of gravity. In addition, the moment of the body or system about the point 0 will also equal $\Sigma a \,\Delta W$, where

ΔW is an increment of the weight of the system and a is the horizontal distance from 0 to the center of gravity of that increment of weight. The distance from the point 0 to the center of gravity

Fig. 2-18

can then be determined by setting these two equations equal to each other and solving for S, or $(\Sigma a \,\Delta W)/W = S$. Referring to Fig. 2-18, this can be illustrated as follows:

$$S = \frac{\Sigma a \,\Delta W}{\Sigma \,\Delta W} = \frac{a_2 W_2 + a_3 W_3}{W_1 + W_2 + W_3}$$

Taking moments about the center of gravity of W_1, if we take $a_2 = 5$ ft, $a_3 = 12$ ft, $W_1 = 3$ lb, $W_2 = 5$ lb, $W_3 = 7$ lb, then the distance from the center of gravity of W_1 to the center of gravity of the system is:

$$S = (5 \times 5 + 12 \times 7)/(3 + 5 + 7) = 7.27 \text{ ft}$$

To prove this, calculate the sum of all the moments about the center of gravity of the system.

$$\Sigma M_{CG} = W_1 \times 7.27 + W_2 \times 2.27 - W_3 \times 4.73$$
$$= 21.81 + 11.35 - 33.11 = 0.05$$

or zero, considering slide-rule inaccuracy, which checks the location of the center of gravity.

Another illustration is afforded by the determination of the centroid of a triangle.

First orient the triangle so that the apex lies on the Y axis and the base is parallel to the Y axis (Fig. 2-19).

$$S = \frac{\int_0^h x \, dA}{A} \qquad dA = b' \, dx$$

$$b' = (x/h) \times b \qquad \text{giving } dA = (b/h) \cdot x \, dx$$

$$A = \tfrac{1}{2}bh$$

$$S = \frac{\int_0^h x \, b/h \, x \, dx}{\tfrac{1}{2}bh} = \frac{b/h \int_0^h x^2 \, dx}{\tfrac{1}{2}bh} = \frac{\tfrac{1}{3}h^3}{\tfrac{1}{2}h^2} = \tfrac{2}{3}h$$

or the centroidal axis of a triangle is two-thirds the distance from the apex to the base. By repeating the above calculations for

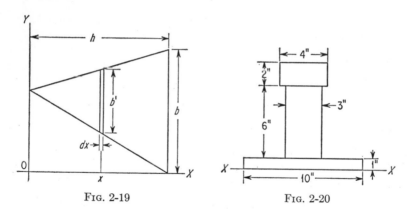

FIG. 2-19   FIG. 2-20

different orientations it may be shown that the centroid is at the intersection of the three lines drawn parallel to each of the three sides at distances one-third the way from the side to the opposite vertex. If the triangle had thickness and weight, the distance to the center of gravity would equal

$$\frac{\int x \, dW}{W} = \frac{\int x \, dA \cdot t \cdot w}{A \cdot t \cdot w} = \frac{\int x \, dA}{A}$$

which is the same as the calculation for the centroid of the area.

Another past examination problem was as follows:

- Find the location of the horizontal centroidal axis of the built-up beam shown in Fig. 2-20.

$$\bar{y} = \frac{\Sigma s \, \Delta A}{A} = \frac{\frac{1}{2}(10 \times 1) + (1 + 3)(6 \times 3) + (1 + 6 + 1)(2 \times 4)}{10 \times 1 + 6 \times 3 + 4 \times 2}$$
$$- 3.91 \text{ in.}$$

Another problem was stated as follows:

- A horizontal plate rests on three posts: A, B, C. Material of uniform density is piled on the plate at a depth increasing uniformly from zero at the right edge to a maximum at the left edge. If the total weight of the material is 1,000 lb, what are the reactions at A, B, and C? Disregard the weight of the plate. (See Fig. 2-21.)

This problem can be solved by determining the location of the center of gravity and then proceeding as if all the weight were concentrated at that point. The center of gravity will be located two-thirds of the distance from end C to end AB and midway between the 9-ft edges A and B.

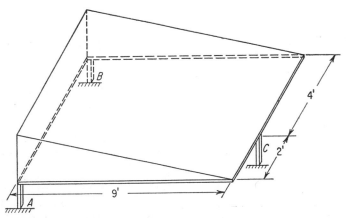

Fig. 2-21

From
$$\Sigma F_y = 0 = -1{,}000 + A + B + C$$
$$\Sigma M_{A-B} = 0 = -1{,}000 \times 3 + 9C$$
which gives
$$C = 333 \text{ lb}$$
$$\Sigma M_{\text{edge}\,B} = 0 = -3 \times 1{,}000 + 4C + 6A$$
$$A = \frac{1{,}667}{6} = 278 \text{ lb}$$
$$B = 1{,}000 - 278 - 333 = 389 \text{ lb}$$
or, taking
$$\Sigma M_{\text{edge}\,A} = 0 = -1{,}000 \times 3 + 2C + 6B$$
$$B = \frac{2{,}334}{6} = 389 \text{ lb}$$

which checks.

One more example, illustrating that the center of gravity or centroid need not always lie within the piece, is afforded by a past examination problem:

> • Find the location of the centroid of the figure shown in Fig. 2-22.

Find the distance of the centroidal axis from the left edge.

$$\frac{(5 \times 2) \times 1 + (6 \times 1)(2 + 3)}{(5 \times 2) + (6 \times 1)} = 2.50 \text{ in.}$$

Next determine the distance of the centroidal axis above the base

$$\frac{(5 \times 2) \times 2\tfrac{1}{2} + (6 \times 1) \times \tfrac{1}{2}}{(5 \times 2) + (6 \times 1)} = 1.75 \text{ in.}$$

To summarize, the resultant of the weight of a body or system will pass through one point in the body, or the body extended, for all orientations of the body; this point is defined as the center of gravity of the body or system. The centroid of an area corresponds to the center of gravity of a thin plate and may be determined as the center of gravity is determined, by assuming the area to be a thin plate.

2-9. Friction and Friction Angle. The next important topic to be discussed is the effect of friction. A frictional force will always be

Fig. 2-22

in such a direction as to resist motion. It is a passive force and can never exceed whatever force may be applied to an object. It can never cause motion; it may vary from zero to a maximum. The maximum frictional force which can be exerted on an object is equal to the coefficient of friction times the force *normal* to the surface along which the frictional force is exerted. This is easily demonstrated in its simplest form by the forces acting on a block resting on an inclined plane (Fig. 2-23). In this figure we see that the frictional force is equal to $W \cos \varphi \times \mu$, or the normal force times the coefficient of friction between the block and the plane.

FIG. 2-23. μ = coefficient of friction between block and plane.

FIG. 2-24

The force parallel to the face of the plane tending to cause the block to slide down the plane is equal to $W \sin \varphi$. If the angle of the plane is adjusted so that slipping impends, or if the block is pushed to start it moving and the velocity of the block down the plane remains constant, the value of the angle φ is termed the "friction angle." In this case the frictional force resisting motion will be just equal to the force component $W \sin \varphi$. This gives the relationship $W \sin \varphi = \mu W \cos \varphi$, which reduces to $\mu = \tan \varphi$, or the coefficient of friction between the block and the plane is equal to the tangent of the friction angle. This concept of a friction angle is extremely useful and considerably simplifies the working of the more complicated friction problems. A brief analysis will show the reader that it is possible to add the friction angle to whatever mechanical angle is being considered (or subtract the friction angle from the mechanical angle) to obtain an equivalent angle of a frictionless system, and the answer can be readily calculated. The method is illustrated as follows:

- Referring to Fig. 2-24, how large a horizontal force F must be applied to a block of weight W resting on an incline of

angle α to cause motion to impend up the slope?   The coefficient of friction between the block and the slope is μ.

The force acting up the plane parallel to it equals $F \cos \alpha$.   The
forces resting motion are the force down the slope due to the weight
of the block, equal to $W \sin \alpha$, and the frictional resistance equal
to the force exerted by and on the block normal to the plane—N
times the coefficient of friction μ. N is made up of two components,
$W \cos \alpha$ and $F \sin \alpha$.

Adding the forces acting, we have

$$F \cos \alpha = W \sin \alpha + (W \cos \alpha + F \sin \alpha)\mu$$

and if we substitute $\tan \varphi$ for its equivalent, μ, we get

$$F \cos \alpha = W \sin \alpha + (W \cos \alpha + F \sin \alpha) \frac{\sin \varphi}{\cos \varphi}$$

or

$$F \cos \alpha \cos \varphi = W \sin \alpha \cos \varphi + W \cos \alpha \sin \varphi + F \sin \alpha \sin \varphi$$

which gives

$$F(\cos \alpha \cos \varphi - \sin \alpha \sin \varphi) = W(\sin \alpha \cos \varphi + \cos \alpha \sin \varphi)$$

which reduces to

$$F \cos (\alpha + \varphi) = W \sin (\alpha + \varphi)$$
or
$$F = W \tan (\alpha + \varphi)$$

which is the same result we should have obtained had we considered
the slope angle to be $\alpha +$ the friction angle, or $(\alpha + \varphi)$, and considered the surfaces to be frictionless.

Utilizing the concept of friction angle, resketch the problem as
shown in Fig. 2-25.   In this case we get:

$$F \cos (\alpha + \varphi) = W \sin (\alpha + \varphi)$$
$$F = W \tan (\alpha + \varphi)$$

as before.

Similarly it can be shown that to find the force to just hold
the block in place we can consider the friction angle as being
subtracted from the slope angle and again treat the system as if it
were frictionless.

From Fig. 2-26, $F \cos (\alpha - \varphi) = W \sin (\alpha - \varphi)$
or $F = W \tan (\alpha - \varphi)$

By adding or subtracting the friction angle it is possible to incorporate the effects of friction without treating the frictional components separately.

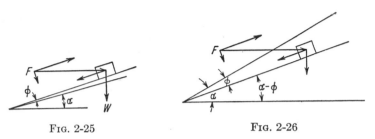

Fɪɢ. 2-25   Fɪɢ. 2-26

One implication of the friction-angle concept is immediately discernible, i.e., if the friction angle is greater than the angle of the slope, the system will be statically stable.

Figure 2-27 shows the condition of a statically stable wedge where $\varphi > \alpha$ and the weight will not slip.

On the other hand, Fig. 2-28 shows a wedge which is not statically stable. The weight would slide as if on a frictionless plane with a slope of $\alpha - \varphi$; or the wedge would shoot out if the force F were

Fɪɢ. 2-27   Fɪɢ. 2-28

removed. Also, if the sum of the slope angle plus the friction angle equals or exceeds 90°, it would be impossible to push the block up the slope with a force which is applied horizontally.

A word of caution should be given about the use of the friction angle. Do not change the direction of the application of the force. As an example, if it is desired to determine the force required to push a block up a plane, the direction of the force must not be changed when the friction angle is added to the slope angle to determine the resisting force (Fig. 2-29).

$$F \cos \alpha = W \sin (\alpha + \varphi)$$

$$F = \frac{W}{\cos \alpha} \sin (\alpha + \varphi)$$

where F is the force parallel to the face of the plane required to push the block up the plane.

FIG. 2-29   FIG. 2-30

A more involved type of wedge and friction problem is illustrated in Fig. 2-30.

- For the wedge system shown, find the force F required to raise the weight W. The coefficient of friction for all surfaces is equal to $\mu = \tan \varphi$.

Applying the principle of friction angle to the problem we can

FIG. 2-31

construct a new figure which will incorporate the effects of the friction angles and give us an equivalent frictionless system (Fig. 2-31). Here we can determine the relationship between F and W by means of the conservation of energy (or equivalence of work); i.e.,

$$FS = Wh_{\text{effective}}$$

$h_{\text{effective}}$ will be made up of two parts:

$$h_{eff} = S[\tan(\alpha + \varphi) + \tan \varphi] + h'$$

where h' is the additional elevation due to the movement to the left which results from the movement of the upper right corner

FIG. 2-32

of the weight in the figure along the back angle of the vertical incline. These quantities are shown in Fig. 2-32.

$$\frac{M}{\sin \varphi} = \frac{h}{\sin \gamma} \qquad h' = M \sin(\alpha + \varphi)$$

$$\gamma = 90 - (\alpha + 2\varphi)$$

$$\sin \gamma = \cos(\alpha + 2\varphi)$$

$$h' = \frac{\sin \varphi}{\sin \gamma} \times h \times \sin(\alpha + \varphi)$$

or

$$h' = \frac{\sin \varphi \times \sin(\alpha + \varphi)}{\cos(\alpha + 2\varphi)} \times h$$

$$h_{eff} = S[\tan(\alpha + \varphi) + \tan \varphi]\left[1 + \frac{\sin \varphi}{\cos(\alpha + 2\varphi)} \sin(\alpha + \varphi)\right]$$

which gives

$$F = W[\tan (\alpha + \varphi) + \tan \varphi] \left[1 + \frac{\sin \varphi}{\cos (\alpha + 2\varphi)} \sin (\alpha + \varphi) \right]$$

If we take $W = 1,000$ lb, $\mu = 0.3$, and $\alpha = 5°$, this will give

$$F = W(\tan 21.7° + \tan 16.7°) \left(1 + \frac{\sin 16.7°}{\cos 38.4°} \sin 21.7° \right)$$

$$= W(0.398 - 0.300) \left(1 + \frac{0.288}{0.784} \times 0.370 \right)$$

$$= 793 \text{ lb}$$

It is of interest that the force required to lift the weight would be less if the taper, instead of being on the underside of the weight,

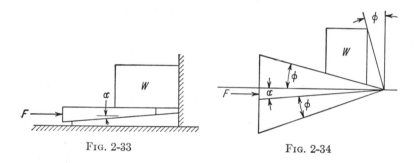

FIG. 2-33   FIG. 2-34

were supplied by a supplementary complementing wedge (Fig. 2-33). Here, as before, we shall determine the relationship between F and W by means of friction angles. μ for all surfaces is the same. The equivalent frictionless system is shown in Fig. 2-34. Note that for this case the angle α is below the horizontal. It can be seen that the frictional force acting horizontally on the block is less than before, which in turn reduces the friction acting downward. This reduces the load to be raised by the wedge and thus reduces the magnitude of the required force F. For this case we find (Fig. 2-35)

$$F = W[\tan \varphi + \tan (\alpha + \varphi)] \left(1 + \frac{\sin \varphi}{\cos 2\varphi} \sin \varphi \right)$$

Substituting the same numerical values as before gives

$$F = 0.698 \left[1 + \frac{(\sin 16.7°)^2}{\cos 33.4°} \right] \times W$$
$$= 0.698 \times 1.1335 \times W$$
$$F = 768 \text{ lb}$$

The same results may be obtained by a combination of the principles of friction angle and concurrent forces in a way which is prob-

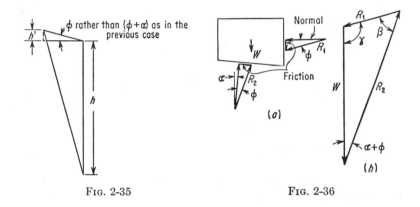

FIG. 2-35   FIG. 2-36

ably an easier method.   To use this procedure it is first necessary to draw the free-body diagrams of the block and wedge and to show all the forces acting at their effective angles (Fig. 2-36).

Referring to the figure,

$$\frac{W}{\sin \beta} = \frac{R_2}{\sin \gamma} \qquad \gamma = 90 + \varphi$$
$$\sin \gamma = \cos \varphi$$
$$\beta = 90 - (\alpha + 2\varphi)$$
$$R_2 = \frac{\cos \varphi}{\sin \beta} W = \frac{0.958}{0.784} W = 1.223W$$

The concurrent-force diagram for the wedge is shown in Fig. 2-37.

$$\frac{F}{\sin (\alpha + 2\varphi)} = \frac{R_3}{\sin \theta} \qquad \theta = 90 - \alpha$$

$$R_3 = -R_2$$

$$F = \frac{\sin (\alpha + 2\varphi)}{\sin \theta} R_3 = \frac{\sin 38.4°}{\sin 73.6°} R_2 = \frac{0.621}{0.959} 1.223W$$

$$F = 0.793W = 793 \text{ lb}$$

which checks with the result obtained by the other method.

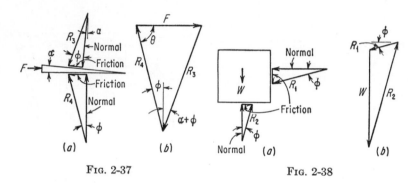

FIG. 2-37   FIG. 2-38

For the alternate case, in which the taper is supplied on the bottom of the wedge and the top of the wedge is maintained horizontal, the force diagrams are shown in Figs. 2-38 and 2-39.

Referring to Fig. 2-38,

$$\frac{R_2}{\sin (90 + \varphi)} = \frac{W}{\sin (90 - 2\varphi)}$$

giving

$$R_2 = \frac{\cos \varphi}{\sin (90 - 2\varphi)} W = 1.15W$$

From Fig. 2-39,

$$\frac{F}{\sin (\alpha + 2\varphi)} = \frac{R_3}{\sin [90 - (\alpha + \varphi)]}$$

$$F = \frac{\sin (\alpha + 2\varphi)}{\cos (\alpha + \varphi)} R_2 = \frac{0.621}{0.929} 1.15W = 768 \text{ lb}$$

which checks with the answer obtained by the previous method.

Another example is afforded by the problem illustrated in Fig. 2-40. Here it is required to determine the force F for motion to impend. Determine also the force F' which must be applied to the end of the wedge to prevent movement of blocks A and B after

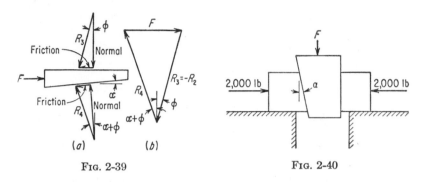

FIG. 2-39   FIG. 2-40

they have been pushed apart as far as desired. $\alpha = 10°$; $\mu = 0.3$ all surfaces.

Like most problems in mechanics, this one can be solved by a number of different methods. We shall examine two different methods here for comparison. Let us first solve the problem by applying the principle of the friction angle. We must first draw the equivalent frictionless diagram of the system, adding the friction angle φ wherever friction acts. This diagram is shown in Fig. 2-41.

FIG. 2-41

We may assume which block will move by intuition, but intuition is sometimes (!) in error, so to be safe let us analyze both possibilities, i.e., that of the left block moving and that of the right block moving. Taking first the case in which the left block moves, and assuming that the right-hand block remains stationary (if one block moves first, i.e., with a lower applied force F, the other will remain stationary), then, by equivalent work, the left block will move a distance D when the force moves a distance S, and

Left block   Right block

Fig. 2-42

$FS = 2,000 D.$ $D = S[\tan (\alpha + \varphi)$ $+ \tan \varphi] +$ distance caused by block's moving upward and outward because of its rise on the frictional slope, which additional distance we shall term D' (Fig. 2-42).

$$D' = M \cos \varphi$$
$$\frac{M}{\sin (\alpha + \varphi)} = \frac{h}{\sin \theta}$$
$$\theta = 90 - (\alpha + 2\phi)$$
$$\sin \theta = \cos (\alpha + 2\varphi)$$
$$M = \frac{\sin (\alpha + \varphi)}{\cos (\alpha + 2\varphi)} h$$

where $h =$ rise on the friction slope owing to the movement outward of $S[\tan (\alpha + \varphi) + \tan \varphi] \tan \varphi$

$$F \times S = S[\tan (\alpha + \varphi) + \tan \varphi]$$
$$\left[1 + \frac{\sin (\alpha + \varphi)}{\cos (\alpha + 2\varphi)} \tan \varphi \cos \varphi\right] 2,000$$

substituting for D'.   Substituting numerical values,

$$F = (0.503 + 0.300)\left(1 + \frac{0.451}{0.727} \times 0.300 \times 0.958\right) \times 2,000$$
$$= 1,890 \text{ lb}$$

If we now take the other possibility, i.e., that the right-hand block moves and the left-hand block remains stationary, we find, by a similar analysis, that

$$F = [\tan (\alpha + \varphi) + \tan \alpha]\left(1 + \frac{\sin \varphi \tan \varphi}{\cos 2\varphi} \cos \varphi\right) 2,000$$
$$F = (0.803)(1 + 0.099)2,000 = 1,770 \text{ lb}$$

This is less than the force required to move the left-hand block, so the right block will move and the left block will remain stationary. The difference lies in the equivalent distance D' due to the work against friction which is greater in the case of the left block, as shown in the sketch.

$$D' = M \cos \varphi \qquad \frac{M}{\sin \varphi} = \frac{h}{\sin (90 - 2\varphi)} = \frac{h}{\cos 2\varphi}$$

$$D' = \frac{\sin \varphi \cos \varphi}{\cos 2\varphi} \tan \varphi [\tan (\alpha + \varphi) + \tan \varphi] S$$

The other method to be considered is the method of concurrent forces combined with the application of the friction-angle principle.

Fig. 2-43

Fig. 2-44

To employ this method we must construct the free-body diagrams of the wedge and the blocks. Taking again the left block first (from Fig. 2-43),

$$\frac{R_1}{\sin (90 + \varphi)} = \frac{2{,}000}{\sin [90 - (\alpha + 2\varphi)]}$$

From Fig. 2-44,

$$\frac{F}{\sin (\alpha + 2\varphi)} = \frac{R_3}{\sin (90 - \varphi)}$$

FIG. 2-45

but $R_3 = -R_1$, which gives

$$F = \frac{\sin (\alpha + 2\varphi)}{\cos \varphi} \frac{\sin (90 + \varphi)}{\cos (\alpha + 2\varphi)} \, 2{,}000 = 2{,}000 \tan (\alpha + 2\varphi)$$
$$F = 1{,}890 \text{ lb}$$

$$\frac{R_4}{\sin (90 + \varphi)} = \frac{2{,}000}{\sin (90 - 2\varphi)}$$

From the sketch in Fig. 2-45,

$$\frac{F}{\sin (\alpha + 2\varphi)} = \frac{R_4}{\sin [90 - (\alpha + \varphi)]}$$
$$F = \frac{\sin (\alpha + 2\varphi)}{\cos (\alpha + \varphi)} R_4 = \frac{\sin (\alpha + 2\varphi)}{\cos (\alpha + \varphi)} \frac{\cos \varphi}{\cos 2\varphi} \, 2{,}000$$
$$F = \frac{0.687}{0.893} \frac{0.958}{0.835} \, 2{,}000 = 1{,}770 \text{ lb}$$

Since the friction angle exceeds the wedge angle α, no force need be applied to the end of the wedge to prevent movement of blocks A and B.

2-10. Jackscrew. One other example is the derivation of the mechanical efficiency of a jackscrew (Fig. 2-46). First assume a square thread, with a pitch P.

$$\text{Pitch} = \frac{1}{\text{No. of threads/in.}}$$

We shall also consider the screw to be single-threaded (lead equal to pitch). The coefficient of friction is equal to μ, and the mean thread diameter is D_m. From Fig. 2-47 we can see that if we unwind the thread, the lead angle λ is easily determined; it is equal to $\tan^{-1} (lead/D_m)$.   The friction angle φ is equal to $\tan^{-1} \mu$.   The equivalent angles of frictionless screws are $\lambda + \varphi$ if the load is being raised and $\lambda - \varphi$ if the load is being lowered.   A torque

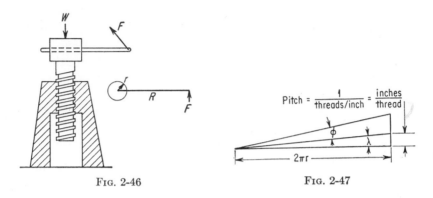

FIG. 2-46   FIG. 2-47

T_q, lb-in., applied to the jackscrew will supply a force F equal to $2T_q/D_m$ at the thread.

$$\text{Torque} = FR \qquad \text{lb-in.}$$

The equivalent force at a distance of 1 in. from the axis is then equal to the torque, or $(FR)/1 = $ torque, and the work done per revolution of the screw equals $2\pi \times$ torque.   This also equals the work done in raising the weight a distance equal to the pitch P plus the work done against friction, or

$$2\pi Tq = \pi 2r \tan (\lambda + \varphi)W$$
$$Tq = \frac{D_m \tan (\lambda + \varphi)}{2} W = r \tan (\lambda + \varphi)W = FR$$

If $\varphi > \lambda$, the jackscrew will be statically stable and will require no force on the handle to maintain the load in its position.   On the other hand, if $\lambda > \varphi$, the weight will lower by itself if all force is removed from the handle.   This case is similar to that of the wedge, and the effective angle is $\lambda - \varphi$ (Fig. 2-48).

You may have noticed that the torque in the preceding example was calculated from the equivalence of the work done on the system and the energy of the system. This is a very important relationship based on the theory of the conservation of energy. The change in energy of a system—potential energy plus kinetic energy (and heat energy resulting from friction) —will equal the work done on the system, or by the system. This will be discussed further in the next section.

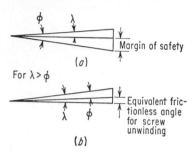

For $\lambda > \phi$

FIG. 2-48. Torque required to lower weight.

$$F \times R = Wr \tan (\varphi - \lambda)$$

2-11. Dynamics. Just as the subject of statics is based on Newton's first law of motion, the subject of dynamics is based on Newton's second law plus effects of Newton's other two laws. The first law has already been stated in the section devoted to statics, but we shall repeat it here with the other two of Newton's laws so that we shall have them all together. The three laws may be stated as follows:

1. Every body persists in its state of rest or of uniform motion in a straight line unless it is compelled by some force to change that state.

2. The rate of change of the momentum of a body is proportional to the force acting upon it and it is in the direction of the force.

3. Action and reaction are equal and opposite.

2-12. Equations of Linear Motion. The word "dynamics" implies motion and the study of dynamics is based upon the effects of motion, so we should probably start our discussion with a review of the fundamentals of motion. Linear motion, or motion along a straight line, is called "velocity," where velocity is a vector quantity (it possesses both magnitude and direction) and is equal to the rate of change of distance with time. Average velocity equals displacement/elapsed time, and if we take the distance covered as $s - s_0$ in the time interval $t - t_0$, the average velocity

$$v_{avg} = \frac{s - s_0}{t - t_0}$$

This can also be written as $v = \Delta s/\Delta t$, which, as Δt approaches zero, has the limiting value $v = ds/dt$. Similarly, the rate of change of velocity with time is termed "acceleration," and the limiting value of the acceleration, $a = dv/dt = d^2s/dt^2$. If we start with a constant acceleration, $a = dv/dt$, and integrate, we get $v = at + c_1$, where c_1 is the constant of integration. Replacing v by its equivalent, we have $ds/dt = at + c_1$, which, upon integration, gives us $s = \frac{1}{2}at^2 + c_1t + c_2$, where c_2 is the constant resulting from the second integration. If $s = s_0$ and $v = v_0$ at time $t = 0$, we can solve for the constants of integration. Substitution of these gives us the general relationship for distance: $s = s_0 + v_0t + \frac{1}{2}at^2$.

If $s = 0$ at $t = 0$, this gives us the more familiar relationship $s = v_0t + \frac{1}{2}at^2$. If the equation $v = v_0 + at$ is solved for t and the value substituted in the equation for s, we get $v^2 = v_0^2 + 2as$. Thus we can easily derive the four basic equations of linear motion:

$$v = v_0 + at$$
$$v^2 = v_0^2 + 2as$$
$$\text{avg } v = \frac{v + v_0}{2}$$
$$s = v_0t + \frac{1}{2}at^2 \quad \text{or} \quad s = v_{avg}t$$

An example of the use of these equations is afforded by a past examination problem, which asked:

• An automobile starting from rest increased its speed in 18 sec to 66 fps. What was its final speed in miles per hour? What was its average speed in miles per hour during the 18 sec its speed was increasing? Assume uniform acceleration. Find also the acceleration and the distance traveled during the 18 sec.

From $v = v_0 + at$, $v = 66$ fps, $v_0 = 0$, $t = 18$ sec, and

$$a = {}^{66}\!/_{18} = 3.67 \text{ ft/sec}^2$$

the final speed in miles per hour equals

$$66 \text{ fps} \times 3,600 \text{ sec/hr} \times 1/5,280 \text{ miles/ft}$$

which equals 45 mph.

The average speed $= (45 + 0)/2 = 22.5$ mph, and the distance traveled equals average $v \times t = {}^{66}\!\!/\!_2 \times 18 = 594$ ft.; or the distance may be calculated from

$$s = \tfrac{1}{2}at^2 = \tfrac{1}{2} \times 3.67 \times 18^2 = 594 \text{ ft}$$

2-13. Flight of a Projectile. One other example of the use of the equations of linear motion is afforded by a past examination problem which asked for details regarding the flight of a projectile. The problem and its analysis are as follows:

- A bullet leaves a gun muzzle at a velocity of 2,700 fps at an angle of 30° with the horizontal.
  - a. What is the maximum height to which the bullet will travel?
  - b. What is the maximum distance the bullet will travel horizontally measured along the same elevation as the gun muzzle? Disregard air resistance.

First sketch the figure and determine the velocity components (Fig. 2-49). The vertical component of the velocity $v_y = v \sin \alpha$,

FIG. 2-49

and the component $v_x = v \cos \alpha$. In the vertical direction the bullet will be subjected to the acceleration of gravity, and if air resistance is disregarded the acceleration will equal g. The time required for the bullet to reach its apogee can be determined from the fact that at the top the vertical velocity will equal zero. Then, from $v = v_0 + at$, we have $0 = v_y - gt$, or

$$\text{Time to apogee} = \frac{v_y}{g} = \frac{v \sin \alpha}{g}$$

The time for the bullet to fall back to the earth will equal the time to rise to the apogee, or the total time of flight will equal $2 \times [(v \sin \alpha)/g]$. The maximum height can be calculated from the relationship $v_{y\,\text{avg}} \times t = h$, where $v_{y\,\text{avg}} = (v_y + 0)/2$. The time t

to rise to the height h has already been determined, and

$$h = \frac{v_y}{2}\frac{v_y}{g} = \frac{(v_y)^2}{2g}$$

The height h can also be determined from the relationship

$$v^2 = v_0^2 + 2as$$

which gives $(v_y)^2 = 2gh$, or $h = v_y^2/2g = (v^2 \sin^2 \alpha)/2g$. The range R will equal the distance traveled horizontally during the total time of flight at the constant horizontal velocity $v_x = v \cos \alpha$. $R = v \cos \alpha \times (2v \sin \alpha)/g = 2[(v^2 \cos \alpha \sin \alpha)/g]$. This last relationship could be reduced to $R = (v^2 \sin 2\alpha)/g$, by substituting equivalent angle-function relationships, but this additional step is no advantage to the occasional user.

The numerical answers will be:

$$h = \frac{v^2 \sin^2 30°}{2g} = \frac{2,700^2 \times 0.500^2}{2 \times 32.2} = 28,300 \text{ ft}$$

$$R = 2\frac{v^2 \cos \alpha \sin \alpha}{g} = 2\frac{2,700^2 \times 0.866 \times 0.500}{32.2} = 196,000 \text{ ft}$$

Note that the only equations necessary for the solution of this problem are the basic velocity relationships: $v = v_0 + at$, $s = v_{avg}t$, and $v^2 = v_0^2 + 2as$.

2-14. Momentum and Impulse. The momentum of a body is equal to the product of its mass times its velocity, or $M = mv$. Newton's second law of motion states that $F = k(dM/dt)$, where k is the constant of proportionality. If we consider the mass as being constant, dM/dt reduces to $m(dv/dt)$, and if we select the proper units, k is equal to 1. This gives us the familiar relationship $F = ma$. A falling body has a force acting on it equal to its own weight, and the acceleration equals the acceleration of gravity; thus $W = mg$, or mass $= W/g$. Newton's second law of motion can then be stated as $F = ma$, where $m = W/g$. This is a very important relationship and is the foundation of the study of dynamics.

In addition to this, we see from Newton's second law of motion that if no external force acts, the momentum of a system will remain constant. This leads to the concept of the conservation of momentum. Since momentum is equal to $m \times v$, or is the product of a vector and a scalar, it is a vector quantity and thus must possess both magnitude and direction.

From $F = ma$ and $a = dv/dt$, we obtain $F\,dt = m\,dv$, from which we see that $F\,dt = mv_2 - mv_1$. The integral of $F\,dt$ is termed the "impulse," and the quantity $m(v_2 - v_1)$ is the change in momentum of mass m. This gives us the relationship that impulse equals change in momentum, where impulse is also a vector quantity.

To illustrate some of the above relationships let us take as an example a golf ball which is struck by a club. High-speed photography shows that the club is in contact with the ball for approximately one-half-thousandth of a second and the velocity of the ball is 250 fps immediately after being struck. What force is exerted by the club if the ball weighs $1\frac{2}{3}$ oz? We shall assume that the force is constant during the period of contact, so the impulse will equal $0.0005F$. The change in momentum of the golf ball will equal mv, or $[1.67/(16 \times 32.2)]250 = 0.810$ lb-sec, or 0.810 slug-ft/sec. Since the change in momentum is equal to the impulse, $F = 0.810/0.0005 = 1{,}620$ lb.

This problem could also have been worked using the relationships $F = ma$ and $a = \Delta v/\Delta t$, giving

$$F = \frac{1.67}{16 \times 32.2} \frac{250}{0.0005} = 1{,}620 \text{ lb}$$

It will be true of most problems in dynamics that the solution can be obtained by two or more different methods; this serves to illustrate that the relationships in mechanics are all related and that there are many ways of employing them to obtain correct answers to problems. Another example of the conservation of momentum is illustrated by the following problem:

- A plastic body weighing 100 lb is moving with a velocity of 20 fps and overtakes another plastic body, weighing 150 lb, moving in the same direction with a velocity of 15 fps. What is the final velocity, and what is the loss in kinetic energy?

From the principle of the conservation of momentum we have

$$m_1v_1 + m_2v_2 = (m_1 + m_2)v_r$$

The resulting velocity

$$v_r = \frac{m_1 v_1 + m_2 v_2}{m_1 + m_2} = \frac{100 \times 20 + 150 \times 15}{100 + 150}$$
$$= 17 \text{ fps}$$

Note that a $1/g$ factor was canceled out of each term.

$$KE \text{ initially} = \tfrac{1}{2}m_1 v_1^2 + \tfrac{1}{2}m_2 v_2^2$$
$$= \frac{100}{2g} \times 20^2 + \frac{150}{2g} \times 15^2$$
$$= 1{,}144 \text{ ft-lb}$$
$$KE \text{ final} = \tfrac{1}{2}(m_1 + m_2)v_r^2$$
$$= \frac{100 + 150}{2g} \times 17^2$$
$$= 1{,}120 \text{ ft-lb}$$

The loss in kinetic energy $= 24$ ft-lb.

Note that energy is not a vector quantity and that the direction has no bearing on the amount of kinetic energy possessed by a moving body. Momentum, on the other hand, is a vector quantity, and direction of motion is very important. It might also be mentioned that even though 24 ft-lb of mechanical energy has been lost in the impact, the total energy of the system is constant, and this lost mechanical energy will have been converted into heat because of the force of the impact and the subsequent deformation of both bodies.

The impact in this sample problem is a plastic impact or a completely inelastic impact with a coefficient of restitution equal to zero. If a small body rebounds from a very large one, such that the change of velocity of the large body is negligible, the coefficient of restitution $e = -(v_2/v_1)$. (It must be remembered that velocity is a vector quantity; thus v_2 will be opposite in sign to v_1.) If a ball rebounds or bounces up after being dropped onto a fixed plate, then

$$e = -\frac{v_2}{v_1} = \frac{\sqrt{2gh_2}}{\sqrt{2gh_1}} = \sqrt{\frac{h_2}{h_1}}$$

or the coefficient of restitution is equal to the square root of the height of bounce divided by the height of drop. If the impact is between two objects which do not differ greatly in mass, then

$$e = - \frac{v_2 - u_2}{v_1 - u_1}$$

where $v_1 - u_1$ = relative velocity before impact

$v_2 - u_2$ = relative velocity after impact

As an example of the use of this relationship, determine the velocities after impact of an 8-lb ball traveling with a velocity of 20 fps which overtakes and strikes a 12-lb ball traveling in the same direction with a velocity of 8 fps if the coefficient of restitution is 0.75 (Fig. 2-50).

$v_1 = 20$ ft/sec   8 lb $u_1 = 8$ ft/sec   12 lb

FIG. 2-50

$$e = 0.75 = - \frac{v_2 - u_2}{20 - 8}$$

or

$$9 = u_2 - v_2$$

but also

$$m_1 v_1 + m_2 u_1 = m_1 v_2 + m_2 u_2$$

$$\frac{8}{g} \times 20 + \frac{12}{g} \times 8 = \frac{8}{g} v_2 + \frac{12}{g} u_2$$

$$32 = v_2 + 1.5 u_2$$

$$9 = -v_2 + u_2$$

$$u_2 = 16.4 \text{ fps}$$

$$v_2 = 7.4 \text{ fps}$$

The velocity of the 8-lb ball reduces from 20 to 7.4 fps, and the velocity of the 12-lb ball is increased from 8 to 16.4 fps.

If the coefficient of restitution is 1, we have a perfectly elastic collision and no energy is lost. Referring to the first example in this section, if the plastic bodies had been given as elastic bodies we should have had

$$m_1 v_1 + m_2 u_1 = m_1 v_2 + m_2 u_2$$
$$\frac{1}{2} m_1 v_1^2 + \frac{1}{2} m_2 u_1^2 = \frac{1}{2} m_1 v_2^2 + \frac{1}{2} m_2 u_2^2$$

which reduces to

$$42.5 = v_2 + 1.5 u_2$$
$$737.5 = v_2^2 + 1.5 u_2^2$$

which can be solved simultaneously to give $v_2 = 14$ ft/sec and $u_2 = 19$ ft/sec.

The same result can be obtained by utilizing the relationship that

$$e = -(v_2 - u_2)/(v_1 - u_1)$$

The two cases considered have concerned bodies moving along the same line. Should the bodies be moving at an angle to each other, the same relationships would apply, but it would be necessary to consider the components of velocity in the X and Y directions and the components of momentum in the X and Y directions. This is a more complex problem, involving four equations, and will not be discussed further here.

One other important concept of linear momentum is that the linear momentum of any moving-mass system is the product of the mass of the whole system and the velocity of the mass center of the system, and its direction agrees with that of the velocity of the mass center.

The equations of equilibrium, $\Sigma F_x = 0$ and $\Sigma F_y = 0$, state that if the sum of the external forces acting on a system equals zero, the acceleration of the center of mass of that system equals zero. This means that if there is no external force acting on a system, the center of mass of the system remains at rest or continues its motion in a straight line at a constant speed. This is an example of the con-servation of momentum and may be stated as follows: "If the result-ant of the external forces which act on a body equals zero then the linear momentum of the body remains constant."

Note that the forces considered are external forces; it can, there-fore, be stated that the action of an internal force cannot result in a displacement of the center of mass of a system, or if no work is done upon (not inside) a system the location of the center of mass of the system cannot change in a horizontal direction. As an example, a 200-lb man is standing at the rear of a 450-lb barge 18 ft in length. The front of the barge is 2 ft away from a pier, but the barge is float-ing freely in the water and is not tied to anything. The man walks forward in the barge. Will he be able to reach the pier? Assume no frictional drag of any kind on the boat, i.e., no external force acting.

Since no external force is acting, the location of the center of mass of the system must remain constant. Then the moment of the system about point A must also remain constant (Fig. 2-51).

450 lb   200 lb
(a)

200 lb   450 lb
(b)

Fig. 2-51

$$M_A = -11 \times 450 - 20 \times 200$$
$$= -8{,}950 \text{ ft-lb}$$

The moment of the system about point A will be the same after the man has walked the 18 ft to the front end of the barge, so the barge must move outward x ft.

$$-8{,}950 = -450(11 + x)$$
$$- 200(2 + x)$$

$x = 5.54$ ft, or the barge will move 5.54 ft away from the pier. The man would then be 7.54 ft from the pier—a long reach; or, assuming the man moves and then the system (barge and man) moves, the 200-lb man moves 18 ft, so the 650-lb system must move

$$\frac{200}{650} \times 18 = 5.54 \text{ ft}$$

or man impulse equals barge impulse, i.e., $200(18 - x) = 450x$, giving $x = 5.54$ ft.

One further example is the classical problem of the monkey and the bananas (Fig. 2-52). Monkey and bananas weigh the same, the rope and pulley are massless, and the system is frictionless. What happens as the monkey climbs the rope?

The tension in the rope must be the same over its entire length. Thus the impulse produced by the monkey is the same as the impulse acting on the bananas, and since their masses are the same the velocities must be equal. The distance between the monkey and the bananas will, then, stay the same—at least until the bananas jam the pulley.

Fig. 2-52

Note that the location of the center of gravity in a vertical direction changes as the monkey climbs the rope. Since gravity is always acting on any earthly system, there will always be an external (gravitational) force acting. If the action of the internal force is in a vertical direction work will be done against the external force of gravity and the location of the center of gravity may change. This is evidenced by the change in potential energy of the system. This is not in conflict with the previous statements, since the complete system would include the earth; as the monkey (and the bananas) moved, so would the earth, and the center of mass of the entire system in relation to a star would not change.

2-15. Conservation of Energy. Another important relationship, which has been mentioned before, is that of the conservation of energy. The work done on a system must equal the change in energy of the system plus the energy lost in the process (e.g., energy lost in overcoming friction), if we disregard any affects of nuclear fission or change in mass. Furthermore, the work done by a force F on a body while the body undergoes a displacement is defined as the product of the displacement and the component of the force in the direction of the displacement. $W = F \cos \theta$. The magnitude of the force need have little bearing on the amount of work done. As an example, take the case of a man pushing a crate across a loading platform. The sum of the forces acting on the crate includes the force of the platform acting upward, the retarding force of friction, and the force exerted by the man causing motion. Disregarding, for the moment, the frictional force, the total force acting on the crate $= \sqrt{50^2 + 500^2} = 502$ lb (Fig. 2-53). But the work is equal to $R \times S \times \cos \theta$, or $50 \times S$. Another way of looking at it is that any work done must appear either as work against something (friction) or as an increase in kinetic or potential energy.

It is important to keep in mind that work is equal to the product of the distance times the component of the acting force in the direction of the distance. The mechanical energy of a body is the energy it possesses

FIG. 2-53

because of its position and its velocity. The energy due to position, termed the "potential energy," is equal to the weight of

the body times its height above
some arbitrarily selected datum
plane. The change in potential energy is equal to the weight of the object times the change in elevation,
or PE = $W \, \Delta h$, ft-lb. The kinetic
energy is the energy possessed by
a body by virtue of its velocity
and equals $\frac{1}{2}mv^2$. The equality

Fig. 2-54

between these two can easily be seen by taking as an example a
weight W at a height h with an initial velocity of zero. After the
weight falls the distance h it will experience a loss in potential energy
equal to $W \times h$. The force acting through the distance h will have
been W, and the object will have been subjected to a constant
acceleration g. The velocity at the end of the fall will then be
equal to $\sqrt{2gh}$ (from $v^2 = v_0^2 + 2as$, where $a = g$ and $s = h$). The
total energy is constant, so ΔKE equals $Wh = \frac{1}{2}mv^2$, which gives
$Wh = \frac{1}{2}m(2gh) = mgh$, so the loss in potential energy equals the
increase in kinetic energy. Another way of looking at it is that the
increase in potential energy is exactly equal to the work done on the
body.

As an illustrative example, let us take the case of an object which
slides down a chute onto a horizontal table, as shown in Fig. 2-54.

- Assume that the initial horizontal velocity is the same as that
  gained in sliding from A to B. What distance S along the
  horizontal plane will the object slide before coming to rest
  if the coefficient of friction is 0.3?

We can work this problem a number of different ways; let us look at
three of them.

First we shall find the answer using the velocity and acceleration
relationships. The force parallel to the surface of the plane tending
to cause the object to slide is $0.60W$. The resisting frictional force f
is equal to the normal force $(0.80W)$ times the coefficient of friction,
which gives $f = 0.24W$. The resultant force causing the object to

accelerate down the plane is then $0.60W - 0.24W = 0.36W$. Since $F = ma$, the acceleration is $a = 0.36W/(W/g) = 0.36g$. The velocity at the point B is then found to equal $\sqrt{2 \times 0.36g \times 50} = 6\sqrt{g}$, from the relationship $v^2 = v_0^2 + 2as$. The force acting on the object as it slides horizontally is equal to $-0.3W$, giving an acceleration of $-0.3g$. Since the final velocity will be zero,

$$S = \frac{v_0^2}{-2a} = \frac{36g}{0.6g} = 60 \text{ ft}$$

The second method of determining the desired distance is by means of the theory of the conservation of energy. In sliding down the plane the block will lose $30W$ ft-lb of potential energy. This must all be dissipated in work done in overcoming friction. The frictional work will equal $0.24W \times 50$ while sliding down the plane and $0.30W \times S$ while sliding along the horizontal. Then

$$30W = 0.24W \times 50 + 0.30W \times S$$

and
$$S = \frac{30 - 12}{0.30} = 60 \text{ ft}$$

You will note that this method is quicker and less complicated than the previous method.

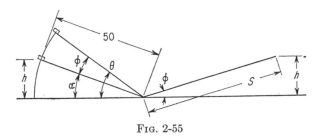

Fig. 2-55

The third method shown is an example of the use of the friction angle (Fig. 2-55). By the use of friction angles we eliminate the effects of friction, and the height which the object falls in sliding down the left side must equal the height to which the object will rise in sliding up the imaginary plane on the right side. Note that the lengths of the hypotenuses of the triangles, or the lengths of the slopes, remain constant.

$$\alpha = \theta - \varphi = 36.9° - 16.7° = 20.2°$$
$$h = h' \quad \text{or} \quad 50 \sin \alpha = S \sin \varphi = S \sin \beta$$
$$S = \frac{50 \sin \alpha}{\sin \beta} = \frac{50 \sin \alpha}{\sin \varphi} = 50 \frac{0.345}{0.287}$$
$$S = 60 \text{ ft}$$

2-16. D'Alembert's Principle. The subject of dynamics can be considerably simplified for many persons by the application of D'Alembert's principle. By this means problems in dynamics can be considered as problems in statics and can be treated by the methods of statics. D'Alembert's principle is based upon the use of a fictitious "inertial force," which is equal and opposite to the force causing the acceleration.

The existence of this imaginary inertial force follows from Newton's third law—action and reaction are equal and opposite. This states that the object pushes just as hard against the force as the force pushes against the object. These two forces must be equal in magnitude and opposite in sense. The equation $F = ma$ can then be written $F - ma = 0$, where ma equals the resisting "inertial force," and F is the resultant of all real external forces acting on the body. The sum of the forces acting on the body is zero, and the problem reduces to an equilibrium which can be treated by the methods of statics.

An example of the use of this principle is illustrated in Fig. 2-56. In this figure is shown a 50-lb block resting on a horizontal plane. The block is pulled by a cord which goes over a frictionless, inertialess pulley and is then attached to a 25-lb weight, which is allowed to fall. The forces on both weights, including the inertial forces, are added,

Fig. 2-56

and the problem is seen to reduce to a problem in statics which can be solved by means of the relationship that the summation of all forces acting must equal zero.

The force acting downward is the weight of the block, or 25 lb. This is balanced by two forces upward, the tension in the cord, T, and the D'Alembert or inertia force, which equals mass times acceleration, giving $T = 25 - (25/g) \times a$. The forces acting on the 50-lb block are next added, and since the tension in the cord is the same over its entire length, the force acting to cause motion of the 50-lb weight is equal

Fig. 2-57

to T. This is balanced by two resisting forces, the frictional force —$50 \times 0.2 = 10$ lb—and the D'Alembert force—$(50/g) \times a$, which gives $T = (50/g) \times a + 10$ (Fig. 2-57). Since $T = T$, $25 - (25/g) \times a = (50/g) \times a + 10$; $a = 0.2g$, and $T = 20$ lb.

2-17. Rotational Motion. The concepts of linear velocity, displacement, and acceleration all have their exact counterparts in rotational motion. So, too, have the concepts of force and mass. These concepts and their counterparts are listed below.

Linear concepts	*Rotational concepts*
Displacement, s, ft..................	θ, radians
Velocity, v, fps.....................	ω, radians/sec
Acceleration, a, ft/sec²..............	α, radians/sq sec
Force, pounds......................	Torque, ft-lb
Mass $= W/g$, slugs.................	$I =$ moment of inertia, slug-ft²

The corresponding relationships are:

$$s = v_0 t + \tfrac{1}{2}at^2 \qquad \theta = \omega_0 t + \tfrac{1}{2}\alpha t^2$$
$$v = v_0 + at \qquad \omega = \omega_0 + \alpha t$$
$$F = ma \qquad T = I\alpha$$
$$KE = \tfrac{1}{2}mv^2 \qquad KE = \tfrac{1}{2}I\omega^2$$

The relationships $T = I\alpha$ and $KE = \tfrac{1}{2}I\omega^2$ are somewhat different, and the moment of inertia I is also different. These can be related to the linear relationships by some brief reasoning.

2-18. Moment of Inertia. If a force F is applied to a mass m which is connected to a weightless, rigid rod of length r (Fig. 2-58), the other end of which is pivoted, the work done by the force will equal $F \times r\,d\theta$, where $r\,d\theta$ is the distance through which the force travels. $F \times r$ is the torque about the pivot point, so we have $dW = T_q \, d\theta$. The velocity attained by the mass will equal v, where $v = \omega r$. The work done on the mass will result in an increase in kinetic energy, or $dW = d(\frac{1}{2}mv^2)$, which becomes

FIG. 2-58

$$T \, d\theta = mv \, dv = m(\omega r)(r d\omega) = mr^2\omega \, d\omega$$

or $T_q = mr^2\omega(d\omega/d\theta)$. $\omega = d\theta/dt$, and $\alpha = d\omega/dt$, so $\omega(d\omega/d\theta) = \alpha$ (obtained by substituting $\omega/d\theta = 1/dt$ from $\omega = d\theta/dt$, the equation for angular velocity).

Substituting this relationship in the former equation gives $T = (mr^2)\alpha$, which corresponds to $F = ma$. The quantity mr^2 is termed the moment of inertia, and for a body where the mass is not concentrated at a distance r from the center point $I = \Sigma \, \Delta mr^2$, or the moment of inertia of a body equals the sum of the products of all the point masses which make up the total mass of the body times the square of their distances from the axis about which the moment of inertia is desired. To return for a moment to the equation for kinetic energy, we see, for the concentrated mass used in the illustration, that $\frac{1}{2}mv^2$ becomes $\frac{1}{2}mr^2\omega^2$, which equals $\frac{1}{2}I\omega^2$.

2-19. Radius of Gyration. From the equation $I = mr^2$ comes also the relationship $r = \sqrt{I/m}$, where r is termed the radius of gyration or the distance from the axis at which the mass m could be concentrated to give the same moment of inertia. The radius of gyration is usually indicated by k rather than r.

$$I = k^2m$$

Note that, in general, the mass of a body cannot be considered as acting at its center of mass for the purpose of calculating the moment of inertia. This can be illustrated easily by calculating the moment of inertia of a uniform, slender rod about an axis through one end and perpendicular to the rod (Fig. 2-59). The mass of the rod will equal $\rho A L$, where ρ is the density in slugs/cubic feet, A the cross-sectional area in square feet, and L

FIG. 2-59

the length in feet. The dm of the relationship $I = \int r^2\, dm$ will then be $\rho A\, dl$, and

$$I = \int_0^L l^2 \rho A\, dl$$

$\frac{1}{3}\rho AL^3 = \frac{1}{3}mL^2$, since $m = \rho AL$. Similarly, the moment of inertia of a slender, uniform rod about an axis through its center and perpendicular to the rod will equal

$$\frac{L}{2} \int_{-L/2} l^2\, dm = \frac{1}{12}ML^2 \qquad \text{(Fig. 2-60)}$$

In the case of the rod pivoted at one end, the center of mass is at a distance of $L/2$ but the radius of gyration equals $L/\sqrt{3}$. The

Fig. 2-60   Fig. 2-61

moment of inertia of the plane of a rectangular surface about an axis through its center and lying in the plane can be determined similarly (Fig. 2-61).

$$I = \sum x^2\, \Delta A = \int_{-h/2}^{h/2} x^2 b\, dx = \frac{bh^3}{12}$$

The moment of inertia about an axis in the plane of an area is called the "plane moment of inertia"; the moment of inertia of an area about an axis perpendicular to the area is termed the "polar moment of inertia." There is a definite relationship between these two, which is stated in the next section.

2-20. Polar Moment of Inertia. The polar moment of inertia of an area with respect to any axis is equal to the sum of the moments of inertia of the area with respect to any two rectangular axes in the plane of the area which intersect on the given polar axis.

$$J_Z = \Sigma r^2\, \Delta A = \Sigma(x^2 + y^2)\, \Delta A$$

where J_z = polar moment of inertia about the perpendicular axis 0 (Fig. 2-62)

$$J_z = \int x^2 \, dA + \int y^2 \, dA = I_x + I_y$$

Application of this principle aids in simplifying a calculation of some of the moments of inertia of the different areas. As an exam-

FIG. 2-62   FIG. 2-63

FIG. 2-64   FIG. 2-65

ple, determine the moment of inertia of a circular section about the Y axis (Fig. 2-63).

$$I_y = \int_{-r}^{r} x^2 \, dA = \int_{-r}^{r} x^2(2y \, dx) = \int_{-r}^{r} (r^2 - y^2)(2y \, dx)$$

which becomes involved.

If we utilize the relationship that $J_z = I_y + I_x = 2I_y$, we can determine I_y much more easily (Fig. 2-64).

$$J_z = \int_0^r \rho^2 \, dA = \int_0^r \int_0^{2\pi} \rho^3 \, d\rho \, d\theta = 2\pi \int_0^r \rho^3 \, d\rho$$

Since $dA = (\rho \, d\theta) \times d\rho$,

$$J_z = 2\pi \frac{r^4}{4} = \frac{\pi r^4}{2}$$

$$J_y = \tfrac{1}{2} J_z = \frac{\pi r^4}{4}$$

or by a different method (Fig. 2-65),

$$J_z = \int_0^r \rho^2 \, dA \qquad dA = 2\pi\rho \, d\rho$$

$$J_z = \int_0^r 2\pi\rho^3 \, d\rho = \frac{\pi r^4}{2}$$

as before.

2-21. Parallel-axis Theorem. If it is desired to calculate the moment of inertia about an axis different from the moment of

FIG. 2-66

FIG. 2-67

inertia about the centroid of an area, this can be done by means of the "parallel-axis" theorem. As an example, determine the moment of inertia of an area about an axis $X - X$ given that the moment of inertia about an axis $0 - 0$ through the centroid of the area equals I_0. Axis $X - X$ is parallel with axis $0 - 0$ (Fig. 2-66).

$$I_x = \int_{-r}^r (s - r)^2 \, dA = \int_{-r}^r r^2 \, dA - \int_{-r}^r 2rs \, dA + \int_{-r}^r s^2 \, dA$$

$$= \int_{-r}^r r^2 \, dA - 2s \int_{-r}^r r \, dA + s^2 \int_{-r}^r dA = I_0 + As^2$$

since $\int_{-r}^r r^2 \, dA$ equals the moment of inertia about the axis $0 - 0$.

$\int_{-r}^{r} r\, dA$ about the centroid of the area must equal zero, since that defines the location of the centroid, as discussed previously.

2-22. Centripetal Acceleration. It can be shown that an object which is moving in a circular path has an acceleration toward the center of the circle of motion equal to the product of the square of the angular velocity times the radius. From Fig. 2-67 we can see that $v = r(d\theta/dt) = r\omega$. The change of velocity Δv equals the distance CB, since velocity is a vector quantity.

As the angle $d\theta$ gets smaller and smaller, point A approaches point C and angle γ approaches $d\theta$. At the instant $d\theta$ vanishes we have $dv = r(d\theta/dt) \sin d\theta = r(d\theta/dt)\, d\theta$. Acceleration toward the center $= dv/dt = r(d\theta/dt)(d\theta/dt) = r\omega^2 = a_c$
$ =$ centripetal acceleration ($d\theta/dt = \omega =$ constant, so the derivative is zero).
From the figure we also see that

$$v = r\frac{d\theta}{dt} = r\omega$$

$$a_c = \frac{v^2}{r}$$

since $ \omega = \frac{v}{r} \frac{d\omega}{dt} = \frac{dv}{dt}\frac{1}{r}$

or $ \alpha = \frac{a}{r}$

$$a = \alpha r$$

where $\alpha =$ angular acceleration
$ a =$ circumferential acceleration

2-23. Centripetal Force. Since we have an acceleration, if we also have a mass then we must have a force from $F = ma$, where the force equals $m \times \omega^2 r$ or $m(v^2/r)$. This force is exerted toward the center and is termed the "centripetal" force. It is balanced by an equal and opposite outward force termed a "centrifugal" force, centrifugal meaning "fleeing a center." We recognize the centrifugal force as an example of the application of D'Alembert's principle.

Two points should be noted in connection with centrifugal force.

The first is that the forces and accelerations discussed are instantaneous; even if the path of the body is not a true circle it will have an instantaneous center of curvature, and there will thus be an instantaneous centripetal acceleration (and an instantaneous centripetal force) toward this center of curvature which can be calculated from the relationships given. If the object is moving in essentially a straight line, then the distance to the center of curvature will be so large that the term v^2/r will be so small as to be negligible. The second point of importance is that if the body moving in a curved path is too large to be considered as a point, then the mass should be considered as concentrated at the center of mass and the location of the center of mass will determine the values of the radius of curvature and the tangential velocity.

Fig. 2-68

An example of the application of these principles is afforded by the past problem:

- What superelevation (slope of roadway) is required on a highway for 60-mph traffic on a 2,500-ft-radius curve so that a 200-lb driver will exert no sideward force on the car seat? What force will the driver exert perpendicular to the seat?

First, draw a figure showing the forces acting (Fig. 2-68). The forces acting on the car (or any object in the car) are shown in the sketch. Any variation due to a variation in the radius will be negligible, since 2,500 ft is so much greater than any distance which would be measured inside the car. The centrifugal force equals $\omega^2 rm$, or $(v^2/r) \times m$, and the force of gravity acting downward $= W = mg$.

$$\tan^{-1}\left[\frac{(v^2/r)m}{mg}\right] = \tan^{-1}\left(\frac{v^2}{rg}\right)$$

$$60 \text{ mph} = \frac{60 \times 5{,}280}{60 \times 60} = 88 \text{ fps}$$

$$\alpha = \tan^{-1}\left(\frac{88^2}{2{,}500 \text{ g}}\right) = 5.5°$$

The superelevation of the roadway should be 5.5°.

$$R = \sqrt{[(v^2/r)m]^2 + (mg)^2} = m\sqrt{9.6 + 1{,}036.8} = 32.35m$$
$$R = \frac{200}{g}\,32.35 = 201\text{ lb}$$

which is the force exerted by the driver perpendicular to the seat.
Another problem was as follows:

- An armature is keyed to a shaft 4 in. in diameter, which rests transversely on two parallel steel rails inclined to the horizontal with a slope of 1:12. The shaft rolls, without slipping and without rolling friction, a distance of 6 ft along the rails from rest in 1 min. What is the radius of gyration of the armature and its shaft about the longitudinal axis?

Fig. 2-69

Make a sketch (Fig. 2-69). The energy possessed by the armature at the end of 1 min equals $\frac{1}{2}mv^2 + \frac{1}{2}I\omega^2$.

$$v_{\text{avg}} = \tfrac{6}{60} = 0.1\text{ fps} = \frac{(0 + v)}{2};\; v = 0.2\text{ fps},\; \omega = \frac{v}{r}$$

$$\text{KE} = \tfrac{1}{2}m(0.2)^2 + \tfrac{1}{2}I\,\frac{v^2}{r^2} \qquad r = 2\text{ in.} = 0.167\text{ ft}$$

$$I = k^2 m$$
$$k = \text{radius of gyration}$$
$$\text{KE} = \tfrac{1}{2}m(0.04) + \tfrac{1}{2}(k^2 m)\,\frac{0.04}{(\frac{1}{6})^2} = m(0.02 + 0.72k^2)$$

This increase in kinetic energy must equal the decrease in potential energy, since no work is done against friction. $\alpha = \tan^{-1}(\frac{1}{12})$, giving $\sin \alpha = 0.083$.

$$\Delta\text{PE} = W\sin\alpha \times 6 = mg \times 0.083 \times 6 = 16.05m$$
$$16.05m = m(0.02 + 0.72k^2)$$
$$k = \sqrt{\frac{16.05 - 0.02}{0.72}} = 4.72\text{ ft}$$

The same result can be obtained by determining the acceleration of the armature (Fig. 2-70).

$$s = v_0t + \tfrac{1}{2}at^2$$
$$6 = 0 + \tfrac{1}{2}a(60)^2 \qquad a = \tfrac{1}{300} \text{ ft/sec}^2$$
$$F = W \sin \beta = 0.083W$$

$$T_q = I\alpha = I\frac{a}{r}$$

$$T_q = F' \times r = F \times r$$

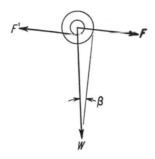

Fig. 2-70

since there is no slipping and $F' = F$.

$$F \times r = I\frac{a}{r} = k^2m\frac{a}{r}$$

$$mg \sin \beta \times r = k^2m\frac{a}{r}$$

$$k^2 = \frac{0.083gr^2}{a}$$

$$= \frac{0.083g(\tfrac{1}{6})^2}{\tfrac{1}{300}}$$

$$= 22.3$$

$$k = 4.72 \text{ ft} \qquad \text{radius of gyration}$$

A word might be in order here about the summation of the forces acting on the armature. The force F (Fig. 2-71) is just equal to the frictional force f and is balanced by it. There is, then, no excess force to cause linear acceleration of the armature, and the total acceleration is angular. If F exceeded f and the armature slipped as well as rolled, then there would be a linear acceleration in addition to that resulting from the angular acceleration.

Another problem asked:

- A 64.4-lb cylinder of radius $R = 2$ ft is pushed by a moving bulldozer. The coefficient of friction at points A and B is 0.20. Determine (a) the minimum acceleration of the bulldozer if the cylinder is to move to the right without rotating, (b) the maximum acceleration of the bulldozer if the cylinder is to roll without slipping.

Make a sketch (Fig. 2-72). The maximum frictional force at point A will equal $0.20W$. The net torque acting on the cylinder

FIG. 2-71

FIG. 2-72   FIG. 2-73

will equal $f_A \times R - f_B \times R$, so if $f_B > f_A$ (Fig. 2-73) the cylinder will not roll, and if $f_B < f_A$ the cylinder will roll. If $f_B = f_A$, then the inertia force, or D'Alembert's force, must equal $W = mg = ma$, so if the cylinder is to move to the right without rotating the acceleration must be greater than g, and if the cylinder is to roll without sliding the acceleration must be less than g.

There are a few other phases of mechanics which have been emphasized in past examinations; they will be discussed here briefly.

2-24. Springs. It has, upon occasion, been necessary to determine the energy absorbed by a spring because of the impact of a weight. The energy lost by the weight will, of course, be matched by an increase in the energy contained in the spring. The energy required to compress a spring a distance dx equals $F\,dx$, where the force will be equal to kx; k is the spring constant, and x is the distance the spring has been compressed. The total work to compress the spring a distance S will then equal $\int_0^S kx\,dx$, which equals $\frac{1}{2}kS^2$.

An example illustrating this is:

- A mass weighing 25 lb falls a distance of 5 ft upon the top of a helical spring with a spring constant of 20 lb/in.
  a. What will the velocity of the mass be after it has compressed the spring 8 in.?
  b. Calculate the maximum compression of the spring.

The fall of the weight will be 5 ft plus 8 in. when it has compressed the spring 8 in. At that time the spring will have absorbed energy equal to $\frac{1}{2}kS^2 = \frac{1}{2}(20\text{ lb/in.}) \times (8\text{ in.})^2 = 640$ lb-in., or 53.3 lb-ft. The change in potential energy equals

$$W \times h = 25(5 - 0.67) = \Delta PE = 142 \text{ ft-lb}$$

Part of this energy has been absorbed by the spring; the remainder, $142 - 53.3 = 88.7$ ft-lb, must remain as kinetic energy of the mass $= \frac{1}{2}mv^2$.

$$v = \sqrt{\frac{88.7 \times 2}{m}} = \sqrt{\frac{88.7 \times 2g}{25}} = 15.1 \text{ fps}$$

When the spring has been fully compressed the velocity of the mass will be zero and all the change in potential energy of the mass will have been converted into potential energy of the spring.

$$W(5 \text{ ft} + S) = \frac{1}{2}kS^2$$

If S is in inches,

$$W(5 \times 12 + S) = \frac{1}{2}20S^2$$
$$2S^2 - 5S - 300 = 0$$
$$S = \frac{5 \pm \sqrt{25 + 2,400}}{4} = \frac{5 \pm 49.3}{4}$$
$$= 13.6 \text{ in.}$$

which is the maximum compression of the spring.

2-25. Simple Harmonic Motion. Another subject sometimes included in a fundamentals examination is that of simple harmonic motion (SHM), which is defined as the motion of a point in a straight line such that the acceleration of the point is proportional to the distance of the point from its equilibrium position, or $a = -kx = d^2x/dt^2$.

Simple harmonic motion can be shown to be the same motion to which a suspended mass is subjected by the force of a spring

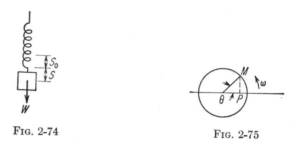

FIG. 2-74   FIG. 2-75

(Fig. 2-74).   The static position of the weight is that position in which the spring is stretched the distance S_0. $S_0 \times k = W$, where k is the spring constant.   If the weight is pulled down farther, a distance S, then the sum of the forces acting on the weight will equal

$$k(S_0 + S) - W = kS$$

Since the distance S is down and the force is up, we have $F = -kS$, giving $ma = -kS$, or $a = (-k/m) \times S$, where k/m is a constant, and we have the defining relationship for simple harmonic motion.

The velocity and time relationships for simple harmonic motion are usually determined by means of a "reference circle."

It can be shown that if a point moves with constant speed in a circular path, the motion of the projection of the point on a diameter of this reference circle is a simple harmonic motion (Fig. 2-75).

$$x = r \cos \theta = r \cos \omega t$$

where ω = a constant

$$v_p = \frac{dx}{dt} = -\omega r \sin \omega t = -\omega y$$

$$a_p = \frac{dv_p}{dt} = -\omega^2 r \cos \omega t = -\omega^2 x$$

This last equation is the equation defining simple harmonic motion. The time for P to make one complete oscillation is the same as the time for the point M to make one complete revolution, or $T = 2\pi/\omega$, and the frequency equals $1/T = \omega/2\pi$. A numerical example illustrating simple harmonic motion is as follows:

- A truck body lowers 5 in. when a load of 25,000 lb is placed on it. What is the frequency of vibration of the truck if the total spring-borne weight is 40,000 lb?

The frequency $= 1/T = \omega/2\pi$, and the acceleration of the weight $a = -\omega^2 x$, but $F = ma$, and the force acting on the mass $= -kx$, so $-kx = -\omega^2 mx$, and $\omega = \sqrt{k/m} = \sqrt{kg/W}$; then

$$f = \frac{\omega}{2\pi} = \frac{1}{2\pi}\sqrt{\frac{kg}{W}}$$

The spring constant $k = 25,000$ lb/5 in. $= 5,000$ lb/in.

$$f = \frac{1}{2\pi}\sqrt{\frac{5,000 \text{ lb/in.} \times 12 \text{ in./ft} \times 32.2 \text{ ft/sec}^2}{40,000 \text{ lb}}}$$

$$= 1.105 \text{ oscillations/sec}$$

The restoring force acting on the truck body equals $-kx$, where x is the distance the spring is compressed past the neutral point (Fig. 2-76).

2-26. Nuclear Energy. In the discussion of the conservation of energy the remark was made that the energy of a system is constant if we disregard any effects of nuclear fission. The problems in the fundamentals examinations reviewed have included no requirements to calculate the amounts

Neutral point or point to which load would compress the spring if system were at rest

Restoring force at this point $= -kx$

FIG. 2-76

or effects of nuclear energy, but an occasional general question has been asked concerning nuclear energy. Briefly, there is a correlation between energy and mass, and if an atom splits or is split into parts and the resulting mass of the parts is less than the initial mass, there is also a release of energy in the amount of $E = (\Delta m)c^2$, where Δm is the change of mass and c is the velocity of light. Since the velocity of light is so very large, even a very small change in mass will produce a tremendous amount of energy. This is utilized in atomic bombs but seldom needs to be considered in ordinary engineering practice.

REFERENCES

There are many well-written texts on the subject of engineering mechanics. Those with which the author is familiar and which he recommends for further review are:

Seely, F. B., N. E. Ensign, and P. G. Jones: "Analytical Mechanics for Engineers," John Wiley & Sons, Inc., New York, 1952. The older editions of this book, written by Seely and Ensign, are also very good.
Beer, F. P., and E. R. Johnston, Jr.: "Mechanics for Engineers," McGraw-Hill Book Company, Inc., New York, 1957.
Higdon, A., and W. B. Stiles: "Engineering Mechanics," Prentice-Hall, Inc., Englewood Cliffs, N.J., 1955.
Meriam, J. L.: "Mechanics," John Wiley & Sons, Inc., New York, 1959.

SAMPLE PROBLEMS SELECTED FROM PAST EXAMINATIONS

2-1. A chain hangs over a smooth peg, 8 ft of its length being on one side and 10 ft on the other. If the force of friction is equal to the weight of 1 ft of the chain, find the time required for the chain to slide off.

2-2. A falling weight of 1,000 lb is used to drive a pile into the ground. If the weight of the pile is 800 lb and the weight is dropped 20 ft, what will be the depth of penetration of the pile, assuming an average resistance to penetration of 30,000 lb? Assume the impact between the weight and pile to be perfectly inelastic.

2-3. A horizontal force is applied to a block moving in a horizontal guide. When the block is at a distance x from the origin, the force is given by the equation $F = x^3 - x$. What work is done by moving the block from 1 ft to the left of the origin to 1 ft to the right of the origin?

2-4. What are the maximum and minimum weights of the box that can be held in place by the force as shown in Fig. 2-P-4?

Fig. 2-P-4   Fig. 2-P-5

2-5. In the system shown in Fig. 2-P-5, $W = 20$ lb and is observed to vibrate ten times in 15 sec. Disregard the weight of the lever arm and find the stiffness coefficient of the spring S.

2-6. A cable 25 ft long is connected between two points 20 ft apart horizontally and 5 ft apart vertically. If a 5,000-lb load is hung on the cable by use of a frictionless pulley, where will the pulley come to rest, and what will be the total stress in the cable?

2-7. An unbalanced force in pounds that varies with time in seconds as follows—$F = 800 - 120t$, acts on a body with a weight of 3,220 lb for 5 sec. If the body had an initial velocity of 10 fps in the direction of the unbalanced force, what final velocity would the body have? What would be the initial and final power, in horsepower, required?

2-8. Locate the centroid along the center line from side A of the area shown in Fig. 2-P-8.

Fig. 2-P-8

2-9. A wheel 2 ft in diameter weighing 64.4 lb has a radius of gyration of 9 in. If it starts from rest and rolls without sliping down a 30° plane, what will be its speed when it has moved 20 ft?

2-10. A jackscrew having eight threads to the inch, i.e., 18-in. threads, is operated manually by a handle. The point at which the handle is gripped moves through a 12-ft circumference.

a. If friction is disregarded, what force must be applied at the grip on the handle to just raise a load of 2,300 lb?

b. If a shorter handle three-fourths as long is used as in (*a*), what force would be required at the grip on the short handle to just raise the same load as in (*a*)?

2-11. For the truss loaded as shown in Fig. 2-P-11, find the force in member U_4L_4 and in U_3U_4.

Fig. 2-P-11

2-12. An armature is keyed to a shaft 4 in. in diameter, which rests transversely on two parallel steel rails inclined to the horizontal with a slope of 1:12. The shaft rolls, without slipping and without rolling friction, a distance of 6 ft along the rails from rest in 1 min. What is the radius of gyration of the armature and its shaft about the longitudinal axis?

2-13. A rectangular *door* swings horizontally, is 3 ft wide, and weighs 60 lb uniformly distributed. The door is supported by frictionless hinges installed along one of its vertical sides. It is controlled by a spring which exerts on it a torque proportional to the angle through which it is turned from its closed position. If the door is opened 90° and released, the torque due to the spring is then 3 lb-ft. Determine the angular velocity at the time it has swung back and is passing through the 45° position.

2-14. The bracket shown in Fig. 2-P-14 is fastened to a vertical wall at points *B*, *C*, and *D*, point *D* being 3 ft higher than *C*, with member *AB* horizontal. Find stress in members *AB*, *AC*, and *AD*.

Fig. 2-P-14

2-15. A body is moving in a straight line according to the law

$$S = \tfrac{1}{4}t^4 - 2t^3 + 4t^2$$

When S = distance traveled in time t,
  a. Find its velocity formula and its acceleration formula.
  b. When is its velocity at a maximum?
  c. During what interval is it moving backward?

2-16. The coefficient of friction between the 10-lb block A and the 20-lb block B, shown in Fig. 2-P-16, is 0.40. The coefficient of friction between B and the horizontal plane is 0.15. Determine the force P required to cause motion of B to impend to the right.

FIG. 2-P-16

2-17. A solid sphere weighing 1,000 lb is held at rest on a 45° inclined plane by means of cables a, b, and c, of which a is attached to the center of the sphere. Solve for the tension in each cable and for the reaction of the plane on the sphere. (See Fig. 2-P-17.)

FIG. 2-P-17

2-18. A locomotive is traveling round a curve of mean radius 1,000 ft at a speed of 40 mph. Find the correct amount of superelevation so that there shall be no side thrust on the flanges of the wheels at that speed. If the gauge of the railway track is 5 ft and the height of the center of gravity of the locomotive is 4 ft above rail level, find the greatest speed at which the locomotive could travel round the curve without actually overturning.

2-19. A belt 8 in. wide and ¼ in. thick drives a pulley 12 in. in diameter at 1,650 rpm. The maximum tension the belt may have is 200 psi. If the slack side has three-fourths the tension of the tight side, what horsepower may be transmitted?

2-20. Locate the centroid of the shaded area shown in Fig. 2-P-20.

FIG. 2-P-20

2-21. A steel block is 8 in. square and 12 in. high. A cylindrical hole 6 in. deep is to be drilled from the upper end. Compute the necessary diameter of the hole required so that the center of gravity of the block will be 5 in. from the bottom of the block.

2-22. Find stress in members CH and CD of the truss shown in Fig. 2-P-22.

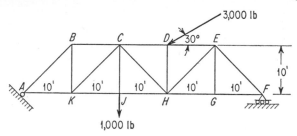

Fig. 2-P-22

2-23. A hoisting cable has a safe working strength of 40,000 psi of cross-sectional area. What is the greatest weight that can be raised with an acceleration of 8.05 ft/sec² by a cable 1½ in. in diameter? Disregard friction.

2-24. A kite is 120 ft high, with 150 ft of cord out. If the kite moves horizontally 4 mph directly away from the boy flying it, how fast is the cord being paid out in feet per second?

2-25. A bullet leaves a gun muzzle at a velocity of 2,700 fps at an angle of 45° to the horizontal.

a. What is the maximum height to which the bullet will travel?

b. What is the maximum distance the bullet will travel horizontally, measured along the same elevation as the gun muzzle?

Disregard air resistance.

2-26. An airplane has a true air speed of 240 mph and is heading true north. A 40-mph head wind is blowing 45° from true north from the Northeast.

a. Draw a velocity vector diagram for the conditions outlined above.

b. Solve for the ground speed.

c. Solve for the true course the airplane is making with reference to the ground.

2-27. The rifling in a 30-caliber rifle causes the bullet to turn one revolution per 10 in. of barrel length.

a. If the muzzle velocity of the bullet is 2,900 fps, how many rpm is the bullet rotating at the instant it leaves the muzzle?

b. Assuming constant acceleration for the bullet for the 22 in. of barrel travel, what is the magnitude of the acceleration?

2-28. A faster-moving body is directly approaching a slower-moving body going in the same direction. The speed of the faster body is V_1; the speed of the slower body is V_2. At the instant when the separation of the two bodies is d, the faster body is given a constant deceleration of a. Determine the formula for the minimum value of d, so that there will be no collision.

2-29. A parachutist is falling with a speed of 176 fps when his parachute opens. If the air resistance is $Wv^2/256$ lb, where W is the total weight of the man and parachute, find his speed as a function of time after the parachute is opened.

2-30. At the beginning of the drive, a golf ball has a velocity of 170 mph. If the club stays in contact with the ball for $\frac{1}{25}$ sec, what is the average force on the ball? The weight of the ball is 1.62 oz.

2-31. An artificial satellite is circling the earth at a radius of 4,500 miles. Assume that the pull of gravitation is the same at that elevation as at the earth's surface.

a. What speed in radians per second is required to maintain the satellite at that radius?

b. What is total kinetic energy in the satellite if it weighs 50 lb?

2-32. Solve for the magnitude and direction of the stresses in the members AC, BC, and DC of the frame shown in Fig. 2-P-32. Distances between lettered points are as indicated. Plane ABC is horizontal, and plane CDE is vertical.

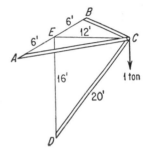

Fig. 2-P-32

2-33. The fire door shown in Fig. 2-P-33 is hung from a horizontal track by means of wheels at A and B. The door weighs 200 lb. The wheel at A has rusted on its bearing and slides, rather than rolls, on the track, the coefficient of friction being one-third. Wheel B rolls freely, and friction is negligible. Determine the force P necessary to give the door an acceleration of 8 fps. Compute the horizontal and vertical components of the reactions at A and B.

Fig. 2-P-33   Fig. 2-P-34

2-34. A truck of dimensions and weights shown in Fig. 2-P-34 is rolling across a 30-ft bridge.

a. What is distance X for maximum moment?

b. Calculate maximum moment and where it is located.

2-35. A balloon is ascending vertically at a uniform rate for 1 min. A stone let fall from it reaches the ground in 5 sec. Find:

a. Velocity of the balloon

b. Height from which the stone fell

2-36. A body takes just twice as long to slide down a plane at 30° to the horizontal as it would if the plane were smooth. What is the coefficient of friction?

2-37. How far from the center of a phonograph record turning at 78 rpm will a pickle lie without being thrown off, if the coefficient of friction is 0.30?

2-38. Figure 2-P-38 shows how a weight can be raised by an ideal frictionless wedge.

a. Find the relation between the load W and the applied force F and the wedge angle.

b. Find the forces transmitted by the three rows of balls.

c. For what angle can a weight W be raised that is ten times as large as the applied force F?

FIG. 2-P-38   FIG. 2-P-39

2-39. *a.* Calculate stress in member L_1-U_2 in the truss shown in Fig. 2-P-39.

b. Calculate stress in member U_0-U_1.

2-40. A weight of 4,000 lb is supported at the midpoint of a cable HNK which is 18 ft long (Fig. 2-P-40). If the safe tension in the cable is 2,600 lb determine:

a. Maximum distance between H and K so that the 2,600 lb tension will not be exceeded

b. Angle θ for the condition in (*a*)

c. Direction and magnitude of the horizontal forces at H and K

d. Distance BN (B is midway between H and K)

FIG. 2-P-40

2-41. Total length of rope $A + B = $ 60 ft (Fig. 2-P-41). Weight on sheave is free to move on rope. Disregard the weight of rope.

a. Find tension in rope A and in rope B.

b. Find moment at base of pole, point C.

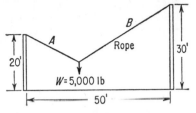

FIG. 2-P-41

2-42. a. Find center of gravity of area of figure shown in Fig. 2-P-42.

b. What is moment of inertia about Y-Y axis through the center of gravity?

FIG. 2-P-42

FIG. 2-P-43

2-43. A wooden beam is made up of full-dimension timbers, as shown in Fig. 2-P-43.

a. What is the moment of inertia about axis x-x?

b. What load concentrated at center of such a beam 12 ft long can be supported with a stress of 1,200 lb?

2-44. Refer to Fig. 2-P-44 which shows a Fink truss, and determine the stresses in members labeled a and b. Express your final answer in pounds and state whether the stress is *tension* or *compression*.

FIG. 2-P-44

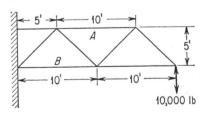

FIG. 2-P-45

2-45. A cantilever beam is hinged to the wall as shown in Fig. 2-P-45. What are the amount and direction (compression or tension) of stress in members A and B?

2-46. *a.* Tractor as shown in Fig. 2-P-46 is on level ground. What pull X will remove all weight from front wheels?

b. Assume same tractor is going up a slope 20° from horizontal: what will X be in pounds?

FIG. 2-P-46   FIG. 2-P-47

2-47. Given a truss as shown in Fig. 2-P-47. Assume the horizontal components of the reactions at A and B are equal.

a. Determine the horizontal and vertical components of the reactions at A and B.

b. Determine the stresses in AE, AD, BF, and BD. Be sure to state kind of stress in each case.

c. Check your results by analyzing joints D and C.

2-48. Find the least force P and the angle α just sufficient to move the wheel shown in Fig. 2-P-48, radius r, which weighs W, over the curb of height h.

FIG. 2-P-48   FIG. 2-P-49

2-49. Block A (Fig. 2-P-49) weighs 200 lb and is placed 5 ft from the edge of the table. A string passing over a smooth pulley connects blocks A and B as shown. Block B weighs 50 lb and is 2 ft from the floor. The coefficient of sliding friction for block A is 0.15. Block B is released from rest in this position.

a. With what velocity does B strike the floor?

b. How far from the edge of the table will block A come to rest?

2-50. A cast-aluminum drum, 2 ft in diameter and 1 ft in length, is supported by an axial shaft on smooth bearings. A light cord wrapped on the drum is pulled by a constant force of 20 lb until 15 ft of cord is unwrapped and then let go. What is the rpm of the drum when the pull on the cord has ceased?

2-51. Find the location of centroid and moment of inertia about axis X-X through centroid of welded plate and angle girder shown in Fig. 2-P-51.

$\frac{1}{2}" \times 12"$ plate

$2\frac{1}{2}" \times 2\frac{1}{2}" \times 5.0$ lb $\angle$s

$1" \times 10"$ plate

$4" \times 3" \times 9.8$ lb $\angle$s

FIG. 2-P-51

2-52. A 50-ton car moving at a speed of 3 mph strikes a bumping post equipped with a 40,000-lb spring. Assuming that all the shock is absorbed by the spring, how far will the spring be compressed?

2-53. An automobile which weighs 3,700 lb approaches a curve on a concrete paved highway. The radius of the curve is 1,000 ft and the pavement is flat (no superelevation). If the coefficient of friction between the tires and the pavement is 0.15, what is the maximum speed at which the driver may round the curve without skidding sidewise? What should be the transverse slope of the pavement to drive at 60 mph on the curve and keep the resultant forces perpendicular to the pavement? Assume the pavement is 24 ft wide and the distance between treads is 6 ft.

2-54. An elastic body weighing 100 lb is moving with a velocity of 20 fps and overtakes another elastic body, weighing 150 lb, moving in the same direction with a velocity of 15 fps. What is the final velocity, and what is the loss in kinetic energy?

2-55. A body weighing 200 lb starts from rest at the top of a plane which makes an angle of 60° with the horizontal. After sliding 8 ft 4 in. down the plane the body strikes a 100-lb/in. spring. The coefficient of friction is 0.25. The body remains in contact with the plane throughout. Determine the compression of the spring in inches.

2-56. The ends of a cable 21 ft long are fastened to two rigid overhead points 15 ft apart and in the same horizontal plane. A weight of 200 lb is attached to the cable 9 ft from one end.

  a. Determine the stress in each segment of the cable.

  b. If the weight were attached to a roller pulley and permitted to move along the cable, what would be the position of equilibrium, and what would be the stress in each segment of the cable?

2-57. Find the magnitude, direction, and distance from point A of the force required to act on the rigid body shown in Fig. 2-P-57 to hold it in equilibrium.

12 lb   20 lb

$\dfrac{4}{3}$

C D 15 lb

12"

10 lb A 12"   12" B

10 lb

Fig. 2-P-57

2-58. Given the truss as shown in Fig. 2-P-58, determine the stresses in L_0U_2, L_0L_2, U_2U_4, and U_2L_4.

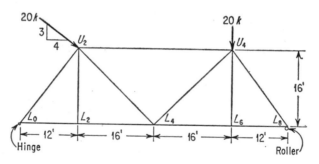

20 k 20 k

$\dfrac{3}{4}$ U_2 U_4

16'

L_0 L_2 L_4 L_6 L_8

12'   16'   16'   12'

Hinge   Roller

Fig. 2-P-58

2-59. A 100-lb wheel 18 in. in diameter, rotating at 150 rpm in stationary bearings, is brought to rest by pressing a brake shoe radially against its rim with a force of 20 lb. If the radius of gyration of the wheel is 7 in., and if the coefficient of friction between the brake shoe and rim is steady at 0.25, how many revolutions will the wheel make in coming to rest?

2-60. A solid cylinder 4 ft in diameter and weighing 12,880 lb is rolling at a linear speed of 40 fps. How far will it roll up a 10 per cent grade before coming to a stop?

2-61. The friction surface on a friction disk type of clutch has an outside diameter of 10 in. and an inside diameter of 3 in. The coefficient of friction for the surfaces in contact may be assumed as 0.3. What pressure must be applied to the plate if the clutch is to transmit 100 hp at 3,300 rpm?

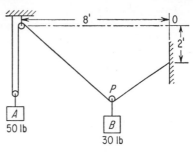

2-62. The weights *A* and *B* (Fig. 2-P-62) are supported by a continuous rope which is attached at points *C* and *D* and passes around frictionless pulleys as shown. Disregard the weight of the rope and pulleys. Find the position of pulley *P* relative to the point 0 for equilibrium.

FIG. 2-P-62

2-63. A homogeneous rod weighing 50 lb is hinged at *A* and rests on a block at *B* (Fig. 2-P-63). The block, weighing 3 lb, rests on a horizontal floor. If the coefficient of friction for all surfaces is one-third, find the horizontal force *P* necessary to cause the block to slide to the left. Consider the hinge at *A* to be frictionless.

FIG. 2-P-63

FIG. 2-P-64

2-64. For the conditions shown in Fig. 2-P-64, compute the weight *W* in pounds and the tension in the cable if the acceleration of the 100-lb body is 10 ft/sec², the coefficient of sliding friction is 0.5, and the pulleys are assumed to be frictionless.

2-65. A body starts from rest, and its velocity *t* sec later is given by the following table:

t, sec	*v, fps*
0	0
0.5	12
1	19.5
2	29.5
3	34
4	31
5	19.8
6	11
7	6.5

   a. Find the distance traveled in the first 5 sec.

   b. Find the acceleration at the instant when $t = 2$ sec.

If another body starts from rest under a uniform acceleration, and travels the same distance in the first 5 sec,

   c. Find its acceleration.

   d. Find its velocity at the instant when $t = 5$ sec.

   2-66. A motor car has a maximum speed of 70 mph on the level, and the engine is then transmitting 60 hp to the road wheels.

   a. Find the resistance to motion in pounds of weight.

   b. Assuming the tractive effort at the wheels to remain constant, while the resistance to motion varies as the square of the speed, find the slope (1 in x) up which the car can maintain 50 mph, the weight of the car being 4,000 lb.

   2-67. What is the moment of inertia about its horizontal neutral axis of a section assembled from four 3- by 3- by 0.5-in. angles and an 11- by 0.5-in. plate as shown in Fig. 2-P-67?

FIG. 2-P-67   FIG. 2-P-68

   2-68. Two smooth cylinders rest as shown in Fig. 2-P-68 on an inclined plane and a vertical wall. Compute the value of the force F exerted by the vertical wall.

   2-69. To measure the muzzle velocity of a bullet fired from a rifle, two cardboard disks mounted on a long axle are rotated at a constant speed, the rifle is mounted parallel to the axle, and, upon firing, the bullet passes through each of the disks in turn. In a test, the disks were 3.5 ft apart on the axle, the speed of rotation was 3,000 rpm, and the bullet hole in the farther disk was displaced 18° with respect to the hole in the nearer disk. Determine the muzzle velocity.

   2-70. A 3-oz bullet is fired horizontally into an 18-lb block suspended vertically so that it can swing as a pendulum. If the center of gravity of the block is caused to rise 8 in., what was the speed of the bullet?

2-71. *a.* Draw a free-body diagram of the slider arm shown in Fig. 2-P-71, indicating all the forces acting on the slider arm when the slider arm has a constant velocity due to the force F.

FIG. 2-P-71

b. In a case where $d = 4$ in., $a = 2$ in., and the coefficient of friction is 0.20, what is the minimum dimension of x so that the force F will result in no movement of the slider arm?

2-72. Referring to Fig. 2-P-72, CD is turning clockwise about D at 60 rpm. What is the tangential velocity of point B for the position shown?

FIG. 2-P-72

FIG. 2-P-73

2-73. A steel plate 30 in. in diameter and 4 in. thick has six 3-in. holes equally spaced on a 20-in.-diameter circle (Fig. 2-P-73). The disk is rotating about an axis through its center at 300 rpm. Calculate the kinetic energy stored in the disk.

2-74. *a.* Three springs, having spring constants of 5 lb/in., 10 lb/in., and 15 lb/in., respectively, are connected in series as shown in Fig. 2-P-74. What is the magnitude of the combined spring constant?

b. If the springs were arranged in parallel in such a way that a load deflects them equally, what is the magnitude of the deflection for a 100-lb load?

FIG. 2-P-74

2-75. A rope wound around a cylindrical drum, which is free to turn in a frictionless bearing about an axis through its center, has a 16-lb weight fastened to its end (Fig. 2-P-75). The drum is 1 ft in diameter and has a moment of inertia of 1.875 slug-sq ft. When the weight has fallen 16 ft,

  a. Find the work done on the system.

  b. Find the kinetic energy of the cylinder.

  c. Find the kinetic energy of the weight.

FIG. 2-P-75

2-76. An elevator and load weighing 10,000 lb after a 2-sec free fall down the shaft strikes a safety device which applies a braking force of 15,000 lb.

  a. What is the rate of deceleration?

  b. What is the total distance traveled including the fall and deceleration to a stop?

2-77. A drop hammer of 1 ton deadweight capacity is propelled downward by a 12-in.-diameter air cylinder. At 100 psi air pressure, what is the impact velocity if the stroke is 28 in.? What is the impact energy?

2-78. A 10-hp 1,750-rpm motor is connected directly to a 30 lb × ft torque brake. The rotating system has a total inertia (WR^2) of 10 lb-ft². How long will it take the system to stop if the brake is set at the instant the motor is shut off? How much energy must be dissipated?

2-79. A train traveling at 75 mph receives a warning that it is approaching a "slow signal," and the engineer immediately reduces speed at a uniform rate of 1.8 ft/sec², so that his speed is 15 mph as he reaches the slow signal. The slow order covers a stretch of 5 miles of track being reconstructed and as soon as he reaches the end of the slow order the engineer increases his speed at such a uniform rate that the train is traveling 85 mph 90 sec thereafter.

  a. What length of time elapsed between the warning and the beginning of the slow-order stretch, and what distance did the train travel during that time?

  b. What distance did the train travel from the end of the slow-order stretch in attaining its speed of 85 mph?

  c. How long will the train have to travel at 85 mph in order to make up the time lost by not running continuously at 75 mph?

2-80. A 30-ton freight car with a velocity of 4 mph in coupling collides with a stationary 20-ton car. Assume half the energy is lost in impact and failure to couple; what will be the velocities of both cars after collision?

2-81. Three men are carrying a heavy 12-ft log of circular cross section 8 in. in diameter at the small end and 12 in. in diameter at the large end. One man takes the small end of the log and the other two place a bar under the log at a point so that each of the three carries an equal load. How far from the small end was the bar placed?

2-82. Find the minimum speed that a ball starting at point P must have to loop the loop on the vertical circular track without leaving it (Fig. 2-P-82). (Assume frictionless contact.)

FIG. 2-P-82

2-83. A mass weighing 25 lb falls a distance of 5 ft upon the top of a helical spring with a spring constant of 20 lb/in.

a. What will the velocity of the mass be after it has compressed the spring 8 in.?

b. Calculate the maximum compression of the spring.

2-84. A circular cylinder, as in Fig. 2-P-84, rolls on a horizontal floor. At a given instant the angular acceleration α equals 8 radians/sec², and the angular velocity ω equals 6 radians/sec. Assume that there is no slipping and that A and C are on a horizontal line. Determine the velocity and the acceleration of point A at this instant.

FIG. 2-P-84

2-85. One end of a ladder 50 ft long is leaning against a perpendicular wall standing on a horizontal plane. Supposing the foot of the ladder to be pulled away from the wall at the rate of 3 fpm.

a. How fast is the top of the ladder descending when the foot is 14 ft from the wall?

b. When will the top and bottom of the ladder move at the same rate? Solve by calculus.

2-86. A boy weighing 100 lb is jumping up and down on a Pogo stick which has a 100 lb/in. spring. The boy jumps so that the lower end of the Pogo stick is 3 ft off the ground at maximum height, and at the bottom of the cycle he pushes down with 25 lb more than is required to stop his downward motion in order to overcome friction and keep up the jumping. How many inches is the spring compressed at the bottom of the cycle?

2-87. Cylinder A weighing 100 lb is placed in a box B (Fig. 2-P-87), the bottom of which is inclined 30° to the horizontal. The box is accelerated to the right at 20 fpsps. Determine the forces F_1 and F_2.

Fig. 2-P-87

2-88. The wheel A in Fig. 2-P-88 is a solid cylinder weighing 1,000 lb, with a diameter of 8 ft and free to turn on a frictionless axle. It is desired to arrange a brake as shown, by means of which the speed of the wheel may be reduced from 120 rpm to zero in 10 sec. Determine the ratio b/c of the available force. $P = 100$ lb and the coefficient of brake friction is 0.25.

Fig. 2-P-88

Fig. 2-P-89

2-89. Two weights, A and B, are suspended by a cord over a pulley as shown in Fig. 2-P-89. Assuming that pulley and cord are weightless and frictionless and that the weights are permitted to shift from the position indicated by gravity, when A is 500 lb and B is 750 lb:

a. Determine acceleration of weights.

b. Determine velocity of A when one weight hits the floor.

c. Determine momentum of *A* at the instant when one weight hits the floor.

d. Determine tension in cord.

2-90. The weightless beam shown in Fig. 2-P-90 is suspended at each end by cables at (1) and (2).   Find:

a. Value of tension in the cable at (2), which is at an angle θ_2 of (60°) with the horizontal

b. Angle θ_1

c. Tension F_1 in the cable supporting the beam at (1)

FIG. 2-P-90

2-91. The hoisting rig in Fig. 2-P-91 is composed of two symmetrical column members *bd* and *cd* with pin joints at *b* and *c* and a steel cable *ad*.   A vertical load *L* of 8 tons is supported at *d*.   The distance *ae* is 21 ft and *ef* is 11 ft.   The angle *daf* is 30°, *def* is 60°, *dbc* is 60°.   The distance *af* = 32 ft.   Determine:

a. Tension in the cable F_{ad}

b. Tension or compression in the legs *cd* and *bd*, F_{bd} and F_{cd}

c. Horizontal forces along the line *bc*, F_{bc}

FIG. 2-P-91

Fluid Mechanics

The review of fluid mechanics or hydraulics can be split into two general subdivisions—hydrostatics and hydrodynamics. Hydrostatics will be discussed first. The phases of this general subdivision which have been included in many of the past fundamentals examinations include the following: pressure due to a head of fluid, pressure gauges and manometers, the location of the center of pressure and the resultant force due to the applied fluid pressure, and Archimedes' principle of buoyancy.

3-1. Hydrostatics. Hydrostatics is the name applied to the study of fluids at rest; the term "fluids" includes both liquids and gases. In this discussion we shall be concerned primarily with the properties of liquids, taking as a guide the emphasis shown in past fundamentals examinations.

Liquids are distinguished from solids by the fact that their particles are readily displaced. If sufficient time is allowed for the change of shape to take place, then only an infinitesimal force is required to alter the form of a liquid. A liquid, depending upon its viscosity, may offer a considerable resistance to a rapid change of shape, but this resistance will vanish once the motion has ceased. One definition of the liquid state is that "a liquid in equilibrium offers no resistance to change of shape." From this it follows that the resultant of all the forces acting upon a particle of liquid at the surface of a liquid must be perpendicular to the tangent to the surface at that point. This also follows from the fact that a liquid cannot withstand any shearing force. An example of the usefulness of this concept is shown in the determination of the shape of the

116

surface of the fluid in an upright cylindrical container rotating about its central axis (Fig. 3-1).

First draw a sketch of a section through the center of the cylinder. To determine the required curve of the surface then select any particle of fluid on this surface and add the forces acting on this particular particle. F_x equals the force on the particle due to the rotation about the axis and equals the centripetal force, or

$$F_x = \omega^2 rm$$
$$F_y = \text{gravitational force} = mg$$

Slope of the surface of the liquid at the point x, y

Axis of rotation

(a) (b)

FIG. 3-1

The slope of the surface of the liquid at the point x, y is perpendicular to the slope of the resultant R of the forces acting on the particle of liquid. $\tan \alpha = F_x/F_y$, but also $\tan \alpha = dy/dx$ at this particular point, so

$$dy/dx = (\omega^2 rm/mg)$$

where ω and g are constants, $r = x$, and $dy = (\omega^2/g)\, x\, dx$, or the equation for the curve of the surface is $y = (\omega^2/2g)x^2$ plus a constant of integration. If the axes are selected as shown in the figure, $y = 0$ for $x = 0$ and the constant of integration is zero, the final equation becomes $y = (\omega^2/2g)x^2$, which will be recognized as the equation of a parabola. The curve of the surface of the liquid is then a paraboloid of revolution.

Another example of the application of this principle is afforded by a past examination problem:

- A container partially filled with water and having a total weight of 10 lb is sliding down a 30° inclined plane against a friction factor of $\mu = 0.30$.

  a. At what rate is the container accelerating down the inclined plane?

  b. At what angle is the water surface in the container measured from the horizontal?

In order to simplify your calculations, it is suggested that you

(a)

(b)

Fig. 3-2

solve for the unknowns in the tri-angles graphically. First, draw the figure (Fig. 3-2).

$$f = N \times \mu = W \cos 30° \times 0.30$$
$$f = 0.260W = 2.60 \text{ lb}$$
$$P = W \sin 30° = 5.00 \text{ lb}$$

The net force acting on the container to cause acceleration = 2.40 lb.

$$a = \frac{F}{m} = \frac{2.40}{10/g} = 0.240g$$
$$= 7.73 \text{ ft/sec}^2$$

Taking one particle of water on the surface, we can show the forces acting upon it. If we draw the inertial force of ma at an angle of 30° and the gravitational force of mg at the correct angles, the angle of the resultant can be determined either graphically or analytically.

3-2. Fluid Pressure. The pressure at any point in a liquid is equal to the pressure on the surface of the liquid plus the weight of the column of liquid of unit cross-sectional area extending vertically from the point to the surface of the liquid. Furthermore, the pressure is the same at all points at the same level within a single liquid and the pressure at the particular point is the same regardless of the direction in which the pressure is measured. The pressure at a given depth in a fluid will then depend upon the density of the fluid; columns of unequal heights of different liquids may produce equal pressures. This is the basis of the manometer and the differential manometer.

3-3. Manometers. An example illustrating a differential manom-eter is afforded by a problem which asked:

- Given the compound manometer shown in Fig. 3-3, determine the pressure P_x.

The required pressure can be determined by starting with P_x and adding or subtracting all the incremental pressures between P_x and P_1.

$P_x + 70$ in. water $- 45$ in. Hg $+ 30$ in. water $- 35$ in. Hg
$$- 25 \text{ in. water} = P_1$$

$$P_x = 80 \text{ in. Hg} - 75 \text{ in. water} + 10 \text{ psia}$$

The specific gravity of mercury is 13.6, so

$$P_x = 1,013 \text{ in. water} + 10 \text{ psia}$$

or $P_x = 84.4$ ft of water $+ 10$ psia.

Water weighs 62.4 lb/cu ft, so a column of water 1 in. square

FIG. 3-3   FIG. 3-4

by 1 ft high would weigh $62.4/144 = 0.433$ lb, or the pressure
equivalent for water is 0.433 psi/ft of depth.

$$P_x = 36.6 + 10 = 46.6 \text{ psia}$$

The addition of the incremental pressures follows from the previous
discussion. This is illustrated by the figure, where

$$P_2 = P_x + 70 \text{ in. water}$$
$$P_2 = P_3 = P_4 + 45 \text{ in. Hg}$$
$$P_5 = P_4 \text{ and } P_6 = P_5 + 30 \text{ in. water}$$
$$P_6 = P_7 = P_8 + 35 \text{ in. Hg}$$
$$P_8 = P_1 + 25 \text{ in. water}$$

(P_2 and P_3 are at the same height in the same fluid system, as are
P_4 and P_5, and P_6 and P_7.) Combining these relationships gives

$$P_x = 80 \text{ in. Hg} - 75 \text{ in. water} + P_1$$

as before.

Another example of a manometer problem is illustrated in Fig. 3-4.

• Carbon tetrachloride flows in pipe A in the figure and water flows in pipe B. The two pipes are connected by a differential gauge which contains oil (sp. gr., 0.80) and pipe A is 10 ft above pipe B. If the specific gravity of the carbon tetrachloride is 1.5 and the other dimensions are as shown, what is the difference in pressure (in feet of water) between pipes A and B, and which is the greater?

The notations P_1 and P_2 are added to the figure, and since they are at the same elevation in the same fluid system, $P_1 = P_2$.

$P_A = P_1 + 5$ ft of CCl$_4$ $P_B = P_2 + 2$ ft of oil $+ 13$ ft of water

$P_1 = P_A - 5$ ft of CCl$_4$ $P_2 = P_B - 2$ ft of oil $- 13$ ft of water

$P_1 = P_A - 7.5$ ft of water $P_2 = P_B - 1.60$ ft of water $- 13$ ft of water

$$P_A - 7.5 \text{ ft of water} = P_B - 14.60 \text{ ft of water}$$
$$P_B = P_A + 7.1 \text{ ft of water}$$

Utilizing the same reasoning, we can calculate the total force on

Fluid of specific weight w lb/ft^3

Fig. 3-5

any submerged area. The total force will equal the summation of the pressures at depths h, $h + \Delta h$, $h + 2\Delta h$, . . . times the areas at depths h, $h + \Delta h$, $h + 2\Delta h$, ... This is shown in Fig. 3-5. The force on $dA = P_h \, dA = (P_1 + wh) \, dA$.

$$dA = 1 \times \frac{dh}{\sin \alpha}$$
$$\sum P_h \, \Delta A \rightarrow \int_{h_0}^{h_1} (P_1 + wh) \frac{dh \, l}{\sin \alpha}$$

The force acting on the surface is

$$F = \int_{h_0}^{h_1} (P_1 + wh) \frac{l\,dh}{\sin \alpha}$$

For the rectangular surface shown,

$$F = \frac{l}{\sin \alpha} \left[P_1(h_1 - h_0) + \frac{w}{2} (h_1{}^2 - h_0{}^2) \right]$$

P_1 is ordinarily only atmospheric pressure, which will act on both sides of a gate or dam subjected to hydraulic pressure, so it can be omitted from the equation.   This gives:

$$F = \frac{lw}{2 \sin \alpha} (h_1{}^2 - h_0{}^2) = wA \frac{h_1 + h_0}{2}$$

since $A = l(h_1 - h_0)/\sin \alpha$, $w(h_1 + h_0)/2$ is the average pressure acting on the area.

The same result may be obtained without the use of calculus by constructing the graph of pressure vs. depth and calculating the

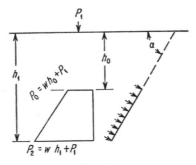

Fig. 3-6

resulting force from the relationship P psf $\times A$ sq ft $= F$ lb (Fig. 3-6).   The total force represented by the trapezoid of pressure is, for a perpendicular surface,

$$F = \left[P_1 + \frac{w(h_0 + h_1)}{2} \right] (h_1 - h_0) \times l$$

where $l =$ width of the perpendicular surface

The actual pressure acts over a larger sloping surface in the ratio of $1/\sin \alpha$, so

$$F = \frac{l}{\sin \alpha}\left[P + \frac{w(h_1 + h_0)}{2}\right] \times (h_1 - h_0)$$

since pressure always acts perpendicular to a surface regardless of the angle of the surface.

This same relationship can be arrived at for a vertical dam in another manner (Fig. 3-7). Pressure increases linearly with the depth, and the force per unit width of the dam will equal $\int p\, dh$; this

Fig. 3-7   Fig. 3-8

is just the area of the pressure triangle shown, which in turn is equal to the product of one-half the altitude times the base or

$$(\tfrac{1}{2}h_d) \times (wh_d) = w\frac{(h_d)^2}{2} \quad \text{lb/ft of width of dam}$$

The same average pressure relationship will hold for any submerged surface that is symmetrical about its horizontal center line. This includes rectangles, circles, and ellipses.

The total net force acting on a surface because of the pressure of the liquid may be considered as the resultant of the hydrostatic forces acting. The hydrostatic force can then be resisted by a single applied force acting against the surface on the side opposite the liquid. This single force must be located at a point about which there will be no moment due to the hydrostatic force; this point is called the "center of pressure." We can determine the center of pressure for a rectangular surface in a fashion similar to that by which we determined the force due to the hydrostatic pressure (Fig. 3-8).

3-4. Center of Pressure. Locating the center of pressure is similar to locating the center of gravity of a surface. The center of pressure might be termed the center of force, since it is that point on the submerged surface about which there is no resultant moment due to the pressure forces acting on the surface. m is the distance from the surface of the liquid to the center of pressure.

$$m = \frac{\Sigma r \, \Delta F}{\Sigma \, \Delta F} = \frac{\int_{h_0}^{h_1} h \times hw \, dA}{\int_{h_0}^{h_1} hw \, dA}$$

For the rectangular surface shown, this becomes

$$m = \frac{\int_{h_0}^{h_1} h^2 w \times l \, dh}{\int_{h_0}^{h_1} hw \times l \, dh} = \frac{lw \, \tfrac{1}{3}(h_1{}^3 - h_0{}^3)}{lw \, \tfrac{1}{2}(h_1{}^2 - h_0{}^2)} = \frac{2}{3} \frac{h_1{}^3 - h_0{}^3}{h_1{}^2 - h_0{}^2}$$

Since $l \, dh = dA$, a more general relationship may be deduced from the above relationship:

$$m = \frac{w \int_{h_0}^{h_1} h^2 \, dA}{w \int_{h_0}^{h_1} h \, dA}$$

where $\int_{h_0}^{h_1} h^2 \, dA$ = moment of inertia of the area about axis 0-0

$$\int_{h_0}^{h_1} h \, dA = \bar{y} \int dA$$

since $\bar{y} = (\int h \, dA)/\int dA$, giving the general relationship $m = I/A\bar{y}$.

The effect of an angle different from 90° can be calculated as before if desired. The intent here is to develop only the simpler relationships, those which you will be able to recall at a later date and which you will be able to utilize effectively. For more complete analyses the reader is advised to consult some of the references listed at the end of the chapter.

We have developed a relationship for finding the center of pressure of a rectangular area located in a direction perpendicular to the surface of the liquid. This specific relationship can easily be modified to cover the case of a rectangular area at an angle to the surface of the liquid. The analysis of other areas is not so simple, however; as it is probably easier to remember the answer alone than the analysis, the general relationship will be stated but not proved.

The equation for determining the distance from a point 0 to the center of pressure of an area is

$$m = \frac{I}{A\bar{y}}$$

where m = distance from point 0 to the center of pressure

    I = moment of inertia of the area about a horizontal axis through 0

    A = area

    $\bar{y}$ = distance from 0 to the center of gravity (or centroid) of the area

In other words, the distance from an axis to the center of pressure of an area is equal to the moment of inertia of the area about that axis divided by the moment of the area about the same axis.

A problem illustrating this is:

- A vertical 4- by 4-ft gate is submerged with the level top 2 ft below the water surface. The gate is exposed to hydrostatic pressure on one side. Find the magnitude and location of these hydrostatic forces.

First draw a figure and label it (Fig. 3-9). The pressure diagram will be a trapezoid, as shown in the figure. The total force acting on the gate because of the pressure of the water will then equal $[(2w + 6w)/2] \times 4$ lb/ft of width $\times$ 4 ft wide; therefore,

$$F = 4w \times 4 \times 4 = 3{,}990 \text{ lb } (w \text{ for water } = 62.4 \text{ lb/cu ft})$$

Note that the atmospheric pressure may be disregarded since it acts equally on both sides of the gate. The location of the center of pressure will be m ft below the surface, where $m = I/A\bar{y}$. The moment of inertia of a rectangle about a transverse axis through its center is $bh^3/12$, which equals $(4 \times 4^3)/12 = 21.3$ ft⁴. The moment of inertia about the surface, 4 ft from the axis of the square, would be:

$$21.3 + AS^2 = 21.3 + 16 \times 4^2 = 277.3 \text{ ft}^4$$
$$A\bar{y} = 16 \times (2 + 2) = 64$$
$$m = 277.3/64 = 4.33 \text{ ft}$$

Another way to calculate the center of pressure of a submerged surface (and one which is probably easier for many shapes) follows from the fact that pressure times area equals force. Force is measured in pounds, so we can draw an equivalent picture of the force acting on the gate and solve for the center of pressure using the relationships from mechanics (Fig. 3-9a). In this analysis the

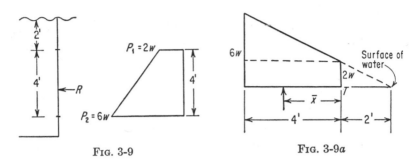

FIG. 3-9   FIG. 3-9a

pressure forces are replaced by their equivalent weight forces, and the problem becomes one in statics. The location of the centroid of the trapezoid of pressure shown in Fig. 3-9a is also the location of the center of pressure, since the loading is constant in a direction perpendicular to the plane of the paper.

Taking moments about T, we find that

$$\bar{x} = \frac{4 \times 2w \times \frac{4}{2} + (4w \times 4)/2 \times \frac{8}{3}}{4 \times 2w + (4w \times 4)/2} = 2.33 \text{ ft}$$

Therefore, the distance from the surface of the water to the center of pressure is $2 + 2.33 = 4.33$ ft, as before. The magnitude of the resultant of the hydrostatic forces is 3,990 lb; its location is 4.33 ft below the surface of the water and midway between the two vertical edges.

Another problem of a similar type was:

- Flashboards placed on the crest of an ogee spillway are designed to fail when the head H is 12 ft. The boards are 4 ft wide and are supported by iron pins mounted in sockets along the crest at 10-ft intervals. Consider only hydrostatic pressure and determine the resisting moment of each pin at the crest of the spillway (Fig. 3-10).

FIG. 3-10

Add an arrow to represent the resultant R. The total force acting on each foot of width of the flashboards will equal

$$\frac{8 + 12}{2} \times w4 \times 1 = 2,500 \text{ lb/ft}$$

(see previous example for sample pressure diagram). The location of the center of pressure $m = I/A\bar{y}$, where I is the moment of inertia of the pressurized area about an axis at the surface of the water, and $\bar{y}$ is the distance below the surface to the center of gravity of the pressurized area.

$$I/\text{ft of width} = \frac{1 \times 4^3}{12} + (1 \times 4)10^2 = 405.3^4/\text{ft}$$
$$A\bar{y}/\text{ft of width} = (1 \times 4)(2 + 8) = 40$$
$$m = 405.3/40 = 10.1 \text{ ft below the surface of the water}$$

Each pin must withstand the force acting on half of the 10-ft width of flashboard on each side of it, or each pin must withstand the hydrostatic force acting on 10 ft of flashboard. Taking moments about an axis at the top of the flashboard we find that the pins must withstand a force of

$$\frac{(2,500 \text{ lb/ft} \times 10 \text{ ft})(10.1 - 8)}{4} = 13,100 \text{ lb/pin}$$

The remainder of the force of 25,000 lb/(10-ft width), or 11,900 lb/ 10 ft of width, must be held at the top of the flashboard.

3-5. Archimedes' Principles of Buoyancy. Another branch of hydrostatics which has received a fair amount of emphasis is buoyancy, or Archimedes' principle. The principles of buoyancy and flotation may be expressed as follows:

1. A body immersed in a fluid is buoyed up by a force equal to the weight of fluid displaced by the body.

2. A floating body displaces its own weight of the fluid in which it is floating.

3. The buoyant force acts upward through the center of gravity of the displaced volume.

The application of these principles can be illustrated by means of an example selected from a past fundamentals examination, which asked:

- A rectangular caisson is being constructed for use in building a bridge pier. The caisson is 50 by 20 by 30 ft high (inside dimensions). The walls are 1 ft thick, and the weight is 18,000 lb. There is no bottom.

  a. How far below the water surface will the bottom edge be when launched?

  b. What additional weight is required to sink the caisson on the bottom of the lake, which is 25 ft deep?

  c. What additional weight is required to hold the caisson on the bottom once it is seated and the water pumped out?

The volume of the walls per foot of depth would equal

$$50 \times 1 \times 2 + 22 \times 1 \times 2 = 144 \text{ cu ft}$$

The volume of water displaced for each foot the open-ended caisson sank below the surface of the water would then be 144 cu ft, and the buoyancy per foot of caisson below the surface would equal

$$144 \times 62.4 = 8,980 \text{ lb/ft}$$

so the answer to part (a) is 18,000/8,980 = 2.0 ft. The additional weight to sink it an additional 23 ft would equal

$$23 \times 8,980 = 207,000 \text{ lb}$$

(b), and the additional weight required to hold the empty caisson on the bottom would equal the weight of the volume of water displaced minus 18,000 lb, which would be (c)

$$(52' \times 22' \times 62.4 \text{ lb/ft}) \times 25 \text{ ft} - 18,000 = 1,785,000$$
$$- 18,000 = 1,767,000 \text{ lb}$$

The same principles are used to measure the specific gravities of fluids. Another question asked in a past fundamentals examination was:

- A hydrometer bulb and stem displace 0.5 cu in. when immersed in fresh water. The stem has an area of 0.05 sq in. What is the distance on the stem between the graduations for 1.00 and 1.10 sp gr?

The hydrometer bulb and stem displace 0.5 cu in. of water, so the

bulb and stem weigh $(0.5/1,728) \times 62.4$ lb. They will displace this
same weight of liquid when floating in the 1.1-sp-gr liquid, so the
volume of liquid displaced will equal

$$\frac{0.5}{1,728} \times 62.4 \times \frac{1,728}{1.1 \times 62.4} = 0.455 \text{ cu in.}$$

The difference in the volume of fluid displaced (or the volume of bulb
and stem immersed) will be $0.500 - 0.455 = 0.045$ cu in. Since
the stem has a cross-sectional area of 0.05 sq in., the stem will

FIG. 3-11

stick out of the liquid 0.045 cu in./0.050 sq in. = 0.90 in. higher
in the 1.10-sp-gr fluid than it did out of the 1.00-sp-gr fluid, and the
distance on the stem between the graduations for 1.00 and 1.10 sp gr
would then equal 0.90 in.

Another problem illustrating the application of Archimedes' principles was:

- A cubical block of wood 10 cm on a side and of density
  0.5 g/cu cm floats in a container of water. Oil of density
  0.8 g/cu cm is poured on the water until the top of the oil
  layer is 4 cm below the top of the block.
  a. How deep is the oil layer?
  b. What is the gauge pressure at the lower face of the block
  in dynes/sq cm?

First draw a sketch (Fig. 3-11). The mass of the block is
$10 \times 10 \times 10 \times 0.5 = 500$ g. The total volume of fluid displaced
equals $(10 - 4) \times 100 = 600$ cu cm. The density of water is
1 g/cu cm, and the weight of the block must equal the weight of the
fluid displaced, so

$$100y \times 0.8 \text{ g/cu cm} + 100(6 - y) \times 1 \text{ g/cu cm} = 500 \text{ g}$$
$$y = 5 \text{ cm}$$

or the oil layer is 5 cm deep. The gauge pressure at the lower face of the block would equal (5 × 0.8 × 980) dynes/sq cm due to oil + 1 × 980 dynes/sq cm due to water; $P = 4,900$ dynes/sq cm.

Another problem in the same vein was as follows:

- A 50-gal steel barrel which weighs 40 lb when empty is full of fuel oil of 0.93 sp gr and is placed in a fresh-water lake. Will it float or sink? Show calculations used to arrive at answer.

Fifty gallons of fuel oil would weigh 50 × 0.93 × 8.34 lb; 50 gal of water displaced would weigh 50 × 8.34 lb. The buoyant force acting on the 50 gal of oil would then equal

$$50 \times (1 - 0.93) \times 8.34 = 29.3 \text{ lb}$$

The steel barrel itself would also possess some buoyancy. The 40 lb of steel will displace $40/(7.86 \times 62.4) \times 62.4 = 5.1$ lb of water, which must be added to the buoyancy of the oil; this gives a total buoyant force of 29.3 + 5.1 = 34.4 lb, which is less than the 40-lb weight of the steel drum by 5.6 lb, so the drum and contents would sink.

A slightly different approach is to calculate the total weight of the full drum and the volume of the full drum so that the weight of the water displaced can also be calculated:

Weight of filled barrel = 40 + (50 × 0.93 × 8.34) = 427.6 lb

$$\text{Volume of barrel and contents} = \frac{40}{7.86 \times 62.4} + \frac{50}{7.48 \text{ gal/cu ft}}$$
$$= 6.76 \text{ cu ft}$$

giving 6.76 × 62.4 = 422 lb, weight of water displaced. Again the filled barrel weighs 427.6 − 422 = 5.6 lb more than the water displaced, so it will sink.

The subject of bulk modulus should probably also be mentioned here. Liquids are generally considered to be incompressible. Relative to the compressibility of gases this is true, but liquids as well as gases can be compressed, i.e., the volume of a liquid will be reduced under the application of pressure. The ratio of the change in volume divided by the original volume equals the pressure applied divided by the bulk modulus of the fluid, or $\Delta V/V = P/BM$, which equals the percentage reduction in volume. The bulk modulus of water is about 300,000 psi. This means that the volume of a given amount of water will be reduced by $5{,}000/300{,}000 = 1.7$ per cent if the pressure acting on the water is increased by 5,000 psi.

3-6. Hydrodynamics. Fluids in motion are governed in large part by the same principles that were discussed under Dynamics in Chap. 2, Mechanics. To analyze the characteristics of the flow of liquids we must also, however, include the effects of viscosity; and analysis of the flow of gases must in addition include a consideration of the thermodynamic effects.

The bulk of the problems on this subject in past examinations have been concerned with the flow of liquids and have included examples covering flow through pipelines, open channels, orifices, and venturi tubes. Other phases covered have included the conservation of momentum, pump analyses, and a few problems concerning drag, and model theory.

3-7. Bernoulli's Equation. Perhaps the one most important fundamental relationship dealing with hydrodynamics is Bernoulli's equation. This equation is based on the concept of the conservation of energy; it states in algebraic form that the total energy at one point of a closed system is equal to the total energy at any other point in the system plus the energy lost between those two points. Bernoulli's equation may be written as:

$$\frac{P_1}{w} + \frac{v_1^2}{2g} + Z_1 = \frac{P_2}{w} + \frac{v_2^2}{2g} + Z_2 + h_{L_{1-2}}$$

where P_1 and P_2 = respective static pressures at points 1 and 2, psf

w = specific weight of the fluid flowing, lb/cu ft

v_1 and v_2 = respective velocities, fps

g = acceleration of gravity = 32.2 ft/sec²

Z_1 and Z_2 = elevations of points 1 and 2 above some selected datum plane

$h_{L_{1-2}}$ = head loss measured in feet of fluid flowing between points 1 and 2

The head loss results from the frictional resistance of the fluid because of its viscosity. An example of the use of Bernoulli's equation is the solution of the following sample examination problem:

• From the information given on the sketch (Fig. 3-12) calculate the diameter at section B in inches. The diameter at section A is 4.00 in. Disregard friction. Kerosene is flowing at the rate of 2.5 cfs (sp gr, kerosene = 0.80). Area of 1-in.-diameter circle equals 0.00545 sq ft.

Gauge reads 10 psi

FIG. 3-12

First, write out Bernoulli's equation:

$$\frac{P_A}{w} + \frac{v_A{}^2}{2g} + Z_1 = \frac{P_B}{w} + \frac{v_B{}^2}{2g} + Z_2$$

Let the elevation at point A be the zero reference plane. This gives:

$$Z_1 = 0 \quad \text{and} \quad Z_2 = 10 \text{ ft}$$

$$\frac{P_A}{w} = \frac{(10 \times 144) \text{ lb/sq ft}}{62.4 \times 0.80} + 2 = 28.9 + 2 = 30.9 \text{ ft}$$

$$\frac{P_B}{w} + 1.55 \text{ ft} = 3 \text{ in. Hg} = \left(\frac{3 \times 13.6}{12} \text{ ft of water}\right) \times \frac{1}{0.80}$$
$$= 4.25 \text{ ft of kerosene}$$

$$\frac{P_B}{w} = 4.25 - 1.55 = 2.70 \text{ ft}$$

$$v_A = \frac{Q}{A} = \frac{2.5 \text{ cfs}}{(4/12)^2 \times \pi/4 \text{ sq ft}} = 28.7 \text{ fps}$$

$$\frac{v_B{}^2}{2g} = \frac{P_A}{w} - \frac{P_B}{w} + \frac{v_A{}^2}{2g} - Z_2 = 30.9 - 2.70 + \frac{28.7^2}{64.4} - 10$$

$$\frac{v_B{}^2}{2g} = 30.95 \qquad v_B = \sqrt{1,995} = 44.7 \text{ fps}$$

$$A_B = \frac{Q}{v_B} = \frac{2.5}{44.7} = 0.0560 \text{ sq ft} \qquad \text{or} \qquad 8.06 \text{ sq in.}$$

$$D_B = \sqrt{8.06/0.785} = 3.20 \text{ in.}$$

3-8. Flow Measurement. Many flow-measuring devices are based upon application of Bernoulli's principle. The ones we are most interested in are the orifice, the venturi tube, the nozzle, and the pitot tube. The orifice, the nozzle, and the venturi tube are quite similar in that all are reductions in flow area; the correlation between pressure and velocity upstream of these devices and at the sections of reduced area gives the velocity of flow through the throat and thus provides a measure of the flow rate.

3-9. Orifices. None of these three devices conforms exactly to Bernoulli's equation, however, because of fluid friction and the contraction of the jet of liquid as it flows through the section of reduced area. This leads to a correction factor called the coefficient of discharge C, which, in the case of an orifice, is the product of a velocity coefficient C_v and a coefficient of contraction C_c. For a sharp-edged orifice, $C_c = 0.62$, $C_v = 0.98$, and $C = 0.61$. This means that for a sharp-edged orifice placed in a pipe the velocity of flow through the orifice would equal $C\sqrt{2gh}$, where h would equal $\Delta P/w$. This is illustrated by means of the following selected past examination problem:

- If a 1-in. orifice has a head of 200 ft and the coefficient of contraction is 0.98, calculate the velocity of flow.

This is not a well-worded question, and we shall have to make some assumptions in order to work it. The velocity at the vena contracta is equal to $C_v\sqrt{2gh}$, where C_v is the velocity coefficient. The coefficient of contraction is the ratio of the area of the vena contracta to the area of the orifice, and the discharge coefficient is equal to $C_v \times C_c$. What is probably meant here is, "What is the quantity of flow for a discharge coefficient of 0.98?" Proceeding upon this premise,

$$Q = A \times 0.98 \sqrt{2g \times 200} = (\tfrac{1}{12})^2 \times \frac{\pi}{4} \times 0.98 \sqrt{64.4 \times 200}$$

$$Q = 0.607 \text{ cu ft/sec} \qquad \text{or} \qquad 0.607 \times 60 \times 7.48 = 272 \text{ gpm}$$

In the case of an orifice in a pipe, the fluid approaching the orifice will have a velocity which must be considered in the calculation of the orifice coefficient. If we apply Bernoulli's equation to a point upstream and at the throat of the orifice, we obtain:

$$\frac{v_o{}^2}{2g} + \frac{P_o}{w} = \frac{v_p{}^2}{2g} + \frac{p_p}{w}$$

where the subscript o refers to the orifice and the subscript p refers to the pipe, since the same quantity of liquid flows through both pipe and orifice.

$$v_p = v_o \frac{A_o}{A_p}$$

$$v_o{}^2 = \left(\frac{P_p - P_o}{w}\right) \times 2g + v_o \frac{A_o{}^2}{A_p}$$

where $\dfrac{P_p - P_o}{w} = h$ ft of fluid

$$v_o{}^2 = \left[1 - \left(\frac{A_o}{A_p}\right)^2\right] 2gh$$

$$v_o = \sqrt{\frac{2gh}{1 - (A_o/A_p)^2}}$$

To this must be added the effect of the previously discussed orifice coefficients, giving

$$v_o = c \sqrt{2gh} \times \frac{1}{\sqrt{1 - (A_o/A_p)^2}}$$

where $1/\sqrt{1 - (A_o/A_p)^2}$ is termed the "velocity-of-approach factor."

3-10. Venturi Meters. Another past examination problem illustrating Bernoulli's principle was:

- A 3- by 1-in. venturi meter carries oil with a specific gravity of 0.86. A differential gauge connected between the pipe and the throat contains water with oil above the water in the manometer tubes. If the gauge shows a deflection of 57.6 in. and if the meter coefficient is 0.975, find the rate of discharge.

First, sketch the figure.   Assume that the pipe and venturi meter are horizontal and that both are at the same elevation (Fig. 3-13).

FIG. 3-13

The difference in pressure between throat and body can be determined from the manometer reading.

$$P_B + 57.6 \text{ in. of oil} = P_T + 57.6 \text{ in. of water}$$
$$P_B - P_T = 57.6 - 57.6 \times 0.86 = 8.06 \text{ in. of water}$$
$$\frac{P_B - P_T}{w} = \frac{8.06}{12} \times \frac{1}{0.86} = 0.782 \text{ ft of oil}$$

Bernoulli's equation gives:

$$\frac{P_B}{w} + \frac{v_B{}^2}{2g} + Z_B = \frac{P_T}{w} + \frac{v_T{}^2}{2g} + Z_T$$

but

$$Z_B = Z_T$$

and

$$v_B = \frac{A_T}{A_B} \times v_T = \frac{v_T}{9}$$

$$\frac{P_B - P_T}{w} = \frac{v_T{}^2 - v_B{}^2}{2g} = \frac{80 v_T{}^2}{162 g}$$

$$v_T = \sqrt{\frac{0.782 \times 162 g}{80}}$$

if the meter coefficient were 100 per cent.   Actually

$$v_T = 0.975 \sqrt{\frac{0.782 \times 162 g}{80}} = 6.97 \text{ fps}$$

$$Q = (\tfrac{1}{12})^2 \times \frac{\pi}{4} \times 6.97 = 0.0380 \text{ cfs} \qquad \text{or} \qquad 17.1 \text{ gpm}$$

3-11. Pitot Tubes. A pitot tube is used to measure the velocity of a fluid by converting the energy due to the velocity (velocity head) to potential energy or pressure head. Referring to Bernoulli's equation we get the relationship that $v = \sqrt{2gh}$, and since there is no flow, no flow coefficient is needed as in the previous example.

Fig. 3-14

A further description of a pitot tube and an example of the calculations required to solve such a sample examination problem are as follows:

- A pitot tube having a coefficient of unity is inserted in the exact center of a long smooth tube of 1-in. ID in which crude oil (sp gr = 0.90)($\mu = 35 \times 10^{-5}$lb-sec/sq ft) is flowing. Determine the average velocity in the tube if the velocity pressure is (*a*) 2.3 psi, (*b*) 3.9 in. water.

First make a sketch of the system under consideration (Fig. 3-14). Bernoulli's equation gives us the velocity at the center of the tube. The velocity of the fluid in contact with the pitot tube is all converted into pressure head.

$$\frac{P_1}{w} + \frac{v_1^2}{2g} + Z_1 = \frac{P_2}{w} + \frac{v_2^2}{2g} + Z_2$$

where $Z_1 = Z_2$
$v_2 = 0$

$$\frac{v_1^2}{2g} = \frac{P_2 - P_1}{w}$$

For case (*a*)

$$\frac{P_2 - P_1}{w} = \frac{(2.3 \times 144) \text{ lb/sq ft}}{(62.4 \times 0.9) \text{ lb/cu ft}} = 5.9 \text{ ft} \qquad \text{of oil}$$

For case (*b*)

$$\frac{P_2 - P_1}{w} = \frac{3.9}{0.90} \times \frac{1}{12} = 0.361 \text{ ft} \qquad \text{of oil}$$

The velocity at the center of the tube would then be

$$v_a = \sqrt{5.9 \times 2g} = 19.5 \text{ fps}$$
$$v_b = \sqrt{0.361 \times 2g} = 4.82 \text{ fps}$$

3-12. Average Velocity in a Pipe.　The average velocity can be determined from the velocity at the center of the tube, which is the maximum velocity.　In the case of viscous flow, $v_{avg} = v_{max}/2$, and the average velocity in the case of turbulent flow is equal to $0.82v_{max}$.

Turbulent flow occurs for Reynolds numbers (see below) greater than 4,000; flow is ordinarily viscous for Reynolds numbers less than 2,000.

$$\text{Re} = \frac{\rho Dv}{\mu} = \frac{62.4 \times 0.90}{32.2} \frac{\text{lb-sec}^2}{\text{ft}^4} \times (\tfrac{1}{12})\text{ft} \times \frac{1}{35 \times 10^{-5}} \frac{\text{ft}^2}{\text{lb-sec}}$$
$$\times v \text{ ft/sec}$$

$$= 415 \times v$$

For case (a)

Re = 8,100—turbulent flow

For case (b)

Re = 2,000—viscous flow

Average velocities will then be

For case (a)
$$v_{avg} = 0.82 \times 19.5 = 16 \text{ fps}$$

For case (b)
$$v_{avg} = 0.50 \times 4.82 = 2.41 \text{ fps}$$

3-13. Reynolds Number.　The next important topic is that of Reynolds number; with it are reviewed some of the fundamentals of viscous and turbulent flow and pressure drop (or head loss) due to the flow of liquids through pipes and channels.　Reynolds number, abbreviated Re, is a dimensionless number equal to $\rho Dv/\mu$, where ρ = density of the fluid flowing, slugs/cu ft, $\rho = w/g$; v = fluid velocity, fps; μ = absolute viscosity in lb-sec/sq ft, or μ = centipoises/47,800; and D = four times the hydraulic radius (D = the diameter of a circular pipe).　Reynolds number also equals Dv/ν, where ν is the kinematic viscosity measured in ft²/sec (ν = centistokes divided by 93,000).

3-14. Hydraulic Radius. The hydraulic radius is equal to the cross-sectional flow area divided by the wetted perimeter. For a circular pipe,

$$R_H = \frac{(\pi/4)D^2}{\pi D} = \frac{D}{4}$$

For a rectangular duct of width w and height h,

$$R_H = \frac{w \times h}{2w + 2h} = \frac{wh}{2(w + h)}$$

For a square of side length s, $R_H = s/4$. In calculating the hydraulic radius of an open trough or flume, it is important to remember the phrase "wetted perimeter." R_H for the trough shown in Fig. 3-15 of width w with water flowing at a depth h would equal $(w \times h)/(w + 2h)$, since the top is open and the "wetted perimeter" includes only the two sides and the bottom.

Fig. 3-15

3-15. Turbulent and Viscous Flow. The Reynolds number (Re) is a measure of the amount of turbulence in the flowing fluid; for Re less than 2,000 the flow is generally considered to be laminar or viscous, for Re greater than 4,000 the flow is generally considered to be turbulent. The range of Re between 2,000 and 4,000 is called the "critical zone," and the flow in this region is neither completely laminar nor completely turbulent.

3-16. Frictional Head Loss. The head loss due to frictional flow of fluid flowing full in a pipe or duct can be determined from the relationship (Darcy's equation)

$$h_L = f \frac{Lv^2}{2gD}$$

where h_L = head loss, ft of fluid flowing
L = length of pipe or duct through which the fluid flows, ft
v = fluid velocity, fps
g = acceleration of gravity
D = four times the hydraulic radius (or the diameter of a circular pipe), ft
f = friction factor, which is dimensionless and depends upon the value of the Reynolds number

FIG. 3-16. For descriptive legend see opposite page.

For viscous flow, $f = 64/\text{Re}$ and f is independent of any ordinary internal pipe roughness. In the turbulent range, the value of f is somewhat dependent upon the roughness of the pipe and is usually taken from a curve of f vs. Re, such as is shown in Fig. 3-16.

- What sized pipe will be required to transport 2 cu ft/sec of oil with a drop in pressure of 1 psi/1,000 ft of pipe? The specific gravity is 0.85, and the absolute viscosity is 12 centipoises at a temperature of 70°F. Assume steel pipe.

$$h_L = f \frac{Lv^2}{2gD}$$

where h_L is measured in feet of fluid flowing.

$$h_L = \frac{1 \times 144 \text{ lb/sq ft}}{62.4 \times 0.85 \text{ lb/cu ft}} = 2.72 \text{ ft/1,000 ft}$$

$$\frac{2gh_L}{L} = f \frac{v^2}{D} = \frac{2g \times 2.72}{1,000} = 0.175 = f \frac{v^2}{D}$$

Now, determine the Reynolds number.

$$\mu = \frac{0.12 \text{ poise}}{478} = 2.50 \times 10^{-4} \text{ lb-sec/sq ft}$$

$$\text{Re} = \frac{\rho Dv}{\mu} = \frac{62.4 \times 0.85}{32.2} \times \frac{1}{2.50 \times 10^{-4}} \times Dv = 6,580Dv$$

$$2 \text{ cu ft/sec} = Q = v \times A = v \times \frac{\pi}{4} D^2$$

FIG. 3-16. Plot of Reynolds number vs. friction factor.

TABLE OF VALUES OF ABSOLUTE ROUGHNESS ϵ FOR NEW PIPES

Feet

Drawn tubing, brass, lead, glass, centrifugally spun concrete, bituminous lining, transite	0.000005
Commercial steel or wrought iron	0.00015
Welded-steel pipe	0.00015
Asphalt-dipped cast iron	0.0004
Galvanized iron	0.0005
Cast iron, average	0.00085
Wood stave	0.0006–0.003
Concrete	0.001–0.01
Riveted steel	0.003–0.03

ϵ/D for use with curves of Fig. 3-16 found by dividing the value given above for ϵ by diameter of pipe in feet.

giving $v\dot{D}^2 = 2.55$.   These three relationships reduce to

$$\text{Re} = \frac{17{,}500}{D} \quad \text{and} \quad f = 0.0269D^5$$

From Fig. 3-16, using the curve for steel pipe, $\epsilon/D = 0.00015$ if D is 1 ft,

$$\text{Re} = 17{,}500$$

and $f = 0.028$, so D should be slightly larger to satisfy the requirements exactly.   The theoretical inner diameter would be approximately $12\frac{1}{8}$ in., but standard pipe is actually a little less than 12 in. ID (Schedule No. 40 pipe, 11.938 in. ID for 12-in. nominal pipe size), and this ordinarily has a $\pm\frac{1}{32}$-in. tolerance.   In addition, the calculated pressure drop is not absolutely accurate, and the friction factor f may vary as much as ± 10 per cent for commercial pipe.   Considering these various factors, standard 12-in. pipe would be the best selection.   The 12-in. ID pipe would give:

$$v = \frac{2}{0.785} = 2.55 \text{ fps}$$

$$\text{Re} = \frac{62.4 \times 0.85}{32.2} \frac{1 \times 2.55}{2.50 \times 10^{-4}} = 16{,}800$$

giving $f = 0.028$

$$h_L = 0.028 \frac{1{,}000 \times (2.55)^2}{2g \times 1} = 2.82 \text{ ft}/1{,}000 \text{ ft}$$

$$2.82 \text{ ft} \times (62.4 \times 0.85) \text{ lb/cu ft} \times \frac{1 \text{ sq ft}}{144 \text{ sq in.}} = 1.04 \text{ psi}/1{,}000 \text{ ft}$$

estimated pressure drop.

Another sample problem from a past examination asked:

• Find the hydraulic radius of the section shown in Fig. 3-17 when the water is flowing 4 ft deep in the channel.

FIG. 3-17

The hydraulic radius is equal to the area of the cross section divided by the wetted perimeter.

The cross-sectional area of a trapezoidal section equals

$$\frac{\text{(Width at top } - \text{ width at bottom)}}{2} \times \text{height}$$

The width at the top $= 10 + 2[4 \times (1/1.5)] = 15.34$ ft.
The length of each side is

$$\sqrt{4^2 + \left(4 \times \frac{1}{1.5}\right)^2} = 4.81 \text{ ft} = S$$

or

$$S = \frac{4}{\sin \alpha} \qquad \alpha = \tan^{-1}\frac{1.5}{1} = 56.3°$$

$$S = \frac{4}{0.832} = 4.81 \text{ ft}$$

$$R = \frac{(10 - 15.34)/2 \times 4}{10 - 2(4.81)} = 2.59 \text{ ft}$$

A further application of these principles is illustrated by another sample problem:

- What quantity of water, in cubic feet per second, will flow in a 450-ft 10-in. ID pipe if the static head is 35 ft? The friction factor may be considered essentially constant, having a value of 0.025. Disregard entrance and exit losses (Fig. 3-18).

FIG. 3-18

Apply Bernoulli's equation, taking as the two points the top of the reservoir and the discharge end of the pipe.

$$\frac{P_1}{w} + \frac{v_1^2}{2g} + Z_1 = \frac{P_2}{w} + \frac{v_2^2}{2g} + Z_2 + h_{L_{1-2}}$$

P_1 and P_2 are equal to atmospheric pressure, and v_1 is negligible, since the area of the reservoir is many times that of the pipe cross section. $Z_1 - Z_2 = 35.0$ ft, the difference in elevation between the two points.

$$35 = \frac{v_2{}^2}{2g} + h_L = 0.0155v_2{}^2 + h_L$$

$$h_L = f\frac{Lv^2}{2gD} = 0.025\frac{450v^2}{2g(10\!\!/\!\!12)} = 0.210v^2$$

$$35 = 0.0155v_2{}^2 + 0.210v_2{}^2 \qquad v = \sqrt{\frac{35}{0.226}} = 12.45 \text{ fps}$$

$$Q = v \times A = 12.45 \times (10\!\!/\!\!12)^2 \times \frac{\pi}{4} = 6.80 \text{ cfs}$$

3-17. Open-channel Flow. If the flow is in a pipe which is not running full or if it is in an open channel, the flow rate is usually calculated by means of the Manning formula:

$$v = 1.486\frac{R^{2\!/\!3}S^{1\!/\!2}}{n}$$

where R = hydraulic radius

S = slope of the channel, ft/ft

n = Manning factor, which depends upon the material of which the channel is made and the roughness of the inside of the channel

An illustration of the use of this equation is afforded by the past examination problem:

- A sewer made of concrete pipe (Manning coefficient 0.013) 4 ft in diameter is to carry 32.2 cfs when running half full. What is the minimum slope in feet per 1,000 ft required?

Sketch the pipe (Fig. 3-19). Using Manning's formula for flow in open channels, given above,

$$R = \frac{\text{cross-sectional area}}{\text{wetted perimeter}} = \frac{\frac{1}{2}(\pi/4)D^2}{\frac{1}{2}\pi D} = \frac{D}{4} = 1 \text{ ft}$$

$$\text{Required } v = \frac{Q}{A} = \frac{32.2}{\frac{1}{2}(\pi/4)D^2} = \frac{32.2}{6.28} = 5.13 \text{ fps}$$

$$5.13 = 1.486\frac{1^{2\!/\!3}S^{1\!/\!2}}{0.013}$$

$$S = \left(\frac{5.13 \times 0.013}{1.486}\right)^2 = 0.00202$$

Fig. 3-19   or the slope must equal 2.02 ft/1,000 ft of line.

3-18. Centrifugal Pumps. The next main topic under the general heading of fluid mechanics is that of pumps and pumping systems. Briefly, a pump is a device to add "head" or pressure to a fluid. In a centrifugal pump the fluid leaves the periphery of the impeller at a higher velocity than that at which it enters; this velocity is partly converted into pressure by the pump casing before the fluid leaves the pump through the nozzle. Thus a centrifugal pump is a device which supplies kinetic energy to a fluid (velocity head) and then converts it into potential energy (pressure head). If we apply Bernoulli's equation to a pump we see that the head added to the fluid can be determined from the relationship

$$H = H_d - H_s + \frac{v_d{}^2}{2g} - \frac{v_s{}^2}{2g}$$

where H_d = discharge head measured at the pump discharge and referred to the pump shaft center line, and is expressed in feet of the fluid being pumped

H_s = suction head measured at the pump intake, also referred to the same datum plane of the pump shaft (Note that if the suction pressure is negative, it must be added.)

v_d and v_s = the velocity at the discharge and at the suction of the pump

The terms v_d and v_s give the difference in velocity head into and out of the pump. If the suction and discharge nozzles of the pump are the same size, these terms cancel each other. The horsepower supplied to the fluid by the pump would equal $H/33,000$ hp/lb/min pumped, or $8.33H/33,000 = H/3,960$ hp/gpm pumped.

3-19. Specific Speed. There are a few other important points regarding centrifugal pumps; they will be discussed very briefly. The first of these is the specific speed of a pump. The specific speed

$$n_s = \frac{nQ^{1/2}}{H^{3/4}}$$

where n_s = specific speed

n = speed of rotation, or impeller speed, rpm

Q = flow, gpm

H = head, ft of fluid flowing

The physical meaning of specific speed is the rpm needed to produce 1 gpm at 1-ft head with an impeller similar to the one under consideration but (probably) reduced in size. The physical meaning of specific speed has no practical significance; the number is used as a "type" number for a particular style of pump. The specific speed as a type number is constant for all similar pumps and does not change with speed for the same pump. Specific speed is a criterion of similarity for centrifugal pumps. The efficiency for a particular specific speed of a pump will remain essentially constant even though the output is varied. The efficiency vs. specific speed relationship will also hold for larger or smaller pumps of the same design (models which have been scaled up or down in size).

3-20. Pump Affinity Laws. The specific speed relationship is derived from the pump affinity laws, which are expressed by the following formulas:

$$\frac{Q_1}{Q_2} = \frac{n_1}{n_2} \qquad \frac{H_1}{H_2} = \frac{n_1{}^2}{n_2{}^2} \qquad \frac{HP_1}{HP_2} = \frac{n_1{}^3}{n_2{}^3}$$

These state that the pump capacity Q varies directly as the speed; the head, or pressure output, varies as the square of the speed; and the power varies as the cube of the speed.

3-21. Net Positive Suction Head. One other point which should be discussed is the suction pressure requirement. A pump must "suck" fluid into its intake. As we know, a fluid can withstand little tensile stress, so the absolute pressure at the intake must be great enough to prevent cavitation (or "pulling apart") of the fluid. This pressure requirement, which will be different for different pumps, is called the "net positive suction head," or the NPSH. It is defined as the pressure of the fluid in feet at the inlet to the pump referred to the center line of the pump, minus the vapor pressure of the fluid at the fluid temperature in feet, plus the velocity head of the fluid at this point.

An example of a type of pump problem the examinee may expect is the following:

- Several water piping systems are under consideration for use with a pump which has the operating characteristics shown in Fig. 3-20. Curves showing the operating characteristics of

FIG. 3-20. (a) Curves represent actual pump test information. (b) Curves show head loss for piping systems A, B, C, and D.

the piping systems under consideration are given in the lower figure. It is desired to use the piping system which will permit the pump to operate at its highest efficiency. (1 gal of water weighs 8.33 lb.)

a. Select the piping system which will allow the most efficient pump operation. Show calculations to substantiate your choice.

b. How many gallons per minute will be pumped by the pump through the piping system selected?

c. What is the efficiency of the pump when operating at the chosen flow rate?

d. What size motor would you recommend so that the pump may operate over its full capacity range without overloading?

The first step is to plot the curve of pump efficiency vs. flow. The efficiency will equal the ratio of

$$\frac{\text{horsepower out of pump}}{\text{horsepower input to pump}}$$

The horsepower out of the pump equals the water horsepower, which can be determined from the relationship

$$\text{hp} = \frac{(\text{gpm} \times 8.33)\ \text{lb/min} \times (\text{head})\ \text{ft}}{33{,}000\ \text{ft-lb/min}} = 2.525 \times 10^{-4}\ (\text{gpm})$$
$$\times\ (\text{head})$$

$$\text{Efficiency} = \frac{2.525 \times 10^{-4}(\text{gpm}) \times (\text{head})}{\text{hp input}}$$

Taking different points from the pump data curve gives the following:

Gallons per minute	Feet of head	Water horsepower	Horsepower input	Efficiency, %
25	119	0.75	1.8	42
50	115	1.45	2.5	58
75	110	2.08	3.2	65
100	102	2.58	3.8	68
125	93	2.94	4.3	69
150	68	2.58	4.5	68
175	55	2.43	4.6	53

The resulting curve of efficiency vs. flow can be plotted on the curve showing the head losses for piping systems A, B, C, and D. When this is done (the efficiency curve is shown dotted in the given figure), it can be seen that piping system C will permit the pump to operate more efficiently than any of the other systems. The operating point will be at 145 gpm and 80 ft of head. The pump efficiency at this point is 68 per cent. It would be best to use a 5-hp motor to power the pump, since the operating point requires $4\frac{1}{2}$ hp and if someone opened a valve to drop the back pressure then the flow would increase and the power requirement would rise to almost 5 hp.

Another example selected from a past examination is as follows:

- A pump for the water system shown in Fig. 3-21 is to be selected from the characteristic curves shown. The pump is to service both tanks, pumping into one tank at a time. All piping is 6-in. diameter, new steel (standard strength, schedule No. 40) with $f = 0.017$. The pump desired is to deliver more than 500 gpm to each tank.

  a. Under these conditions, which pump would be the most efficient for the system?

  b. What maximum horsepower *out* of the motor is necessary for operation of the system?

  Use the given graph for solution.

$$\text{F\scriptsize IG}.\ 3\text{-}21$$

Designating the points as R, F, and S for reservoir, first tank, and second tank, we can write Bernoulli's equation for each case.

$$\frac{P_R}{w} + \frac{v_R{}^2}{2g} + Z_R + h_P = \frac{P_F}{w} + \frac{v_F{}^2}{2g} + Z_F + h_{L_{(R-F)}}$$

where h_P = head supplied by pump
This gives

$$h_P = \frac{v_F{}^2}{2g} + 110 + h_{L_{(R-F)}}$$

where v_F = velocity through pipe

The inner diameter of 6-in. schedule No. 40 pipe is given in pipe data tables as 6.065 in.

$$500 \text{ gpm} = \frac{500}{60 \times 7.48} = 1.115 \text{ cu ft/sec}$$

$$\text{Cross-sectional area} = \left(\frac{6.065}{12}\right)^2 \times \frac{\pi}{4} = 0.200 \text{ sq ft}$$

$$v_F = \frac{Q}{A} = \frac{1.115}{0.200} = 5.58 \text{ fps}$$

$$h_{L_{(R-F)}} = f\frac{Lv_F{}^2}{2gD} = 0.017 \times \frac{1{,}500v_F{}^2}{2g6.065/12} = 0.784v_F{}^2$$

$$h_P = (0.0155 + 0.784)v_F{}^2 + 110 = 24.9 + 110 = 134.9 \text{ ft}$$

For the second tank,

$$h_P = \frac{v_S{}^2}{2g} + 95 + h_{L_{(R-S)}}$$

$$h_{L_{(R-S)}} = 0.017\,\frac{2{,}500v_S{}^2}{2gD} = 1.31v_S{}^2$$

$$h_P = (0.0155 - 1.31)v_S{}^2 + 95 = 41.4 + 95 = 136.4 \text{ ft}$$

The pump would then have to supply at least 136.4 ft of head at a flow of 500 gpm, which rules pump C out of the picture. Either pump A or pump B could handle the operation. Pump A is the more efficient at the 500-gpm operating point, but it would actually shift its operating point to almost 600 gpm, where the head loss to the second tank would reach 154 ft.

$$h_P = 95 + 1.32v^2 = 95 + 1.64 \times 10^{-4} \text{ (gpm)}^2$$

which gives 154 ft of head to be supplied by the pump at 600-gpm flow rate. At this operating point the efficiency of pump A drops to 72 per cent.

Pump B would shift its operating point to approximately 515 gpm and 139 ft of head, at which point its efficiency would be 84 per cent.

The pump would pump approximately 525 gpm at 137 ft of head into the first tank, again with an efficiency of 84 per cent.

The maximum horsepower out of the motor would be

$$\frac{525 \text{ gpm} \times 8.34 \text{ lb/gal} \times 135 \text{ ft}}{33{,}000 \times 0.84 \text{ eff}} = 21.3 \text{ hp}$$

The graph of pump characteristics gives "total head" as the item listed on the ordinate. Total head would equal pressure head plus

velocity head. In the example the velocity-head factor was disregarded. Actually, to be perfectly correct, it should be included.
In the case of the 525-gpm flow, the velocity head would equal
$[1.24 \times 10^{-4}(5.25)^2]/2g = 0.53$ ft, which cannot be read on the
graph, so velocity head can safely be disregarded in this particular
case and the answer is correct as previously calculated.

3-22. Fluid Momentum. Another phase of fluid mechanics
treated in past fundamentals examinations is the subject of fluid
momentum and the force exerted by a fluid when it is subjected to a
change in momentum.

We know from our study of mechanics that the impulse equals the
change in momentum, or $F \Delta t = \Delta(Mv)$, which becomes $F \Delta t = M \Delta v$
for a mass which remains constant. This can also be recognized
as an expression of Newton's second law, $F = ma$, or $F = m(dv/dt)$.

The mass M, for the case of fluid flow, can be written as

$$M = \rho Q \, \Delta t$$

and when this relationship is substituted in the impulse-momentum
relationship, an equation is obtained for the calculation of the force
exerted on (and by) the fluid.

$$F \Delta t = \rho Q \, \Delta t \, \Delta v$$

$$F = \rho Q \, \Delta v = \frac{wQ}{g} \, \Delta v$$

where Δv = change in velocity, or $\Delta v = \bar{v}_2 - \bar{v}_1$
where the lines over the v_2 and the v_1 indicate that these velocities
are vector quantities and the subtraction is a vectorial subtraction.
This is important and should be kept in mind. The velocities are
vector quantities and must be treated as such. The resultant force
is also a vector quantity and possesses both magnitude and direction.
These principles are illustrated by means of sample problems, as
follows:

- A horizontal bend in a pipeline reduces the pipe from a 30-in.
  diameter to an 18-in. diameter while bending through an
  angle of 135° from its original direction. The flow rate is
  10,000 gpm, and the direction of flow is from the 30-in. to
  the 18-in. pipe. If the pressure at the entrance is 60 psig,

what must be the magnitude of the resultant force necessary to keep the bend in place? Consider the bend to be adequately supported in a vertical direction.

First draw the figure (Fig. 3-22), and then calculate the velocities and pressures in and out of the bend. Then calculate the changes in momentum and obtain the forces acting on the elbow.

$$10,000 \text{ gpm} \times \frac{1}{60 \times 7.48} = 22.3 \text{ cfs}$$

$$\text{Area}_A = 4.91 \text{ sq ft}$$

$$\text{Area}_B = 1.77 \text{ sq ft}$$

$$v_A = \frac{22.3}{4.91} = 4.54 \text{ fps}$$

$$v_B = \frac{22.3}{1.77} = 12.6 \text{ fps}$$

Fig. 3-22

Determine the pressure at section B by means of Bernoulli's equation:

$$\frac{P_A}{w} + \frac{v_A{}^2}{2g} = \frac{P_B}{w} + \frac{v_B{}^2}{2g}$$

$$P_A - P_B = \frac{w}{2g} (v_B{}^2 - v_A{}^2)$$

$$P_A - P_B = \frac{62.4}{64.4} (159 - 20.6) = 134 \text{ psf} \quad \text{or} \quad 0.931 \text{ psi}$$

The pressure at section B is $P_B = 59$ psi.

The forces resulting from the changes in momentum are proportional to the changes of velocity, since the mass flow is constant through both sections A and B.

$$\Delta v_x = v_A - v_B \cos 135° = 4.54 - (-12.6) \times 0.707 = 13.45 \text{ fps}$$

$$\Delta v_y = 0 - v_B \sin 135° = 0 - (-12.6) \times 0.707 = 8.91 \text{ fps}$$

$$\Delta M_{F_x} = \rho Q \, \Delta v_x = \frac{62.4}{g} \times 22.3 \times 13.45 = 581 \text{ lb} = \Delta M_{F_x}$$

$$\Delta M_{F_y} = \rho Q \, \Delta v_y = 385 \text{ lb}$$

$$\text{Pressure force at } A = \left(30^2 \times \frac{\pi}{4} \right) \times 60 = 42,400 \text{ lb} = F_A$$

$$\text{Pressure force at } B = \left(18^2 \times \frac{\pi}{4} \right) \times 59 = 15,000 \text{ lb}$$

The force at B can be resolved into forces in the x and y directions.

$$F_{B-x} = 15,000 \times 0.707 = 10,600 \text{ lb}$$
$$F_{B-y} = 15,000 \times 0.707 = 10,600 \text{ lb}$$

FIG. 3-23   FIG. 3-24

The total forces add to (see Fig. 3-23):

$$F_x = F_A + F_{B-x} + \Delta M_{Fx} = 53,581 \text{ lb}$$
$$F_y = F_{B-y} + \Delta MF_y = 10,985 \text{ lb}$$
$$F_R = \sqrt{F_x{}^2 + F_y{}^2} = 54,800 \text{ lb}$$
$$\alpha = \tan^{-1}\left(\frac{F_y}{F_x}\right) = \tan^{-1} 0.205 = 11.6°$$

Remember that a force is a vector quantity and that the direction of the action of the force must also be given.

Another problem was as follows:

- A jet strikes a stationary vane, and half of it is deflected in each direction, as shown in Fig. 3-24. Calculate the horizontal and vertical components of the force with which the vane resists the jet. Jet diameter is 6 in.; jet velocity is 80 fps.

$$Q = v \times A = (\tfrac{6}{12})^2 \times \frac{\pi}{4} \times 80 = 15.7 \text{ cfs}$$

Assume a vane efficiency of 100 per cent, with no loss of velocity or energy due to vane friction or impact of liquid. The velocity of the jets after striking the vane will then both equal 80 fps. For the purpose of calculation, assume that the jet is divided into two halves both before and after striking the vane. Taking the upper half,

$$\Delta v_x = v - v \cos 60° = 80(1 - 0.50) = 40 \text{ fps}$$
$$\Delta v_y = 0 - v \sin 60° = -80(0.866) = -69.3 \text{ fps}$$

then
$$\Delta M_x = \rho Q \, \Delta v_x = \rho \times \frac{15.7}{2} \times 40 = 31.4 \times \rho$$

$$\Delta M_y = \rho Q \, \Delta v_y = -54.4 \times \rho$$

Taking the lower half,

$$\Delta v_x = 80(1 - 0.50) = 120 \text{ fps} \qquad \Delta M_x = 94.2 \times \rho$$
$$\Delta v_y = 0 - (-69.3) = 69.3 \text{ fps} \qquad \Delta M_y = 54.4 \times \rho$$

Adding these gives

$$M_{Fx} = (31.4 - 94.2)\rho = 125.6 \times \rho \text{ lb}$$
$$M_{Fy} = (54.4 - 54.4)\rho = 0$$

The force with which the vane resists the jet would then equal 125.6 × ρ lb and would act in a horizontal direction. If the fluid is water,

$$R = \frac{62.4}{g} \times 125.6 = 245 \text{ lb}$$

Fig. 3-25

It is of interest to note the force that would have been required if the flow vane were smooth and if the flow were not split in half. In this case, assuming no shock or loss of velocity (and thus no energy loss), and assuming the plate to be perfectly smooth so that no drag (or force parallel to the face of the plate) is produced on the plate by the fluid, there can be no change of momentum of the fluid in a direction parallel to the face of the plate. The path of the liquid would then be as shown in Fig. 3-25, and the fluid would split into two parts such that

$$(Q_1 - Q_2)\rho v = (Q_1 + Q_2)\rho v \cos \alpha$$
$$Q_1 - Q_2 = (Q_1 + Q_2) \cos \alpha$$
$$Q_1 - Q_2 = Q \qquad \text{the total flow}$$
$$Q_1 = \frac{Q}{2}(1 + \cos \alpha)$$
$$Q_2 = \frac{Q}{2}(1 - \cos \alpha)$$

For the previous example, $\alpha = 60°$, $Q = 15.7$ cfs. Then

$$Q_1 = 11.78 \text{ cu ft/sec}$$

and $\qquad\qquad Q_2 = 3.93$ cfs

For Q_1, $\qquad\qquad \Delta v_x = 80 - 80 \sin \alpha = 40$ fps

$$\Delta v_y = 0 - 80 \cos \alpha = -69.2 \text{ fps}$$

$$F_x = Q_1 \rho \, \Delta v_x = 91.3 \text{ lb}$$

$$F_y = -158 \text{ lb}$$

For Q_2,

$$\Delta v_x = 80 - (-80 \sin \alpha) = 120 \text{ fps} \qquad F_x = 91.3 \text{ lb}$$

$$\Delta v_y = 0 - (-80 \cos \alpha) = 69.2 \text{ fps} \qquad F_y = 52.6 \text{ lb}$$

$$R_x = -(91.3 + 91.3) = -182.6 \text{ lb}$$

$$R_y = -(52.6 - 158) = 105.4 \text{ lb}$$

$$R = 211 \text{ lb} \qquad \text{Angle of action} = \tan^{-1}\left(\frac{105.4}{182.6}\right) = 30° = \beta$$

which checks, since there can be no force parallel to the face of the plate.

3-23. Compressible Flow. There have been only a few references to compressible fluid flow in past fundamentals examinations and most of these could be treated satisfactorily by the application of the principles discussed in the section on incompressible fluid flow. A general relationship to keep in mind is that the error introduced by considering (and treating) a compressible fluid as an incompressible fluid is approximately equal to one-fourth of the square of the Mach number of the fluid flowing for velocities appreciably less than the sonic velocity. In other words,

$$\text{Error} = \text{(approximately)} \frac{1}{4}\left(\frac{v}{c}\right)^2$$

where c = velocity of sound at the existing conditions

The quantity v/c is the ratio of the actual velocity to the local velocity of sound and is known as the Mach number. The sonic velocity can be determined from the relationship

$$c = \sqrt{kgRT}$$

where k = ratio of the specific heats at constant pressure divided
    by the specific heat at constant volume

g = acceleration of gravity

R = gas constant and = (approximately) $\dfrac{1{,}544}{\text{molecular weight}}$

T = absolute temperature of the gas and = °F + 460

The value of k may be taken as 1.66 for monatomic gases such as
helium, 1.40 for diatomic gases such as air, and 1.30 for gases such
as carbon dioxide, ammonia, methane, and acetylene. Illustrative
examples are afforded by a pair of representative past examination
problems.

- A blower-type fan delivers air at the rate of 2,200 cfm against
  a static pressure of 2 in. of water. How much air horsepower
  is being delivered if the air has a density of 0.075 lb/cu ft?
  Velocity pressure may be disregarded.

The very low pressure of compression of 2 in. of water (0.0722 psi)
indicates that the work required to compress the air is negligible
so, as discussed previously, the air may be treated as an incompressible fluid. Disregarding the velocity head,

$$\text{hp} = \frac{\text{ft-lb/min}}{33{,}000}$$

$$= \frac{(2{,}200 \times 0.075)\ \text{lb/min} \times \frac{2}{12} \times 62.4/0.075\ \text{ft of air}}{33{,}000}$$

$$\text{hp} = 0.694$$

where

$$\frac{2\ \text{in. water}}{12\ \text{in./ft}} \times \frac{62.4\ \text{lb/cu ft water}}{0.075\ \text{lb/cu ft air}} = \frac{1}{6}\ \text{ft water} \times 833\ \frac{\text{ft air}}{\text{ft water}}$$

$$= 138.6\ \text{ft of air, equivalent to}$$
$$2\ \text{in. of water}$$

The problem could also be worked by

$$\text{hp} = \frac{\text{cfm} \times \text{psf}}{33{,}000}$$

$$\text{hp} = \frac{2{,}200\ \text{cfm} \times \frac{2}{12} \times 0.433\ \text{psi/ft water} \times 144\ \text{psf}}{33{,}000} = 0.694$$

Another past examination problem was as follows:

- An air-conditioning duct is designed to carry 2,300 cu ft of air per minute (cfm) with a pressure loss of 0.4 in. of water using standard air weighing 0.075 lb/cu ft. During construction it was found that several right-angle turns had to be added to avoid other piping. Upon completion the duct was tested and found to have a pressure loss of 0.6 in. of water at 2,300 cfm, using air having a density of 0.074 lb/cu ft. What is the percentage increase in horsepower required?

The pressure loss in the system will equal the friction loss

$$h_L = f \frac{Lv^2}{2gD}$$

and the losses in the elbows. The losses in the elbows can also be measured in "velocity heads." A velocity head equals $v^2/2g$.

$$\text{hp}_{\text{design}} = \frac{2,300 \text{ cfm} \times 0.4/12 \times 0.433 \times 144 \text{ psf}}{33,000} = 0.145 \text{ hp}$$

$$\text{hp}_{\text{measured}} = \frac{2,300 \text{ cfm} \times 0.6/12 \times 0.433 \times 144 \text{ psf}}{33,000} = 0.217 \text{ hp}$$

or a 50 per cent increase in horsepower will be required.

The use of 0.075 lb/cu ft air and then 0.074 lb/cu ft air does not enter into this method of calculation, since the volume and the pressure were the only factors considered. If the horsepower has been determined by multiplying pounds per minute of air flow times feet of fluid pressure rise, the specific weight terms would have cancelled out, since the pressure differential was measured by a different medium, not with the fluid (air) being pumped.

$$\text{hp} = \frac{(2,300 \text{ cfm} \times 0.075 \text{ lb/cu ft}) \times 0.4/12 \text{ ft water} \times 62.4/0.075}{33,000}$$

$$\text{hp}_{\text{design}} = \frac{2,300 \times 0.075 \times 0.4/12 \times 62.4/0.075}{33,000} = 0.145 \text{ hp}$$

$$\text{hp}_{\text{measured}} = \frac{2,300 \times 0.074 \times 0.6/12 \times 62.4/0.074}{33,000} = 0.217 \text{ hp}$$

A brief comment might be in order here. Even though the question asks only, "What is the percentage increase in horsepower required?" it is doubtful if the response "50 per cent," without

Fig. 3-26

calculations to justify it, would be given much credit. Any answer to an engineering problem should be backed up by the necessary calculations and/or reasoning.

3-24. Lift and Drag Coefficients. The subject of aerodynamics has also been touched upon in past fundamentals examinations and will be mentioned briefly. Two of the most important characteristics of an airfoil are the drag coefficient

$$C_D = \frac{D}{(\rho v^2/2) \times A}$$

and the lift coefficient

$$C_L = \frac{L}{(\rho v^2/2) \times A}$$

where D and L = drag and lift, respectively, lb

ρ = mass density of the medium (air)

v = velocity of the airfoil (or of the air past the airfoil)

A = projected area

An example of an aerodynamics problem is as follows:

• The graph in Fig. 3-26 shows test values for typical lift and drag coefficients for a Clark Y airfoil.

  a. Explain why the peak point of the lift coefficient curve (point *A*) is so important.

  b. When the Clark Y airfoil section was tested at an angle of approach of $\alpha = 5°$, a total drag of 50 lb was measured. What is the magnitude of the total lift under these conditions?

a. Point *A* is the point of maximum lift, or "stall," and determines the stalling angle above which lift no longer continues to increase with the angle of attack. At this point (also called the "burble point") the flow separates from the upper side of the wing and forms a turbulent wake, which increases the profile drag. This increased drag is accompanied by a large drop in lift and lift coefficient because of increased pressure on the upper side of the wing.

b. At 5°, $C_D = 0.08$ and $C_L = 0.8$. The drag force,

$$F_D = C_D A \frac{\rho v^2}{2}$$

and the lift force, $F_L = C_L A[(\rho v^2)/2]$. Since $A[(\rho v^2)/2]$ will be the same for the same test point, $(F_D/F_L) = (C_D/C_L)$, or

$$F_L = \frac{C_L}{C_D} \times F_D \qquad F_L = \frac{0.8}{0.08} \times 50 = 500 \text{ lb}$$

3-25. Model Theory. Model theory is based on similarity, and all the laws of similarity which are applicable to a given case must be satisfied if complete similarity is to exist between fluid phenomena. The first and simplest of these is geometrical similarity, which means that the model and prototype must have the same shape. This in turn means that the ratios between corresponding lengths in model and prototype must all be the same. Dynamic similarity is obtained when various dimensionless coefficients such as the Reynolds, Froude, Cauchy, and Weber numbers are made equal for model and prototype.

Perhaps the commonest application of model theory is in the calculation of the pressure drop for flow through pipelines. Geometric similarity demands that the pipes be the same shape (usually cylindrical) and that different samples have the same percentage of roughness. Complete dynamic similarity is obtained when the Reynolds numbers are equal.

REFERENCES

A very well-written introduction to the subject and one recommended by the author for further review and study of fluid mechanics is:

Vennard, J. K.: "Elementary Fluid Mechanics," John Wiley & Sons, Inc., New York, 1954.

The following text is also well written and gives good coverage:

Daugherty, R. L., and A. C. Ingersoll: "Fluid Mechanics," 5th ed., McGraw-Hill Book Company, Inc., New York, 1954.

Two other excellent books, but a little more advanced than the above, are:

Dodge, R. A., and M. J. Thompson: "Fluid Mechanics," McGraw-Hill Book Company, Inc., New York, 1937.

Rouse, H.: "Elementary Mechanics of Fluids," John Wiley & Sons, Inc., New York, 1946.

SAMPLE PROBLEMS SELECTED FROM PAST EXAMINATIONS

3-1. Find the force on the end of a triangular upright trough having an apex angle of 90° when filled with water to a height of 3 ft.

Fig. 3-P-2

3-2. From the information shown on the schematic diagram in Fig. 3-P-2, calculate the velocity of the fluid at section B in feet per second.

3-3. Water flows over the triangular weir shown in Fig. 3-P-3 with a head of 1 ft, a coefficient of discharge C of 0.60, and the temperature of the water is 140°F. Compute the flow over this weir in gallons per hour.

Fig. 3-P-3

3-4. A piece of glass weighs 125 g in air, 75 g in water, and 92 g in gasoline. What is the specific gravity of the gasoline?

3-5. A 12- by 12-in. timber 12 ft long floats level in fresh water with 4.3 in. above the water surface. One end is just touching a rock which prevents that end from sinking any deeper. How far out from the supported end can a 150-lb man walk before the free end submerges?

3-6. *a.* An 8-in. pipeline, 3,500 ft long, conveys water from a pump to a reservoir whose water surface is 450 ft above the pump which is pumping at the rate of 3 cfs. Use constants for rough cast-iron pipe, disregard velocity head and minor losses, and determine the gauge pressure in pounds per square inch at the *discharge end* of the *pump.*

b. Water is flowing, horizontally, from a reservoir through a circular orifice under a head of 50 ft. The coefficient of discharge is 0.7, and the diameter of the orifice is 4 in. How many cubic feet per second are being discharged from the orifice?

3-7. A swimming pool is being cleaned by a rubber hose 2 in. in diameter with a brush fixture on the end through which the water is drawn by a vacuum pump. The hose is 50 ft long, leading to the pump 12 ft above the bottom of the pool. If the water in the pool is 8 ft deep, what suction (in pounds per square inch) would be required at the pump to draw 600 gpm through the hose? (Assume a loss coefficient at the brush at $0.5V^2/2g$, where V is the velocity in the hose. Assume kinematic viscosity of water $= 1.2 \times 10^{-5}$ sq ft/sec).

3-8. Water flows from a supply tank through 80 ft of welded steel pipe 6 in. in diameter to a hydraulic mining nozzle 2 in. in diameter. The coefficient of the nozzle may be assumed to be 0.90, and the temperature of the water may be assumed to be 75°F with a kinematic viscosity of 0.00001 sq ft/sec. If 1.00 cfs of water is flowing, how far must the nozzle lie below the elevation of the water in the tank?

3-9. A hollow reinforced concrete dam 20 ft high with water to its top has dimensions as shown in Fig. 3-P-9. If the supporting piers are 2 ft thick and are spaced 20 ft on centers, where would the vertical resultant force cut the base *AB*? (The specific weight of the concrete is 150 lb/cu ft.)

Fig. 3-P-9

3-10. Water falling from a height of 100 ft at the rate of 2,000 cfm drives a water turbine connected to an electric generator at 120 rpm. If the total resisting torque due to friction is 400 lb at 1-ft radius and the water leaves the turbine blades with a velocity of 12 fps, find the horsepower developed by the generator.

3-11. A venturi meter with a throat 2 in. in diameter is placed in a pipeline 4 in. in diameter carrying fuel oil. If the differential pressure between the upstream section and the throat is 3.5 psi, how much oil is flowing in gallons per minute?   The discharge coefficient of the venturi meter is 0.97.   The specific gravity of the oil is 0.94, and the specific weight is 58.7 lb/cu ft.

3-12. A rectangular sluice gate, 4 ft wide and 6 ft deep, hangs in a vertical plane.   It is hinged along the top (4-ft) edge.   If there are 21 ft of water above the top of the gate, what horizontal force applied at the bottom of the gate will be necessary to open it?

3-13. A pump on the diagram shown in Fig. 3-P-13 pumps water to an eleva- tion of x feet above the center of the pump.   When the pump is running, the pressure gauge A registers 39.2 psi.   When the pump is shut off, the pressure gauge A reads 10 psi because of the water in the line.   A characteristic curve, as furnished by the manufacturer for the pump, is shown.

a. What is the total head, including the suction head, against which the pump must operate if the friction in the inlet line can be considered negligible?

b. What is the head loss due to friction in the line from the gauge to discharge?

c. How many gallons per minute are being pumped when the pressure gauge registers 39.2 psig?

d. Calculate the efficiency of the pump with 1.25-hp input and 39.2-psig discharge pressure.

Fɪɢ. 3-P-13

3-14. A gravity dam composed of concrete is 45 ft high.   It is 3 ft wide on top and the base is 30 ft wide.   The water side of the dam is vertical and the other side slopes uniformly from top to bottom.   The water behind the dam is 42 ft deep and there is no water pressure under the dam.

a. Compute the position of the resultant at the base of the dam.

b. Compute the pressure in pounds per square foot at the toe and at the heel of the dam.

c. Compute the position of the resultant with the reservoir empty.

d. Would the dam be safe against sliding?

3-15. A smooth nozzle on a fire hose is $1\frac{1}{8}$ in. in diameter and discharges 250 gpm. What is the force with which this stream of water strikes a flat surface normal to the stream if placed only a short distance away?

3-16. A pipe, 12 in. in diameter, carries water by gravity from a reservoir. At a point 500 ft from the reservoir and 28 ft below its surface, a pressure gauge reads 10.5 psi; at a point 8,500 ft from the reservoir and 28.5 ft below its surface, a pressure gauge reads 61.5 psi. Compute the discharge in gallons per minute.

3-17. The instrument readings for a pump test are shown on the schematic diagram in Fig. 3-P-17. Find the following:

a. Kilowatt input to motor
b. Horsepower output of motor
c. Water horsepower output of pump
d. Efficiency of pump under conditions listed

Assume the pipes leading to the gauges are filled with water and the difference between the inlet and outlet velocity head is negligible.

Fig. 3-P-17. 3,460 rpm at 7.89 lb-ft torque; 220 volts, 21.2 amp at 88 per cent power factor single phase; weight of water = 8.33 lb/gal; weight of mercury = 0.49 lb/cu in.

3-18. A horizontal 36-in. pipe curving through an angle of 60° contains water with an average velocity of 7.1 fps and pressure of 50 psi. Find the force exerted on the bend by this discharge (Fig. 3-P-18).

Fig. 3-P-18   Fig. 3-P-19

3-19. The hinged top of a 4-ft square gate is submerged 10 ft below the surface of the water in the tank (Fig. 3-P-19).

a. What is the distance x to the center of pressure on the gate?

b. Find the force F required to balance the water pressure on the gauge.

3-20. A circular concrete culvert 8 ft in diameter and having a slope of 1 ft in 1,000 ft is carrying water 6 ft in depth. Compute discharge in cubic feet per second, disregarding loss of head at entrance. Assume that Manning's coefficient equals 0.013.

3-21. A jet of water is entirely reversed in direction as it hits a vane. If the vane is fixed, the velocity of the jet is 100 fps, the weight flowing equals 200 lb/sec, and friction is such that the water leaves the vane at 0.9 × the velocity with which it strikes it. Determine:

a. The force exerted on the vane

b. The horsepower of the jet and the power exerted on the vane

3-22. *a.* Find the hydraulic radius of the section shown in Fig. 3-P-22 when the water is flowing at a depth of 5.0 ft from the bottom of the V notch.

b. What quantity of water, in cubic feet per second, will flow through this section at the above-mentioned depth, if the slope is 1.0 ft/100 ft, and the coefficient of roughness is 0.013? Manning's equation for velocity is $V = (1.486H^{2/3}S^{1/2})/n$.

Fig. 3-P-22

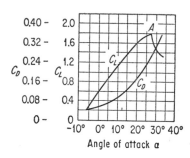

Fig. 3-P-23

3-23. The graph in Fig. 3-P-23 shows test values for typical lift-drag coefficients on a Clark Y airfoil.

a. Explain the reasons why the peak point of the lift coefficient curve (point *A*) is so important.

b. When the Clark Y airfoil section was tested at an angle of approach of $\alpha = 5°$, a total drag of 50 lb was measured. What is the magnitude of the total lift under these conditions?

3-24. A penstock 10 ft in diameter carrying 250 cfs of water bends down through a 45° angle. What is the force F_x at the bend? (See Fig. 3-P-24.)

45° F_x

Fig. 3-P-24

3-25. A hydrometer weighs 50 g. The area of cross section of the stem is 1 sq cm.

a. What is the distance on the stem between the 0.8 gradation and the 0.9 gradation?

b. Will these numbers be placed above or below the 1.0 on the stem?

3-26. In the venturi meter shown in Fig. 3-P-26, the liquid being measured is water and the coefficient of the meter is 0.98. Compute the rate of flow in cubic feet per second.

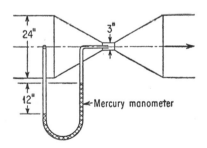

Fig. 3-P-26

3-27. From the sketch shown in Fig. 3-P-27, determine the following:

a. Total loss of head, in feet, from A to B due to fluid friction in the pipe and fittings

b. Head loss due to pipe friction

c. Head loss due to valves and fittings

Fɪɢ. 3-P-27

In Fig. 3-P-27, flow at A = 1.25 cfs; actual inside diameter of pipe = 4.02 in.; actual inside area of pipe = 12.7 sq in.; friction factor for 4-in. pipe = 0.024.

3-28. A manhole of 30-in. diameter in the side of a penstock is closed with a flat plate.   The static head at the center of the manhole is 25 ft (Fig. 3-P-28).

a. What is the total pressure in pounds on the cover plate?

b. Where is the center of pressure with reference to the horizontal center line of the manhole?

Fɪɢ. 3-P-28

3-29. A standard 10-in. galvanized iron pipe 15 ft long, weighing 32 lb/ft, is closed at one end by a pipe cap with a weight attached so that the pipe will float upright.   The cap and weight total 25 lb and displace ½ cu ft of water. How much of the pipe will show above the surface of sea water of 1.025 sp gr?

3-30. A tank in the form of a frustum of a cone, with bases horizontal and axis vertical, is 10 ft in height.   The top diameter is 8 ft; bottom diameter is 3 ft.   What time is required to empty the tank through a 3-in. standard square orifice for which the discharge coefficient is 0.61?

3-31. An oil pipeline has a 10-in. ID, is 100 miles long, and is made of welded steel.   The discharge end is 500 ft above the intake.   The rate of flow is 4 fps.   What is the total pressure in pounds per square inch gauge at intake when the whole length is full of gasoline at 60°F and 0.68 sp gr?

Fɪɢ. 3-P-32

3-32. A wood flume of cross section as in Fig. 3-P-32 is to carry 200 cfs of water.   What slope in feet per 1,000 feet is required?

3-33. A centrifugal motor-driven water pump is connected to a pipeline as shown in Fig. 3-P-33.

a. What is the average velocity in the pipe?

b. If the input to the pump motor is 1,105 watts, what is the combined efficiency of the motor and pump?

c. What is the friction factor for the 300-ft length of pipe?

Fig. 3-P-33. Pipe ID = 2.067 in.; pipe flow area = 3.36 sq in.; 7.48 gal/cu ft.

3-34. A 1-in. diameter cable is used to anchor a buoy near the entrance to a harbor where the ocean current reaches a velocity of 4 mph. A model is made of the buoy and cable to one-tenth scale for tests in the laboratory. Using fresh water in the test, results show that for a velocity of 5 fps the drag on 1 ft of model cable is 2 lb. The density of sea water is 63.8 lb/cu ft. If the relation between the model and prototype can be expressed as $F/(\rho A V^2)$ constant, where F = drag force, ρ = density of fluid, A = area (projected area perpendicular to flow), V = velocity of fluid relative to model or prototype, what is the drag per foot of prototype cable as installed in the harbor entrance?

3-35. A liquid is forced through a pipe 1 meter long with an internal diameter of 0.6 cm by a pressure difference of 1.2×10^5 dynes/sq cm. If 570 cu cm of liquid was discharged in 5 min, what was the viscosity of the liquid in centipoises?

3-36. Disregarding friction, find the gauge pressures and speeds at positions 1, 2, and 3 in Fig. 3-P-36 representing flow of water from a tank with an internal gauge pressure of 15 psi through a discharge pipe. $h = 100$ ft, $y = 50$ ft, $A_1 = 1$ sq ft, $A_2 = \frac{3}{4}$ sq ft, $A_3 = 12$ sq ft.

Fig. 3-P-36

3-37. Turpentine is stored in a tank on the second floor of a plant making paints. A pipeline is to be installed to a mixer on the first floor feeding the turpentine by gravity through an equivalent length of 55 ft of straight steel pipe. The bottom of the tank is 15 ft above the point of discharge to the mixer. Calculate the minimum pipe diameter which will ensure a flow of 10 gpm to the mixer. Minimum temperature may be taken at 60°F, at which temperature the viscosity of turpentine is 1.6 centipoises and the specific gravity is 1.025.

3-38. A cubical block of wood 10 cm on a side and of density 0.5 g/cu cm floats in a container of water. Oil of density 0.8 g/cu cm is poured on the water until the top of the oil layer is 4 cm below the top of the block.

a. How deep is the oil layer?

b. What is the gauge pressure at the lower face of the block in dynes per square centimeter? (See Fig. 3-P-38.)

Fɪɢ. 3-P-38

3-39. Estimate the total time required to empty a tank which is a paraboloid of revolution with every horizontal section a circle whose radius equals the square root of the height above the bottom, through which is cut a 1-in. round, sharp-edged orifice. The depth of water at the start of time is 10 ft.

3-40. A 12-in. ID smooth cast-iron pipe, 4,000 ft in length, conveys water from a pump to a reservoir whose water surface is 250 ft above the pump, which is pumping at a rate of 3 cfs. Determine the gauge pressure, in pounds per square inch above atmospheric, at the pump discharge. Assuming the efficiency of the pump to be 89 per cent, determine the horsepower input.

3-41. A pitot tube having a coefficient of unity is inserted in the exact center of a long, smooth tube of 1-in. ID in which crude oil (sp gr $= 0.9$; $\mu = 35 \times 10^{-5}$ lb-sec/ft²) is flowing. Determine the average velocity in the tube if the velocity pressure is (*a*) 2.3 psi; (*b*) 3.9 in. of water.

3-42. Water flows through 3,000 linear ft of 36-in.-diameter pipe which branches into 2,000 linear ft of 18-in.-diameter pipe and 2,400 linear ft of 24-in.-diameter pipe. These rejoin, and the water continues through 1,500 ft of 30-in.-diameter pipe. All pipes are horizontal, and the friction factors are 0.016 for the 36-in. pipe, 0.017 for the 24-in. and 30-in. pipes, and 0.019 for the 18-in. pipe. Find the pressure drop in pounds per square inch between the beginning and the end of the system if the steady flow is 60 cfs in the 36-in. pipe. Disregard minor losses.

3-43. A piece of lead (sp gr, 11.3) is attached to 40 cu cm of cork (sp gr, 0.25). When fully submerged the combination will just float. What is the weight of the lead?

3-44. A weighted timber 1 ft square and 6 ft long floats upright in fresh water with 2 ft of its length exposed. What will be the length projecting above the surface if the water is covered with a layer of oil 1 ft thick? The specific gravity of the oil is 0.8.

3-45. The outlet and inlet of a venturi meter are each 4 in. in diameter, and the throat is 3 in. in diameter. The inlet velocity is 10 fps. The inlet has a static head of 10 ft of water. If there is no loss due to friction between the inlet and the throat of the meter, what will be the head in the throat?

3-46. A conduit having a cross section of an equilateral triangle of sides b has water flowing through it at a depth $b/2$. Find the "hydraulic radius" (Fig. 3-P-46).

FIG. 3-P-46

3-47. A mass of copper, suspected of being hollow, weighs 523 g in air and 447.5 g in water. If the specific gravity of copper is 8.92, what is the volume of the cavity, if any?

3-48. A 60° pipe bend reduces from a diameter of 8 in. to a diameter of 6 in. The static pressure at the 8-in. diameter is 20 psi. If the flow is 3.0 cfs and the fluid is water, find:

a. Dynamic force on the bend
b. Static force on the bend
c. Total force on the bend

The centers of the 6- and 8-in. apertures lie in the same horizontal plane (Fig. 3-P-48).

FIG. 3-P-48

3-49. A gravity dam has a trapezoidal section 18 ft high, 2 ft wide on top, and 8 ft wide at the base. The water side is vertical. The depth of the water is 15 ft. Assume that the concrete weighs 141 lb/cu ft and that the foundation is sealed so that no water gets under the dam. What is the vertical component of stress on the foundation at the upstream edge of the base? Is this safe?

3-50. For the condition shown in Fig. 3-P-50, find force F needed to open the gate. Width of gate is 4 ft and height is 6 ft.

FIG. 3-P-50   FIG. 3-P-51

3-51. For the arrangement shown in Fig. 3-P-51, calculate the pressure difference (in pounds per square inch) between A and B. (Specific gravity of mercury is 13.6 and of turpentine is 0.8.)

3-52. A 36-in. water main, carrying 60 cfs, branches at point X into two pipes, one 24 in. in diameter and 1,500 ft long, and the other 12 in. in diameter and 3,000 ft long. They come together at Y and continue as a 36-in. pipe. If the factor f is equal to 0.022 in all pipes, find the rate of flow in each of the branches.

3-53. The water system shown in Fig. 3-P-53 is made up of fairly smooth cast-iron pipe.

    a. What quantity of water is flowing past C when 2 cfs is flowing past A?

    b. What is the pressure drop between A and B? Disregard minor losses.

FIG. 3-P-53

Thermodynamics

Thermodynamics seems to cause more difficulty than any other subject among engineers interested in reviewing their fundamentals. This is partly because in the past thermodynamics was often treated largely as a course in steam power plant design; the modern approach is to emphasize the fundamentals of thermodynamics and then to study the application of those principles to the many different types of thermodynamic processes. In this way the fundamental similarities of steam engines, jets, rockets, internal-combustion engines, and other types of thermodynamic power plants are emphasized and grasped at the same time. Extensive study of mechanical adaptations of thermodynamic principles has given way to a study of the thermodynamic principles themselves. Thus it is possible to gain an understanding of the thermodynamic aspects of many different devices without studying any one of the devices in detail.

This same philosophy has been applied in the majority of the fundamentals examinations; an understanding of the basic thermodynamic principles is necessary to handle successfully this portion of most of these examinations. An intimate knowledge of the mechanical details of a steam power plant is not, however, required.

The coverage in past examinations has included questions concerning applications of the general energy equation, different forms of the equation of state, thermodynamic cycles, entropy and enthalpy, heat transfer, the thermodynamics of air, Mollier charts, and other fundamental principles of this branch of engineering.

4-1. General Energy Equation. The first, and perhaps most widely applicable, of these subjects which we shall review is the general energy equation. Just as Bernoulli's equation is universally used in fluid mechanics, so, with the necessary modifications, it is widely applied in thermodynamics. Bernoulli's equation, we recall, merely states that the energy contained in a flowing fluid at point A must be equal to the energy in that same fluid at a later or downstream point B plus the energy lost or minus that gained between the points A and B. With incompressible fluids the energy contained in the fluid at any point is essentially equal to the sum of the kinetic energy and the potential energy due to its elevation and pressure. The difference in the internal energy of the incompressible fluid between points A and B was so slight as to be inconsequential. This is not the case, however, with a compressible fluid; account must be taken of the change in internal energy, and additional terms must be added to Bernoulli's equation to make it applicable to compressible fluids. When these terms are added, Bernoulli's equation becomes, for 1 lb of fluid:

$$\frac{P_1}{w} + \frac{v_1{}^2}{2g} + \text{internal energy}_1 + \text{heat added} + Z_1 = \frac{P_2}{w} + \frac{v_2{}^2}{2g} + \text{internal energy}_2 + Z_2 + W$$

where W = work done by the gas between points 1 and 2

When dealing with gases the change in energy due to the difference in elevation between the two points considered is seldom large enough to affect the accuracy of the result, so Z_1 and Z_2 are usually omitted. The energy is usually given in Btu per pound rather than in foot-pounds per pound as for incompressible fluids, so all the terms in the equation are given in Btu. The specific weight w is generally replaced by its reciprocal for gases $(1/w) = V$, specific volume. The internal energy is denoted by the symbol u, and the heat added to the substance by q, both in Btu per pound. The work done by the substance, W, is also measured in Btu per pound of gas. The equation given then becomes:

$$\frac{P_1V_1}{J} + \frac{v_1{}^2}{2gJ} + u_1 + q = \frac{P_2V_2}{J} + \frac{v_2{}^2}{2gJ} + u_2 + W$$

where J = 778 ft-lb/Btu, the mechanical equivalent of heat

This is known as the general energy equation, but, as we have seen, it is actually just a modification of Bernoulli's equation, with which we are already familiar. As the equation is written, the unit of each of the terms is Btu/pound.

The internal-energy term and the PV/J term are usually combined, since $u + (PV/J) = h$, the enthalpy. The general energy equation then becomes:

$$\frac{v_1^2}{2gJ} + h_1 + Q = \frac{v_2^2}{2gJ} + h_2 + W$$

where the value of h depends upon the pressure and the temperature and may be looked up in a table giving the properties of that particular gas or, more easily, on a Mollier chart.

Examples of the application of the general energy equation are afforded by many past examination problems. One of these asked:

- In thermodynamics the following terms are most generally employed in connection with the steady flow of thermodynamic fluids: Q, h, v^2, Z, and W.
  a. Write the general energy equation between two points (1) and (2) in a system.
  b. Solve this equation for Q.
  c. Write this equation for velocity in a perfect nozzle, assuming the point (1) is the entrance of the nozzle and the point (2) is the exit of the nozzle.

Part (a) is what we have just been discussing, and the general energy equation is written:

$$\frac{v_1^2}{2gJ} + h_1 + Z_1 + Q = \frac{v_2^2}{2gJ} + h_2 + Z_2 + W$$

Part (b) consists merely of rearranging the terms to give

$$Q = \frac{v_2^2 - v_1^2}{2gJ} + (h_2 - h_1) + (Z_2 - Z_1) + W$$

In a perfect nozzle—part (c)—no heat is added or lost and no work is done by the fluid. The nozzle is a device for converting some of the internal energy into kinetic energy. The general energy equation then reduces to:

$$\frac{v_1{}^2}{2gJ} + h_1 = \frac{v_2{}^2}{2gJ} + h_2$$

since $Z_1 = Z_2$, $Q = 0$, and $W = 0$.

This is probably a converging nozzle with a relatively large entrance area, in which case v_1 will be small and may be disregarded, giving $v_2{}^2/2gJ = h_1 - h_2$, limited, however, by the sonic velocity at the throat or discharge section of a converging nozzle, which is the smallest section of the nozzle. In a converging-diverging nozzle the gas will expand in the diverging section and the velocity will be supersonic, provided the critical pressure ratio is exceeded.

Another example of the application of the general energy equation is in the determination of the quality of steam in a line by means of a throttling calorimeter. An example of this is afforded by a past examination problem:

- The pressure and temperature in a throttling calorimeter are 14.7 psia and 240°F, respectively. If the pressure of the steam in the main is 150 psia, what is its quality?

In this case the two points between which the general energy equation should be written are (1) in the main where the quality of the steam is to be found, and (2) in the calorimeter.

The steam flows into the calorimeter through a throttling orifice so that no heat is added or subtracted and no work is done in the process. The elevations of the two points are the same, and the velocity at point (1) is essentially zero, as is the velocity in the calorimeter. The general energy equation then reduces to $h_1 = h_2$, and the enthalpy at point (2) can be found in a table or on a Mollier diagram. From a steam table we find that at point (2) the enthalpy of the steam (14.7 psia and 240°F) is 1164.2 Btu/lb. This means that the enthalpy at point (1) must also equal 1164.2 Btu/lb.

The pressure in the main is 150 psia. The enthalpy of the saturated liquid at 150 psia is 330.51 Btu/lb, that of the saturated vapor is 1194.1 Btu/lb, and the heat of vaporization is 863.6 Btu/lb. Since the enthalpy of the steam in the main is only 1164.2 Btu/lb, it must be wet steam. If we take $1164.2 - 330.5 = 833.7$ Btu/lb, this means that only 833.7 Btu/lb is available for evaporating the saturated liquid into steam, whereas 863.6 Btu/lb is required for total evaporation of the saturated liquid.

Then, 833.7/863.6 = 96.5 per cent of the liquid has been evaporated, and the quality is 96.5 per cent.

A slightly different application of the general energy law occurs in determining the power output of a turbine. An example of this application is afforded by a past examination problem which asks:

- A steam turbine receives 3,600 lb of steam per hour at 110 fps velocity and 1525 Btu/lb enthalpy. The steam leaves at 810 fps and 1300 Btu/lb. What is the horsepower output?

Nothing is said about the efficiency of the energy transfer from the steam to the turbine, so assume it to be 100 per cent, i.e., all the energy given up by the steam appears as work done by the turbine. Applying the general energy equation between points (1) entering the turbine and (2) leaving the turbine, we obtain ($Z_1 = Z_2$ and Q is assumed to be zero):

$$\frac{110^2}{2gJ} + 1525 = \frac{810^2}{2gJ} + 1300 + W \qquad \text{for each pound of steam}$$

$$W = (1525 - 1300) + (0.24 - 1.31) = 224 \text{ Btu/lb of steam}$$

$$\frac{3,600}{60} \text{ lb/min} \times \frac{1}{33,000 \text{ ft-lb/min hp}} \times 224 \text{ Btu/lb}$$

$$\times 778 \text{ ft-lb/Btu} = 317 \text{ hp}$$

Note the almost insignificant effect of the difference between the velocity into the turbine and the velocity out of the turbine.

A slightly different application is the case of an impulse turbine where the heat energy in the steam is converted into velocity through a nozzle and only kinetic energy is extracted from the steam by the turbine blades. A past problem exemplifying this case was:

- In an impulse turbine 5 lb of steam per second impinges upon the buckets at an initial velocity of 4,000 fps and the steam leaves the buckets at a velocity of 1,000 fps. Disregarding friction, what horsepower would be developed and what would be the efficiency?

The general energy equation applies here, but $h_1 = h_2$, $Q = 0$, and $Z_1 = Z_2$, giving:

$$\frac{v_1{}^2}{2gJ} = \frac{v_2{}^2}{2gJ} + W$$

$$W = \frac{v_1{}^2 - v_2{}^2}{2g} = \frac{4{,}000^2 - 1{,}000^2}{2g} = 233{,}000 \text{ ft-lb/lb of steam}$$

$$\text{hp} = \frac{5 \text{ lb/sec} \times 233{,}000 \text{ ft-lb/lb}}{550 \text{ ft-lb/sec hp}} = 2{,}120 \text{ hp developed}$$

When the steam leaves the turbine it still has a velocity of 1,000 fps and possesses $1{,}000^2/2g = 15{,}500$ ft-lb/lb of mechanical energy. When the steam entered the turbine it had $4{,}000^2/2g = 248{,}500$ ft-lb/lb mechanical energy. The turbine then extracted 233,000 ft-lb/lb of mechanical energy from the steam, and the efficiency of the turbine is then $233{,}000/248{,}500 = 93.8$ per cent.

Note that this is a mechanical efficiency and says nothing about the thermodynamic efficiency of the turbine or the conversion of the heat energy originally contained in the steam to power at the turbine shaft. The over-all or thermodynamic efficiency will be considerably less than this.

4-2. Equation of State. Perhaps the next most important single item under the general heading of thermodynamics is the equation of state of an ideal gas and its different modifications. The equation of state may be given, for 1 lb of a gas, as

$$PV = RT$$

where, in English units, P = pressure, psf

V = specific volume, cu ft/lb

T = temperature, °Rankine or °Fahrenheit absolute

R = specific gas constant, ft/°Rankine or ft-lb/(lb)(°Rankine).

The equation of state is written correctly in a number of different ways which are all equivalent. It is sometimes written $P \text{ Vol} = WRT$, where P, R, and T are as before, W = pounds of gas, and Vol = total volume in cubic feet or

$$V \text{ cu ft/lb} \times W \text{ lb} = \text{Vol, cu ft}$$

If we let $W = M$ lb, where M is equally numerically to the molecular weight, we have

$$PMV = MRT$$

where V = specific volume, cu ft/lb
Rearranging terms gives

$$MR = \frac{P(MV)}{T}$$

We remember from Avogadro's law that all perfect gases have the same number of molecules in any given volume at a given temperature and pressure. We remember also, and it follows from Avogadro's law, that a pound mole (a weight of gas equal in pounds to the molecular weight of the gas) of any perfect gas will occupy the same volume as that of any other perfect gas for the same conditions of temperature and pressure. At 32°F and atmospheric pressure this volume is called a *mole volume* and equals 359 cu ft (in the cgs system the mole volume equals 22.4 liters, which is called the "gram-molecular volume" and contains 6.024×10^{23} molecules).

Referring to the equation

$$MR = \frac{P(MV)}{T}$$

we can see that MV (lb $\times$ cu ft/lb) will be a constant number for all perfect gases at a particular pressure and temperature. At standard conditions $MV = 359$ cu ft. We know that PV/T is a constant (equal to R) for a particular gas. Then $[P(MV)]/T$ equals a constant for any perfect gas and MR is a constant for that particular gas. MR is called the universal gas constant or the molar gas constant and is equal to (very nearly) 1,544. With this we can determine R for a given gas from the relationship $R = 1,544/\text{mol. wt.}$

The equation of state will always hold for a perfect gas and will very nearly hold for all common gases in moderate pressure and temperature ranges.

For special cases we have modifications of the equation of state.

For constant pressure we have that, since $PV = RT$,

$$\frac{V_1}{T_1} = \frac{V_2}{T_2} = \text{constant}$$

which is called "Charles' law,"

$$\frac{V_1}{V_2} = \frac{T_1}{T_2} \qquad (P = \text{constant})$$

For constant temperature we have that $P_1V_1 = RT = P_2V_2$, or

$$P_1V_1 = P_2V_2 \qquad (T = \text{constant})$$

This is called "Boyle's law."

The equation of state with the special cases which are variations of it is an extremely useful tool; some of the particular applications will be examined in more detail using past examination problems as examples. One of these examination questions asked:

- When air at atmospheric pressure is pumped into a tire, its volume is compressed to one-third its original value and the temperature rises from 60 to 100°F. What is the gauge pressure of the air in the tire?

The equation of state gives us

$$\frac{P_1V_1}{T_1} = \frac{P_2V_2}{T_2} = R$$

where R is very nearly constant over the range considered. This gives

$$P_2 = P_1 \times \frac{T_2}{T_1} \times \frac{V_1}{V_2}$$

The initial pressure of the air is 14.7 psia.

$$T_1 = 60°F = 60 + 460 = 520°R$$
$$T_2 = 100°F = 100 + 460 = 560°R$$

and the final volume is one-third the initial volume, or $V_2 = \frac{1}{3}V_1$.

$$P_2 = 14.7 \times \frac{560}{520} \times \frac{1}{\frac{1}{3}} = 47.5 \text{ psia}$$

The gauge of the air in the tire would then equal

$$47.5 - 14.7 = 32.8 \text{ psig}$$

Another example is afforded by the question:

- A completely air-tight cylinder 300 cm long is divided into two parts by a freely moving, air-tight, heat insulating piston. When the temperatures in the compartments are equal and equal 27°C, the piston is located 100 cm from one end of the cylinder. How far will the piston move if the gas in the smaller part of the cylinder is heated to 74°C, the temperature of the larger section remaining constant? Assume perfect gas laws hold, and disregard the thickness of the piston.

For this problem it is best to draw the figure first (Fig. 4-1).

This problem may be done in two steps, or the answer may be found in only one step. Let us take it step by step first.

Assume the piston is held stationary while the heat is added, and calculate the pressure increase in volume A.   This would be a constant-volume process.

Fig. 4-1

$$P_{A2} = P_{A1} \times \frac{T_2}{T_1} = P_{A1} \times \frac{74 + 273}{27 + 273} = 1.16 P_{A1}$$

Then let the piston move until the pressures in chambers A and B are equalized, holding the temperatures constant.

$$P_{A2} V'_{A2} = P_{A3} V'_{A3} \qquad \text{and} \qquad P_{B1} V'_{B1} = P_{B3} V'_{B3}$$

plus the equation $V'_{B1} - V'_{B3} = V'_{A3} - V'_{A2}$
or $V'_{A2} + V'_{B1} = V'_{A3} + V'_{B3}$

since the total volume remains constant. Here we are using the relationship $PV' = WRT$, where V' is measured in cubic centimeters.

$$V'_{A2} = 100 \times A \qquad V'_{B1} = 200 \times A$$

where A = the cross-sectional area

The same relationships will hold regardless of what the cross-sectional area might be. To simplify the calculation, let us use $A = 1$.

$$P_{A2} = 1.16 P_{A1} = 1.16 P_{B1}$$
$$V'_{A1} = 100 = V'_{A2} \quad \text{and} \quad V'_{B1} = 200$$
$$1.16 P_{A1} \times 100 = P_{A3} V'_{A3}$$
$$P_{B1} V'_{B1} = P_{A1} \times 200 = P_{B3} V'_{B3}$$
$$P_{A3} = P_{B3} \quad \text{and} \quad V'_{A3} - V'_{B3} = 300$$

Solving these equations simultaneously gives

$$V'_{A3} = 110 \quad \text{and} \quad V'_{B3} = 190$$

The piston will then move 10 cm to the right in the figure as drawn.

To determine the new volume in one step we utilize the same reasoning, regarding cross-sectional area as before, and we have:

$$\frac{P_{A1} V'_{A1}}{T_{A1}} = \frac{P_{A2} V'_{A2}}{T_{A2}} = W_A R \qquad \text{constant}$$

and
$$\frac{P_{B1} V'_{B1}}{T_{B1}} = \frac{P_{B2} V'_{B2}}{T_{B2}} = W_B R \qquad \text{constant}$$

where $P_{A1} = P_{B1}$, $P_{A2} = P_{B2}$, $V'_{A1} = 100$, $V'_{B1} = 200$, $T_{B1} = T_{B2}$, and $V'_{A2} + V'_{B2} = 300$.

$$\frac{100 P_{A1}}{27 + 273} = \frac{P_{A2} V'_{A2}}{74 + 273} \quad \text{or} \quad P_{A1} = 0.00864 V'_{A2} P_{A2}$$
$$P_{B1} \times 200 = P_{B2} \times V'_{B2} \qquad P_{A1} = 0.005 P_{A2} V'_{B2}$$

Combining these two gives $V'_{B2} = 1.728 V'_{A2}$, which, combined with the relationship $V'_{A2} + V'_{B2} = 300$, gives $V'_{A2} = 110$, as before.

For another example let us look at a past examination problem which asks:

- A gas company buys gas at 10 psig and 80°F and sells it at 4 in. of water pressure and 30°F. Assuming no loss in distribution, how many cubic feet are sold for each cubic foot purchased?

Again we have $P_1 V_1 = WRT_1$. Assume W such that $V_1 = 1$ cu ft. Then $P_1/T_1 = WR$, and $(P_2 V_2)/T_2 = WR$, which combine to give the amount sold for each cubic foot purchased, or

$$V_2 = \frac{P_1 \times T_2}{T_1 \times P_2} = \frac{(24.7 \times 144) \times (460 + 30)}{(460 + 80) \times (\frac{4}{12} \times 62.4 + 14.7 \times 144)}$$
$$= 1.51 \text{ cu ft}$$

where $P_1 = [(14.7 + 10) \times 144]$ psf
$P_2 = 4$ in. of water $= [(\frac{4}{12}$ ft $\times 62.4$ lb/cu ft)
$+ (14.7 \times 144)]$ psf

As another example, consider the following past examination problem:

- A tank contains 10 cu ft of oxygen at 500 psia and 85°F. Part of the oxygen was used, and later the pressure was observed to be 300 psia and the temperature, 73°F.
  a. How many pounds of oxygen were used?
  b. What volume would the used oxygen occupy at standard atmospheric pressure and 70°F?

At the beginning we have

$$P_1 V_1 = W_1 R T_1$$
$$R = \frac{1,544}{\text{mol. wt}} = \frac{1,544}{32} = 48.2$$
$$P_1 = 500 \times 144 \qquad V_1 = 10 \text{ cu ft} \qquad T_1 = 460 + 85$$

Then

$$W_1 = \frac{(500 \times 144) \times 10}{48.2 \times 545} = 27.4 \text{ lb} \qquad \text{oxygen at start}$$

At the later time,

$$W_2 = \frac{P_2 V_2}{R T_2} = \frac{300 \times 144 \times 10}{48.2 \times 533} = 16.8 \text{ lb} \qquad \text{oxygen remaining}$$

The amount of oxygen used equaled $27.4 - 16.8 = 10.6$ lb. The specific volume of oxygen may be calculated from the equation of state, $PV = RT$.

$$V = \frac{RT}{P} = \frac{48.2(460 + 70)}{14.7 \times 144} = 12.07 \text{ cu ft/lb}$$

The 10.6 lb of oxygen used would then occupy

$$10.6 \times 12.07 = 128 \text{ cu ft of volume}$$

A further example of the usefulness of the equation of state is afforded by yet another past examination problem:

- A hydrocarbon has the following composition: $C = 82.66$ per cent, $H = 17.34$ per cent. The density of the vapor is 0.2308 g/l at 30°C and 75 mm. Determine its molecular weight and its molecular formula.

The equation of state gives $PV = RT$, or $w = P/RT$, where $w = 1/V = $ g/cu cm. Knowing w, P, and T, we can solve for R, where $R = P/wT$, $p = 75$ mm Hg, and mercury weighs 13.6 g/cu cm.

Therefore, $P = 13.6 \times 7.5$ cm $\times$ 980 dynes/g $= 10^5$ dynes/sq cm
$$w = 2.308 \times 10^{-4} \text{ g/cu cm}$$
$$T = 273 + 30 = 303°K$$
$$R = \frac{10^5}{2.308 \times 10^{-4} \times 303} = 1.43 \times 10^6 \frac{\text{dyne-cm}}{\text{(g)(°K)}}$$
$$= 1.43 \times 10^6 \frac{\text{ergs}}{\text{(g)(°K)}}$$

The universal gas constant in the cgs system equals 8.312×10^7 ergs/(mole)(°K). So

$$\frac{8.312 \times 10^7}{1.43 \times 10^6} = 58.1 \text{ g/mole}$$

or the molecular weight of the gas is 58.1.

The equation of the gas is C_nH_m, and the molecular weight is $n \times 12 + m \times 1.008$, where 12 is the atomic weight of carbon and 1.008 is the atomic weight of hydrogen.

$$n \times 12 = 0.8266 \times 58.1 = 48$$
and $$m \times 1.008 = 0.1734 \times 58.1 = 10.1$$

The required answers are, then: the molecular weight $= 58.1$, and the molecular formula is C_4H_{10}.

Another method of approach is to determine the weight of 22.4 l of the gas at standard conditions. The weight of 1 mole also equals

the molecular weight.   Standard conditions are 1 atm of pressure
(760 mm) and 0°C.

$$P = wRT \qquad R = \text{constant} = \frac{P}{wT}$$

giving $\qquad \dfrac{P_1}{w_1 T_1} = \dfrac{P_2}{w_2 T_2} \qquad w_2 = w_1 \times \dfrac{P_2}{P_1} \times \dfrac{T_1}{T_2}$

$$w_2 = 0.2308 \times \frac{760}{75} \times \frac{273 + 30}{273} = 2.60 \text{ g/l}$$

at standard conditions.

$$2.60 \text{ g/l} \times 22.4 \text{ l} = 58.2 \text{ g/mole}$$

or the molecular weight is 58.2 and the molecular formula may be
determined as before.

Another problem asked:

- Disregarding the friction due to the flow of gas through the
  annular space between the tubing and casing, calculate the
  vacuum which would exist at the bottom of a well 6,000 ft deep
  if the pressure at the top of the well is 15 in. Hg vacuum.
  The specific gravity of the gas is 1.1 compared with that of
  air.   The temperature of the gas may be considered a constant at 100°F, and the atmospheric pressure is 14 psi.

If the gas were incompressible, the pressure at 6,000 ft would equal
$P_0 + (6{,}000w/144)$, or $\int dP = \int_{l_1}^{l_2} w \, dl$. However, w is not constant for the gas and varies with the pressure. Since $P = wRT$,
$w = P/RT$. The same general relationship will hold for

$$\int dP = \int_{l_1}^{l_2} w \, dl$$

giving $dP = w \, dl = (P/RT)dl$; $dP/P = dl/RT$, or $\ln P = 1/RT$,
which gives $P = \text{constant} \times e^{1/RT}$ for $l = 0$, $P = P_0$. Then
$P = P_0 e^{1/RT}$.

Since the specific gravity of the gas is 1.1, the specific weight

$$w_{gas} = 1.1 w_{air}$$

$$w_{air} = \frac{P}{R_{air} T} \quad \text{and} \quad w_{gas} = \frac{P}{R_{gas} T}$$

$$w_{air} R_{air} = \frac{P}{T} \quad \text{and} \quad w_{gas} R_{gas} = 1.1 w_{air} R_{gas}$$

Then $$R_{gas} = \frac{R_{air}}{1.1} = \frac{53.3}{1.1} = 48.5$$

$$P_0 = 14.0 \text{ psia} - 15 \text{ in. Hg} = 14.0 - 15 \times 0.491 \text{ psi/in. Hg}$$
$$= 6.64 \text{ psia}$$

$$P = 6.64 \exp\left(\frac{6,000}{48.5 \times 560}\right) = 6.64 \times 1.247 = 8.28 \text{ psia}$$

$$14 - 8.28 = 5.72 \text{ psi vacuum}$$

or $$\frac{5.72}{0.491} = 11.65 \text{ in. Hg vacuum}$$

A good approximation may be obtained without using calculus by estimating the increase in pressure in 1,000-ft steps and determining the pressure in steps.   This is called "step integrating."

The pressure at 0 ft depth is 6.64 psia.

$$w_0 = \frac{6.64 \times 144}{48.5 \times 560} = 0.0352 \text{ lb/cu ft}$$

The increase in pressure, in pounds per square inch gauge, of 1,000 ft of this

$$\text{Weight of gas} = \frac{1,000 \times 0.0352}{144} = 0.244 \text{ psi} = \Delta p$$

$P_{1,000} = 6.64 + 0.24 = 6.88$ $w_{1,000} = 0.0365$ and $\Delta p = 0.253$
$P_{2,000} = 6.88 + 0.25 = 7.13$ $w_{2,000} = 0.0378$ and $\Delta p = 0.263$
$P_{3,000} = 7.13 + 0.26 = 7.39$ $w_{3,000} = 0.0392$ and $\Delta p = 0.272$
$P_{4,000} = 7.39 + 0.27 = 7.66$ $w_{4,000} = 0.0406$ and $\Delta p = 0.282$
$P_{5,000} = 7.66 + 0.28 = 7.94$ $w_{5,000} = 0.0421$ and $\Delta p = 0.293$
$P_{6,000} = 7.94 + 0.29 = 8.23$

This is reasonably close to the previous answer and could be made as close as desired by using smaller increments of depth.

4-3. Work and Thermodynamic Processes. The equation of state can be used to find the pressure, volume, or temperature of a gas at any point at which two of the three properties are known. It tells nothing, however, about the way in which any of these properties varies between the two points. The work required to change a gas from one state point to another or the work which can be obtained from a gas as it expands from one state point to another depends upon the path which the gas follows as it changes from one point to another. This can be easily shown by an examination of a graph showing the relation between the pressure and volume of a gas as it changes from one state point to another (Fig. 4-2).

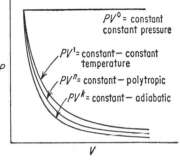

Fig. 4-2

We know from our study of mechanics that Work $= \int F \, ds$. For a gas, Force = pressure $\times$ area, and $ds = (d \text{ Vol})/A$, so we have that

$$F \, ds = P \times A \times \frac{dV}{A} = P \, dV$$

and the work done by an expanding gas equals $\int P \, dV$. We recognize this as equivalent to the area under the P-V diagram. This means that the process by which the gas changes from one state point to another is of extreme importance when it comes to determining the work required by or obtainable from a gas.

The more important processes are:

Constant temperature, isothermal............ $PV = $ constant
Constant pressure, isobaric or isopiestic....... $V/T = $ constant, $P = $ constant
Constant volume, isometric................. $P/T = $ constant, $V = $ constant
Adiabatic................................. $PV^k = $ constant
Polytropic................................. $PV^n = $ constant

where $k = c_p/c_v$, the ratio of specific heats, and n is an exponent, ordinarily somewhat less than k.

The different processes are shown in Fig. 4-2, and the differences in the work required, or developed, are apparent. The work required to go from point (1) to point (2) can be calculated from the relationship Work $= \int_1^2 P \, dV$. For constant pressure we have:

$$W = P \int_1^2 dV = PV_2 - PV_1$$

For the constant temperature, polytropic, and adiabatic processes, we have a similar condition in that the relationship $PV^n = $ constant applies to all three cases, with n equaling 1, n, and k, respectively. Here we have, taking logarithms of both sides,

$$\ln P + n \ln V = \ln C$$

and differentiation gives

$$\frac{dP}{P} + n \frac{dV}{V} = 0$$

or

$$dV = - \frac{V}{n} \frac{dP}{P}$$

then

$$W = \int_1^2 - \frac{1}{n} V \, dP$$

but

$$V = \left(\frac{C}{P} \right)^{1/n}$$

where $PV^n = C$

$$W = - \frac{1}{n} \int_1^2 C^{1/n} P^{-1/n} \, dP = - \frac{C^{1/n}}{n} \frac{1}{1 - 1/n} P^{(1-1/n)} \Big|_1^2$$

$$= - \frac{P^{1/n} V}{n - 1} P^{(1-1/n)} \Big|_1^2$$

which gives

$$W = \frac{P_2 V_2 - P_1 V_1}{1 - n}$$

for work done by the gas. W will be negative if work is done on the gas. This equation can be used to calculate the work done by (or on) the gas for $n = k$ and $n = n$, the polytropic exponent. For an isothermal process where $PV = $ constant and $n = 1$, this relationship gives the indeterminate fraction, 0/0, so the relationship for work for an isothermal process must be found in another way.

$$PV = RT \text{ constant} \qquad P = \frac{RT}{V}$$

$$W = \int P\, dV = \int \frac{RT}{V}\, dV = RT \ln \frac{V_2}{V_1} = RT \ln \frac{P_1}{P_2}$$

$$\text{Work} = P_1 V_1 \ln \frac{P_1}{P_2}$$

In the case of constant volume, $dV = 0$ and no work is done by the gas. There will, however, be a change in the enthalpy of the gas for a change in the pressure when the volume remains constant. This follows from the fact that $h = u + (PV)/J$ or $h = u + (RT)/J$ and also that $du = c_v\, dT$, where u, the internal energy of the gas, is a function of temperature alone. There will, then, be a change in both the internal-energy term and also the PV/J term for a constant-volume process.

Utilizing the same relationships, it can be seen that an isothermal process is a constant-enthalpy process and also a constant-energy process for a perfect gas.

With the relationships given, the work done by a gas (positive or negative) to go from one state point to another can be calculated.

The work may also be determined by the application of the general energy equation; often this will be simpler than calculating the integral of $P\, dV$. We have

$$W = \frac{v_1^2 - v_2^2}{2gJ} + h_1 - h_2 + Z_1 - Z_2 + Q$$

In most cases this can be reduced to $W = h_1 - h_2 + Q$, and it is then only necessary to determine Δh and Q to calculate W.

The enthalpy h is equal to the internal energy u plus the quantity PV/J. For a perfect gas and a reversible adiabatic process, the following relationships will hold:

$$du + P\, dV = 0$$
$$du = c_v\, dT \qquad \text{or} \qquad \Delta u = c_v(T_2 - T_1)$$
$$\Delta h = w c_p\, \Delta T \qquad \text{or} \qquad \Delta h = c_p\, \Delta T$$

$R = c_p - c_v$ for the specific gas, numerically $R = (c_p - c_v)J$
$W = c_v(T_1 - T_2) =$ work done by gas on a piston

$$h_1 - h_2 = \frac{k}{k-1} (P_1V_1 - P_2V_2)$$

also, for an isentropic process, $dh - V\,dP = 0$.   And since

$$h_2 - h_1 = \int_1^2 dh$$

we have $\dfrac{k}{k-1} (P_1V_1 - P_2V_2) = \displaystyle\int_1^2 V\,dP$

For a reversible polytropic process ($Pv^n =$ constant), it can be shown that

$$Q = U_2 - U_1 + \int_1^2 P\,dV = \left(\frac{R}{n-1} - c_v\right)(T_1 - T_2)$$

$$= \frac{c_p - nc_v}{n-1} (T_1 - T_2)$$

The derivation of these relationships is somewhat too lengthy and involved to be included here; the interested reader is referred to any good text on thermodynamics (see references at end of chapter) for a more complete discussion.

For illustration let us look at a past examination problem:

- A centrifugal compressor pumps 100 lb of air per minute from 14.7 psia and 60°F to 50 psia and 270°F by an irreversible process. The temperature rise of 50 lb/min or circulating water about the casing is 12°F. What horsepower is required? Disregard any changes in kinetic energy.

The general energy equation will always apply, and if we write it for the two points of the process we can calculate the work required, provided we can determine the value of the individual components.

$$\frac{v_1^2}{2gJ} + h_1 + Z_1 + Q = \frac{v_2^2}{2gJ} + h_2 + Z_2 + W$$

We have been told to disregard changes in kinetic energy, and we shall assume that the difference in elevation between the inlet and outlet of the compressor is small enough to be ignored without affecting the accuracy of the answer. This gives us the equation for the work:

$$W = h_1 - h_2 + Q$$

Q, the heat lost by the air during the compression process, can easily be determined from the data given for the cooling water.

$$Q = -50 \text{ lb/min} \times 12°F \times 1 \text{ Btu/(lb)(°F)} = -600 \text{ Btu/min}$$

From the relationship $\Delta h = c_p \Delta T$, which holds for a steady-flow process, we find that

$$h_2 - h_1 = 0.24(210) = 50.4 \text{ Btu/lb} = -(h_1 - h_2)$$
$$W = -(100 \text{ lb/min} \times 50.4 \text{ Btu/lb}) - 600 = -5640 \text{ Btu/min}$$
$$\frac{5640 \text{ Btu/min} \times 778 \text{ ft-lb/Btu}}{33,000 \text{ Btu/min hp}} = 133 \text{ hp}$$

which is the required answer, considering the gas as a "perfect" gas.

The process is given as an irreversible one so the work cannot be correctly calculated from the relationship

$$\text{Work} = \int P \, dv$$

This follows from the fact that the process is not reversible and, therefore, is not frictionless and that the amount of work done against friction cannot be calculated from the reversible (or frictionless) work relationships. The path of the process can, however, be described by means of the relationship $PV^n = $ constant. Let us calculate what the work requirement would have been had the compression been a reversible polytropic process. This process can be represented by a sketch in the P-V plane as shown in Fig. 4-3.

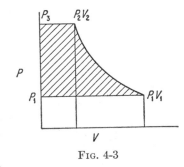

Fig. 4-3

A centrifugal compressor is essentially a centrifugal pump which converts velocity head to pressure head and then pushes the compressed gas at constant pressure to wherever it goes. The curve of the process would be first a constant-pressure intake of air at pressure P_1 from zero volume to V_1. The gas would then be compressed polytropically, in accordance with the relationship PV^n = constant, to the state point represented by P_2V_2. Finally the compressed gas would be pushed out at a constant pressure to the state point represented by $P_3(P_3 = P_2)$. We can assume a clearance of zero since it is a centrifugal compressor. The shaded area of the diagram in Fig. 4-3 indicates the work done on the gas and equals the area under that portion of the curve. The shaded area equals

$$\int_1^2 P \, dV = P_2V_2 - P_1V_1$$

where P_2V_2 is the work represented by the constant-pressure discharge and P_1V_1 is the work represented by the constant-pressure intake at atmospheric pressure.

$$\int_1^2 P \, dV = \int_1^2 CV^{-n} \, dV$$

where $PV^n = C$, giving $P = CV^{-n}$.

$$\int_1^2 CV^{-n} \, dV = \frac{C}{1-n} V^{(1-n)} \Big|_1^2 = \frac{PV^n}{1-n} (V_2{}^{1-n} - V_1{}^{1-n})$$

$$= \frac{P_2V_2 - P_1V_1}{1-n}$$

which is negative, indicating, according to our convention, that work is being done on the gas. This is the work done on the gas during the polytropic compression.

The constant-pressure process work

$$\int_2^3 P \, dV = P(V_3 - V_2) = -P_2V_2$$

This is also negative according to our convention, indicating work done on the gas.

The work done during the intake stroke equals $\int_0^1 P \, dV = P_1V_1$, which is positive, indicating work done by the gas. This gives

$$\text{Work} = \int_0^1 P\,dV + \int_1^2 P\,dV + \int_2^3 P\,dV$$

$$= P_1V_1 + \frac{P_2V_2 - P_1V_1}{1 - n} - P_2V_2$$

which combines to give $n/(1 - n)(P_2V_2 - P_1V_1)$ work done by the gas.

This could also have been obtained from the relationship

$$W = \int V\,dP$$

which also would give the shaded area.

Since $PV^n = $ constant, we find by differentiating that

$$nV^{n-1} P\,dV - V^n\,dP = 0$$

or $V\,dP = -nP\,dV$. This gives $\int V\,dP = -n\int P\,dV$, indicating that the work required to go from P_1V_1 to P_2V_2 equals

$$\left(\frac{n}{1 - n}\right)(P_2V_2 - P_1V_1)$$

as before.

This also represents the difference between flow work and nonflow work. The nonflow work is represented by the shaded area in Fig. 4-4. In this process a given volume of gas is compressed from V_1 to V_2 (or expands from V_2 to V_1). There is no flow of gas here; the quantity of the gas is constant, no gas being added and none removed. Thus we have the term "nonflow work," with the work being represented by $\int_1^2 P\,dV$.

Fig. 4-4

In the case of Fig. 4-3 there is actually a flow of gas. It is taken in at a pressure of P_1 to a volume of V_1, compressed to P_2 and V_2, and then discharged at a pressure P_2. There is an actual flow of gas through the compressor—thus the term "flow work" with the work equal to $\int_1^2 V\, dP$. Since $PV^n = $ constant, $P_1 = 14.7$ psia, $P_2 = 50$ psia, $P_1 V_1{}^n = P_2 V_2{}^n$, and

$$\ln P_1 + n \ln V_1 = \ln P_2 + n \ln V_2$$

$$n = \frac{\ln P_1 - \ln P_2}{\ln V_2 - \ln V_1} = \frac{\ln (P_1/P_2)}{\ln (V_2/V_1)}$$

$V_1 = RT_1/P_1 = 53.3 \times (460 + 60)/(14.7 \times 144) = 13.10$ cu ft/lb

$V_2 = 5.40$ cu ft/lb $\qquad n = \dfrac{\ln (14.7/50)}{\ln (5.42/13.1)} = \dfrac{-1.225}{-0.884} = 1.386$

which gives $W = -40,500$ ft-lb/lb, or 40,500 ft-lb/lb work done on the gas for a reversible (frictionless) polytropic cycle. This amount of work would require 122.5 hp for the 100 lb/min of air handled by the compressor. The frictional work would equal the difference, or 10.5 hp.

A somewhat similar example is provided by another past examination problem:

- Derive an equation in terms of P_1, V_1, P_2, and V_2 for the work required to compress a gas adiabatically from P_1, V_1 to P_2, V_2.

This is similar to the analysis used in the previous example. We know the work will equal the area shown on the P-V diagram (Fig. 4-4).

$$\text{Work} \int_1^2 P\, dV$$

As before

$$\int_1^2 P\, dV = \frac{P_2 V_2 - P_1 V_1}{1 - k}$$

which is negative, indicating work done on the gas.

$$\text{Work} = \frac{P_2 V_2 - P_1 V_1}{k - 1} \qquad \text{ft-lb/lb of gas}$$

to compress the gas adiabatically from $P_1 V_1$ to $P_2 V_2$, where $P = $ psf and $V = $ cu ft/lb.

4-4. Cycles. We have looked at a few processes. If we put together a series of processes so that the beginning and ending points are identical, the sequence is termed a cycle. One of the more important cycles is the Carnot cycle, which consists of a constant-temperature process, a constant-entropy process, a second constant-temperature process, and a second constant-entropy process, as shown in the diagram (Fig. 4-5).

FIG. 4-5

4-5. Entropy. This brings up the question which is so bothersome to many engineers "What is entropy?" We shall discuss this before examining the Carnot and other common cycles.

Entropy cannot be pictured; it has no physical shape or substance. It is actually a mathematical concept and is the name given to the quantity $\int dQ/T$, which appears so frequently in thermodynamic analyses that it seemed desirable to give it a name. Actually, there is no absolute value of entropy; we deal with differences of entropy between state points. We can only equate differences of entropy for reversible processes, and for a reversible process

$$S_2 - S_1 = \int_1^2 \frac{dQ}{T}$$

from which can be obtained other expressions which can be used to solve for differences of entropy for a perfect gas.

$$ds = \frac{dQ}{T} = \frac{du + P\,dV}{T}$$

$$ds = c_v \left(\frac{dT}{T}\right) + R\left(\frac{dV}{V}\right)$$

which can be integrated to give

$$s_2 - s_1 = c_v \ln\left(\frac{T_2}{T_1}\right) + R \ln\left(\frac{V_2}{V_1}\right)$$

$$s_2 - s_1 = c_p \ln\left(\frac{V_2}{V_1}\right) + c_v \ln\left(\frac{P_2}{P_1}\right) = c_p \ln\left(\frac{T_2}{T_1}\right) - R \ln\left(\frac{P_2}{P_1}\right)$$

Also, the increase of entropy during a polytropic process can be shown to equal

$$s_2 - s_1 = \frac{c_p - nC_v}{n-1} \ln\left(\frac{T_1}{T_2}\right) = c_v \left(\frac{k-n}{1-n}\right) \ln\left(\frac{T_2}{T_1}\right)$$

The concept of entropy is a difficult one to grasp; a look at a few sample examination questions regarding this quantity may aid in gaining a better acquaintance with it. One such past examination problem asked:

• What is the difference between entropy and enthalpy?

We recall that enthalpy $h = u + pV$, or

$$dh = du + P \, dV + V \, dP$$

whereas the change in entropy $ds = (du + P \, dV)/T$; these equations combine to give $dh = T \, ds + V \, dP$.

Another question in a past examination asked:

• A volume of gas having an initial entropy of 3000 Btu/°R is heated at constant temperature of 1000°F until the entropy is 4500 Btu/°R. How much heat is added?

We know that $S_2 - S_1 = \int_1^2 dQ/T$, and if T is a constant we can integrate easily, obtaining $S_2 - S_1 = (1/T)(Q_2 - Q_1)$. Then we have $(S_2 - S_1)T = \Delta Q$, or

$$\Delta Q = (4500 - 3000)(1000 + 460) = 2{,}190{,}000 \text{ Btu}$$

added.

Another examination question was:

• A gas has a constant-pressure specific heat of

$$c_p = 6.6 + 7.2 \times 10^{-4} \times T \text{ Btu/[(mole)(°R)]}$$

Determine the entropy of this gas at 2000°R and 5 atm pressure if the base of zero entropy is taken at 520°R and 1 atm.

We note that c_p is given in Btu/[(mole)(°R)]. If we refer to the list of relationships given previously, we see that the relationship $ds = c_p(dT/T) - R(dP/P)$, from

$$s_2 - s_1 = c_p \ln\left(\frac{T_2}{T_1}\right) - R \ln\left(\frac{P_2}{P_1}\right)$$

would appear to apply. We are not, however, given any value for R. We recall that

$$R = \frac{1544}{\text{mol. wt}} \frac{\text{ft-lb}}{\text{lb } ^\circ R}$$

The molecular weight is also the pounds per pound-mole, so we have that $R = 1544[\text{ft-lb}/(\text{mole})(^\circ R)]$. We also know that the mechanical equivalent of heat is 788 ft-lb/Btu, so we can modify this value of R to give $R = 1.985[\text{Btu}/(\text{mole})(^\circ R)]$. Now all that remains is to substitute in the relationship for ds and grind out the answer.

$$ds = (6.6 + 7.2 \times 10^{-4} \times T) \frac{dT}{T} \frac{\text{Btu}}{(\text{mole})(^\circ R)}$$

$$- 1.985 \frac{dP}{P} \frac{\text{Btu}}{(\text{mole})(^\circ R)}$$

$$\int ds = \int 6.6 \frac{dT}{T} + \int 7.2 \times 10^{-4} \, dT - \int 1.985 \frac{dP}{P}$$

$$s_2 - s_1 = 6.6 \ln \left(\frac{T_2}{T_1}\right) + 7.2 \times 10^{-4}(T_2 - T_1) - 1.985 \ln \left(\frac{P_2}{P_1}\right)$$

$$s_2 - s_1 = 8.888 + 1.065 - 3.19 = 6.76 \frac{\text{Btu}}{(\text{mole})(^\circ R)}$$

The difference in entropy between points 1 and 2 is 6.76 Btu/ [(mole)($^\circ$R)]. Since $s_1 = 0$, the entropy of the gas is, then 6.76 Btu/ [(mole)($^\circ$R)] at 2000°R and 5 atm pressure.

Another example:

• One pound of saturated steam at 400°F expands isothermally to 60 psia. Determine (1) change of entropy; (2) heat transferred; (3) change of enthalpy; (4) change of internal energy; (5) work.

From a steam table we find that the pressure corresponding to a saturated-steam temperature of 400°F is 247.3 psia. We also find that $h = 1201$ Btu/lb for saturated vapor, $s = 1.5272$ Btu/ [($^\circ$F)(lb)], and $V = 1.863$ cu ft/lb.

Since the expansion is isothermal, the final product will be superheated steam at 400°F and 60 psia. The steam table gives $h = 1233.6$ Btu/lb, $s = 1.7135$ Btu/[($^\circ$F)(lb)], and $V = 8.357$ for this condition.

The change of entropy will then be

$$1.7135 - 1.5272 = 0.1863 \text{ Btu/[(lb)(°F)]}$$

For a perfect gas $\Delta h = c_p(T_2 - T_1)$, which is zero for an isothermal process. Also, $\Delta u = c_v(T_2 - T_1) = 0$ for an isothermal process for a perfect gas. Steam is not, however, a perfect gas, and the change of enthalpy is $1233.6 - 1201.0 = 32.6$ Btu/lb. From the general energy equation:

$$\frac{v_1^2}{2gJ} + h_1 + Z_1 + Q = \frac{v_2^2}{2gJ} + h_2 + Z_2 + W$$

We see that

$$Q = W + h_2 - h_1$$

since $v_1 = v_2 = 0$ and $Z_1 = Z_2$.

The work $= \int_1^2 P \, dV$, which equals $PV \ln (P_1/P_2)$, as determined previously. Unfortunately,

$$P_1 V_1 = 247.3 \times 144 \times 1.863 = 66,200 \text{ ft}$$

and $P_2 V_2 = 60 \times 144 \times 8.357 = 72,200$ ft, so PV is not a constant and the work calculated by this method will not be quite correct. Averaging the two values, this relationship gives

$$W = 69,200 \ln \frac{247.3}{60} = 98,000 \text{ ft-lb/lb} \qquad \text{work done by the gas}$$

For a reversible isothermal process we have that $Q = T \, \Delta s$. This is not a reversible process, but applying this relationship gives $Q = (400 + 460) \times 0.1863 = 160.2$ Btu/lb heat added to the gas.

Checking, we have $Q - (h_2 - h_1) = 160.2 - 32.6 = 127.6$ Btu/lb, or 99,300 ft-lb/lb, which is close to the average value for W of 98,000 ft-lb/lb.

We recall that the work done by a gas depends upon the path it follows, and since PV is not a constant we do not know the equation of the path accurately. Also the relationship $Q = T \, \Delta s$ Btu/lb is for a reversible process, which this is not. For an ideal gas $\Delta Q = \Delta u + \int P \, dV$. Since $h = u + (PV/J)$, Δh is the same, in the case of an isothermal process, as Δu. In this actual case it is not.

In this case,

$$u_1 = h_1 - \frac{PV_1}{J} = 1201.0 - \frac{66,200}{778} = 1116 \text{ Btu/lb}$$

and

$$u_2 = 1233.6 - \frac{72,200}{778} = 1141 \text{ Btu/lb}$$

The answers are, then:

1. $\Delta s = 0.1863$ Btu/(lb)(°F) increase
2. $\Delta Q = 160.2$ Btu/lb heat added to gas
3. $\Delta h = 32.6$ Btu/lb increase
4. $\Delta u = 25$ Btu/lb increase
5. Work = 99,300 ft-lb/lb, or 127.6 Btu/lb work done by gas

4-6. Carnot Cycle. The ideal Carnot cycle consists of four reversible processes, two isothermals and two adiabatics. Referring to Fig. 4-5:

1. a to b, heat enters the engine at a constant temperature, reversible isothermal expansion
2. b to c, reversible adiabatic expansion until temperature drops
3. c to d, heat removed from the engine at constant temperature, reversible isothermal compression
4. d to a, reversible adiabatic compression until temperature rises to the initial temperature

This cycle is a work cycle, with the engine doing work during the adiabatic expansion. A Carnot cycle can also be run in reverse to act as a refrigerator. As an example, a past examination problem asked:

- If a Carnot refrigerator which extracts heat from a cold-storage plant at $-20°$F and gives it to the atmosphere at $100°$F has a 100-"ton"-per-day capacity, what horsepower is needed to drive the refrigerator?

A "ton" of refrigeration capacity is the amount equal to freeze 2,000 lb of water in 24 hr. Since the heat of fusion of water is 144 Btu/lb, this means 288,000 Btu/24-hr day, 12,000 Btu/hr, or 200 Btu/min.

When the Carnot heat engine cycle is reversed, a refrigeration cycle is obtained. The work supplied to the refrigerator is repre-

sented by the area *abcd* in Fig. 4-5. The heat extracted is represented by the area *dcfe*. This means that work in the amount of
$(T_a - T_d) \Delta S$ is required for the operation of the refrigerator, and
that heat in the amount of $T_d \Delta S$ is extracted from the cold body.
From this we can see that for the normal operating temperature
range, more heat is extracted from the cold body than is required
to operate the Carnot refrigerating machine. In this particular
case we have $(460 - 20) \Delta S = 440 \Delta S$ Btu extracted from the cold
source, while only $(560 - 440) \Delta S$ Btu is required to operate the
engine. This means that for every Btu of energy used to run the
refrigerator,

$$\frac{440 \ \Delta S}{(560 - 440) \ \Delta S} = 3.67 \text{ Btu}$$

is removed from the cold source. This value is called the coefficient
of performance (c.o.p.), which is defined as the ratio of the amount
of refrigeration effected to the work supplied. The c.o.p. may be
greater than 1 or less than 1. Usually it is greater than 1. It
might be noted in passing that the thermodynamic advantage as
evidenced by a c.o.p. is the reason for the development of the heat
pump. In the case of the heat pump all the energy will be transferred to the hot body and the c.o.p. of a heat pump is equal to the
c.o.p. of the same machine used as a refrigerator plus 1. In the
illustration the c.o.p. for this machine used as a heat pump would be

$$\frac{560 \ \Delta S}{(560 - 540) \ \Delta S} = 4.67 \qquad \text{or} \qquad 3.67 + 1.00$$

Since 1 Btu of refrigeration in the example would only require
1/3.67 Btu of work, 100 tons of refrigeration would require

$$\frac{100 \times 200}{3.67} = 5450 \text{ Btu/min} \qquad \frac{5450 \times 778}{33,000} = 128.5 \text{ hp}$$

The horsepower required to drive the refrigerator is 128.5.

It might be noted here that the Carnot efficiency, which equals
work done divided by the heat supplied, is the maximum efficiency
possible for any thermal engine operating between two temperatures. No other cycle may exceed this efficiency and it is not

necessary for a different cycle efficiency to equal it. Other reversible cycles are as efficient as a Carnot cycle, irreversible cycles are not so efficient as a Carnot cycle. No other cycle can be more efficient than a Carnot cycle.

Another interesting past examination problem is:

- A constant-temperature heat source at $t = 1000°F$ supplies heat to a Carnot engine which receives it at 600°F. The engine rejects heat at 100°F to a cold body (or sink) which is at a constant temperature of 60°F. Ten per cent of the energy available to the Carnot engine is converted into friction and lost. 1000 Btu is supplied by the hot body.
  a. What is the efficiency of the cycle?
  b. What is the total increase in entropy due to irreversible processes?
  c. What is the increase in unavailable energy?

The maximum cycle efficiency possible between the two reservoir temperatures would be $(1460 - 520)/1460 = 64.4$ per cent. If the engine receives the heat at 600°F and discharges it at 100°F, the maximum possible engine efficiency would be

$$\frac{(1060 - 560)}{1060} = 47.2 \text{ per cent}$$

The actual efficiency of the cycle will be somewhat less than 47.2 per cent, however, because 10 per cent of the heat supplied (10 per cent × 1000, or 100 Btu) is lost in overcoming friction. This will give us a modified type of Carnot cycle as shown in Fig. 4-5a. The actual engine efficiency will equal the work done by the engine divided by the heat supplied to the engine. Since the heat is supplied to the engine at a constant temperature of 600°F (1060°R), the difference in entropy at the start would equal heat divided by the temperature, or $S = Q/T = 1000/1060 = 0.944$ Btu/°F. The heat discharged at the cold temperature by an ideal Carnot engine would be $Q = T \times S = 560 \times 0.944 = 528$ Btu. The engine loses another 100 Btu in overcoming friction so the total heat lost would equal 628 Btu. The heat utilized in doing useful work would then be $1000 - 628 = 372$ Btu. The cycle efficiency would be 372/1000, or 37.2 per cent. The difference in entropy would increase from 0.944 Btu/°F at the higher temperature to

$$\frac{628}{560} = 1.12 \text{ Btu/°F}$$

at the lower temperature, giving an increase in the difference in

FIG. 4-5a

entropy of 0.18 Btu/°F, or a 19 per cent increase in the difference in entropy. The unavailable energy for the ideal cycle would equal 528 Btu as previously calculated (see also Fig. 4-5a). The real engine would also dissipate 100 Btu in overcoming friction, giving an actual amount of 628 Btu unavailable energy, or a 100 Btu increase over the ideal Carnot cycle. This would be $100/528 = 19$ per cent increase, just as for the increase in the entropy difference from high temperature to low temperature.

Another problem asked:

> • A Carnot engine utilizes a perfect gas as the medium. At the beginning of the isothermal expansion the pressure is 120 psia and the volume is 1 cu ft. At the end of the adiabatic expansion the pressure is 20 psia and the volume is 3 cu ft. What is the efficiency?

The temperatures are not given but may be determined from the relationship $PV = WRT$, since this is a perfect gas and the weight of the gas W will remain constant.

$$T_1 = \frac{P_1 V_1}{WR} = \frac{120 \times 144 \times 1}{WR} = \frac{17,280}{WR}$$

$$T_2 = \frac{20 \times 144 \times 3}{WR} = \frac{8,640}{WR}$$

$$\text{eff} = \frac{T_1 - T_2}{T_1} = \frac{17,280/WR - 8,640/WR}{17,280/WR} = \frac{8,640}{17,280} = 50 \text{ per cent}$$

The cycle efficiency equals 50 per cent.

Three other cycles touched upon in past examinations are the Rankine, diesel, and Otto cycles.

4-7. Rankine Cycle. The Rankine cycle is a more practical cycle for a vapor-liquid system than is the Carnot cycle. It has a lower thermal efficiency than the Carnot cycle but a higher work ratio. This is the theoretical cycle for a steam power plant. We can discuss this cycle by reviewing a past examination problem:

- Draw a Rankine vapor cycle on the pressure-volume diagram shown in Fig. 4-6. Indicate the thermodynamic process involved in each of the following parts of the diagram:
  a. Expansion through turbine
  b. Condensation in condenser
  c. Pumping of condensate into boiler
  d. Change of liquid to saturated vapor in boiler

The Rankine vapor cycle has been sketched over the saturated-steam line in Fig. 4-6. The expansion through the turbine is represented by the line *a*, *b*, *c*. This is a reversible adiabatic expansion of superheated steam, denoted by *a*, into wet steam at point *c*. The transition point from dry to wet steam occurs at point *b*, where the cycle line crosses the saturated-steam line.

From *c* to *d* the wet steam con-

Fɪɢ. 4-6

denses into water at a constant temperature and a constant pressure, reversibly.

The condensate is then pumped into the boiler along a reversible adiabatic line *de*. This is practically a constant-volume process.

The liquid is then changed to superheated steam along the constant-pressure line *e*, *f*, *g*, *a*. From *e* to *f* the water is heated at a constant pressure to the boiling temperature; this is a reversible process. From *f* to *g* the water is vaporized into steam reversibly and isobarically. From *g* to *a* there is a reversible isobaric heating of the steam into superheated steam at a higher temperature.

4-8. Diesel Cycle. The diesel cycle is the cycle which is the basis of the operation of the diesel engine. Another past examination problem was:

- Sketch an ideal diesel cycle diagram (pressure vs. volume). Label the suction stroke, compression stroke, expansion stroke, and exhaust stroke.

The diesel cycle is shown in Fig. 4-7. The intake stroke is shown by the line ab, a constant-pressure process. The air is next compressed adiabatically from b to c. Heat is then added (fuel injected)

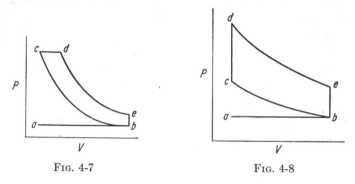

FIG. 4-7   FIG. 4-8

at constant pressure from c to d, and the gas expands adiabatically from d to e. The exhaust valve opens at e and exhaust takes place from e to b and during the exhaust stroke b, a. This is a four-cycle engine as shown, with suction stroke ab, compression bc, expansion c, d, e, and exhaust stroke e, b, a.

4-9. Otto Cycle. The Otto cycle, shown in Fig. 4-8, is the cycle on which the operation of the ordinary gasoline engine is based. The intake stroke is from a to b. The mixture is compressed adiabatically from b to c, at which point ignition takes place and heat is added, raising the temperature and pressure to d. An adiabatic expansion takes place from d to e, at which point the exhaust valve opens and combustion gases flow out. The path eb represents a constant-volume drop in temperature and an extraction of heat. The exhaust stroke is represented by the line ba.

The cycle efficiency of an Otto cycle can be shown to equal $1 - (1/r^{k-1})$, where r is the compression ratio.

4-10. Indicator Diagrams. This seems to be an appropriate place to mention indicator cards, which are P-V diagrams obtained during engine operation. The area under a P-V diagram equals the work done during a cycle, so the net area (work is required to draw air into the cylinder during the intake stroke) is a measure of the work done on a piston during one cycle. The area of the P-V diagram is frequently divided by the length of the stroke to give average pressure; this is known as the "mean effective pressure" (MEP). The indicated horsepower is then:

$$\frac{\text{MEP psf} \times \text{Vol cu ft} \times \text{power strokes/min}}{33{,}000 \text{ ft-lb/min hp}}$$

Sometimes the mean effective pressure is converted to the output of the engine, making allowances for frictional losses in the engine and power transmission system. It is then termed the "brake mean effective pressure," or the BMEP. This is usually calculated from dynamometer readings taken at the output shaft.

4-11. Specific Heat and Latent Heat. Problems concerning specific heat and latent heat are occasionally asked in fundamentals examinations. These merely require a balance of the heat added, lost, and retained. A good illustration is afforded by a past examination problem:

- A tank holds 1,000 lb of water at a temperature of 90°F. A piece of ice at 32°F was added and completely melted in the water, reducing its temperature to 40°F. Assuming no heat losses, find (*a*) how many pounds of ice were added; (*b*) how many pounds of steam at 212°F must be added to bring the tank contents to 140°F? Given data:

  Latent heat of ice = 80 cal/g

  Latent heat of steam at 212°F = 540 cal/g

First we must convert the values for the latent heats to Btu/lb. Since there are 252 cal/Btu and 454 g/lb, the latent heat of fusion of ice will be

$$\frac{80 \text{ cal}}{252 \text{ cal/Btu}} \times \frac{1}{\text{g}} \times \frac{454 \text{ g}}{\text{lb}} = 144 \text{ Btu/lb}$$

The latent heat of steam will be $(540/252) \times 454 = 973$ Btu/lb.

The ice was added at 32°F; it melted and rose to 40°F, so that each pound of ice absorbed (144 + 8) Btu. The 1,000 lb of water would give up 1,000(90 − 40) = 50,000 Btu in cooling. Total ice required = 50,000/152 = 329 lb. The total amount of water at 40°F would then be 1,329 lb. The heat required to raise its temperature to 140°F would equal 1,329(140 − 40) = 132,900 Btu. Each pound of steam would give up 973 + (212 − 140) = 1,055 Btu. The steam required would then be 132,900/1,055 = 126 lb.

4-12. Psychrometry. The subject of psychrometry is occasionally touched upon in fundamentals examinations and seems to cause a fair amount of confusion among examinees. The principal point to remember here is that psychrometry is an application of Dalton's law of partial pressures and the Gibbs-Dalton law. As an illustration let us refer to a past examination problem:

> • Atmospheric air has a dry-bulb temperature of 85°F, and a wet-bulb temperature of 64°F. The barometric pressure is 14.10 psia. Calculate (without the use of the psychrometric chart):
> *a.* Specific humidity in grains per pound of dry air
> *b.* Relative humidity
> *c.* Dew point temperature
> *d.* Enthalpy of mixture in Btu per pound of dry air

As the air passes over the wet bulb it absorbs moisture, thus lowering the temperature of the air and of the water, and increasing the amount of the moisture in the air. The final temperature of the air, when it has absorbed all the moisture it can hold, is the wet-bulb temperature. It is also the dew-point temperature of the air after it has absorbed the additional moisture, which is higher than the dew point of the air originally. This is also called the temperature of adiabatic saturation. The derivation of the relationship used to calculate the specific humidity is somewhat complex and will not be gone through here. The process can be described by means of a temperature-entropy diagram for steam, as shown in Fig. 4-9. Here the vapor in the air is initially at temperature T_c, and the vapor is in the superheat region, as denoted by point 1. If the air, and the vapor in the air, were cooled along the constant-pressure line 1-2, condensation would start to occur at T_a, where the constant-pressure line crosses the saturated-steam line. This is the dew point of the original air-vapor mixture. As the air absorbs moisture, the saturation temperature will rise, and the wet-bulb temperature will be between T_a and T_c at point 3 on the saturated-steam line. From this we can see that the lowest air temperature which could be obtained

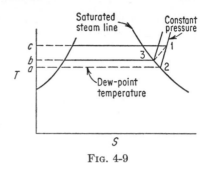

Fig. 4-9

through evaporation of water, evaporative cooling, would be the wet-bulb temperature.

An approximate relationship derived by Carrier and most often used to find humidity is:

$$P_{wv} = P_{swb} - \frac{P - P_{swb}}{2{,}830 - 1.44 t_{wb}}\,(t - t_{wb})$$

where P_{wv} = pressure of water vapor

P_{swb} = saturation pressure at wet-bulb temperature

P = atmospheric pressure

t_{wb} = wet-bulb temperature, °F

t = dry-bulb temperature, °F

For the example problem, $P_{swb} = 0.2951$ psia; $P = 14.10$ psia; saturation pressure at 85°F = 0.5959 psia.

$$P_{wv} = 0.2951 - \frac{14.10 - 0.2951}{2{,}830 - 1.44(64)}\,(85 - 64) = 0.1891 \text{ psia}$$

From Dalton's law of partial pressures we know that the pressure of the air will then be $14.10 - 0.189 = 13.91$ psia.

$$w_{\text{air}} = \frac{13.91 \times 144}{53.3 \times 545} = 0.0692 \text{ lb/cu ft}$$

$$w_{\text{water vapor}} = \frac{0.1891 \times 144}{85.8 \times 545} = 0.000584 \text{ lb/cu ft}$$

Since there are 7,000 grains/lb, a cubic foot of water vapor would weigh 4.09 grains. One pound of dry air would occupy

$$\frac{1}{0.0692} = 14.45 \text{ cu ft}$$

so there would be $4.09 \times 14.45 = 59.1$ grains of moisture per pound of dry air.

The relative humidity will equal the ratio of the actual water vapor pressure to the water vapor pressure at saturation.

$$\text{Relative humidity} = \frac{0.1891}{0.5959} = 31.7 \text{ per cent}$$

The dew-point temperature would be the saturation temperature for the amount of moisture in the air; following down the constant-pressure line in Fig. 4-9 from point 1 to point 2 gives us that the dew point (saturation temperature for $p = 0.1891$ psia) equals $51.8°F$.

The enthalpy of the mixture will equal the sum of the enthalpies of the gases making up the mixture. The steam at $85°F$ is super-heated steam which has a saturation temperature equal to the dew point. The enthalpy of saturated steam at $51.8°F$ is 1084.4 Btu/lb. The steam is then superheated $33.2°F$. The specific heat of steam at low temperature and pressure may be taken as 0.446 Btu/(lb)($°F$), giving an enthalpy for the vapor of

$$1084.4 + 33.2 \times 0.446 = 1099.2 \text{ Btu/lb}$$

The enthalpy of saturated steam at $85°F$ is 1098.8 Btu/lb, which would have served just as well for this purpose.

The enthalpy of the air at low pressures is $c_p(t - t_0)$, and since the point of zero enthalpy for air is $0°F$, the enthalpy of the air is $0.240(85) = 20.4$ Btu/lb.

Since we have $59.1/7{,}000 = 0.00845$ lb of steam per pound of air, the total enthalpy per pound of dry air is:

$$20.4 + 0.00845 \times 1099.2 = 29.68 \text{ Btu/lb} \qquad \text{dry air}$$

4-13. Heat Transfer. The subject of heat transfer has also received some attention in past examinations. The emphasis has been primarily on conduction. If we look at Fig. 4-10 we see that as heat flows from t_1 to t_2 it is hindered first by the film factor on the outside of the first layer of the wall, then by the first layer, the second layer, the third layer, and lastly by the film factor on the inside of the inner layer. These may all be combined to give one equivalent heat-transfer factor for the assembly. The relationship for the combined heat-transfer factor is:

$$\frac{1}{U} = \frac{1}{h_1} + \frac{L_1}{k_1} + \frac{L_2}{k_2} + \frac{L_3}{k_3} + \frac{1}{h_2}$$

where U = over-all heat-transfer coefficient
  h_1 = first film factor
  k_1 = thermal conductivity of the material of first layer
  L_1 = thickness of first layer
  k_2 = thermal conductivity of second layer
  L_2 = thickness of second layer
  k_3 = thermal conductivity of third layer
  L_3 = thickness of third layer
  h_2 = film factor at the other face of the wall

Since k is ordinarily given in Btu/(hr)(sq ft)(°F)/(ft), the units of U will be Btu/(hr)(sq ft)(°F), which must be multiplied by area (sq ft) times temperature differential (°F). The rate of heat transfer through the wall is then:

$$Q = UA(t_1 - t_2) \qquad \text{Btu/hr}$$

This relationship can be easily derived with the aid of Fig. 4-10. Here the flow of the heat is from t_1 to t_2. The temperature drop through the first film is from t_1 to t_a. The temperature drops from t_a to t_b through layer A, from t_b to t_c through layer B, and so on. Since the system has reached a steady state, the same amount of heat will flow through each film and through each layer. We shall call the rate of heat flow Q Btu/hr ft²; that is, Q Btu passes through each square foot of the wall per hour. We can set up relationships for the rate of heat flow through each layer of the resistance.

Fig. 4-10

$$Q = (t_1 - t_a)h_1 \qquad \text{giving} \qquad t_1 - t_a = Q/h_1$$
$$Q = (t_a - t_b)k_1/L_1 \qquad \text{giving} \qquad t_a - t_b = QL_1/k_1$$
$$Q = (t_b - t_c)k_2/L_2 \qquad \text{giving} \qquad t_b - t_c = QL_2/k_2$$
$$Q = (t_c - t_d)k_3/L_3 \qquad \text{giving} \qquad t_c - t_d = QL_3/k_3$$
$$Q = (t_d - t_2)h_1 \qquad \text{giving} \qquad t_d - t_2 = Q/h_2$$

Adding together the relationships on the right we obtain

$$t_1 - t_2 = Q\left(\frac{1}{h_1} + \frac{L_1}{k_1} + \frac{L_2}{k_2} + \frac{L_3}{k_3} + \frac{1}{h_2}\right)$$

which reduces to $Q = U(t_1 - t_2)$ per square foot or

$$Q \text{ Btu/hr} = UA(t_1 - t_2)$$

As an illustration, let us look at a past examination problem which asked:

• Given the air temperature in a room is 75°F and outside temperature 30°F. The inside temperature of the window pane is 45°F and the outside temperature 40°F. The window pane is $\frac{3}{16}$ in. thick and has a conductivity $k = 1.0$ Btu/(hr)(°F)(sq ft surface)(ft thick). The resistances to heat flow consist of the air film on the inside surface, the outside surface air film, and the window pane itself. Calculate the flow of heat per square foot of window pane, and the film coefficients for the inside and outside surfaces of the pane.

This problem must be calculated in steps, and one must remember that the heat which flows through the inner film equals the heat which flows through the pane and the heat which flows through the outer film. This gives us three equations. A sketch of the temperature variation is shown in Fig. 4-11.

The heat which flows out is Q. The heat-transfer coefficient through this film equals h_1, which gives us the relationship

$$Q = h_1(75 - 45) \text{ Btu/hr}$$

for 1 sq ft area.

This same amount of heat must flow through

FIG. 4-11

the pane, and the inverse of the coefficient of heat transfer through the pane will equal

$$\frac{1}{U} = \frac{L}{k} = \frac{\frac{3}{16} \times \frac{1}{12}}{1.0} = 0.01563$$

giving $U = 64$ Btu/(hr)(sq ft)(°F).

$$Q = U(t_1 - t_2) = 64(45 - 40) = 320 \text{ Btu/(hr)(sq ft)}$$

Similarly, the flow through the outer film will be $Q = 10h_2$. This gives us:

$Q = 320$ Btu/hr   for each sq ft of window pane
$Q = 30h_1$ $h_1 = 10.7$ Btu/(hr)(sq ft)(°F)
$Q = 10h_2$ $h_2 = 32$ Btu/(hr)(sq ft)(°F)

Flow of heat through pipe insulation is a bit different because the area of the insulation and of heat flow increases as the radius

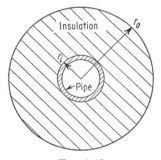

Fig. 4-12

increases. This gives rise to a different relationship for the heat transfer, namely:

$$Q = \frac{2\pi r_m l(t_1 - t_2)}{r_m/(r_o h_o) - (r_o - r_i)/k_m - r_m/(r_i h_i)} \qquad \text{Btu/hr}$$

where r_m = the logarithmic mean radius = $(r_o - r_i)/(\ln r_o/r_i)$
       r_i = inner radius (Fig. 4-12)
       r_o = outer radius
       l = length of pipe
       k_m = mean thermal conductivity

As can be seen, this equation ignores the insulating effect of the metal pipe which can safely be disregarded in most cases.

As an example, let us look at a past examination problem:

- A 1½-in. pipe is lagged with 85 per cent magnesia insulation 1¼ in. thick. The pipe temperature is 230°F, and the outside temperature of the lagging is 85°F.
  a. Calculate the heat loss per hour for 200 ft of pipe
  b. What is the average area of heat transfer per foot of pipe?
  c. Calculate the coefficient of heat transfer based on the (1) inside area, (2) outside area, (3) average area.

Consideration of the film coefficients has been eliminated through the specification of the temperatures at the inner and outer edges of the insulation.

If we assume that the outer diameter (OD) of the pipe is 1½ in., then $r_i = 0.75$ in. and $r_o = 2.00$ in.

$$r_m = \frac{1.25}{\ln 2.67} = 1.27$$

$$Q = \frac{2\pi \times (1.27/12) \times 200(230 - 85)}{1.25/(12 \times 0.041)} = 7580 \text{ Btu/hr}$$

The average area would be $2\pi(r_o - r_i)/2 \times \frac{1}{12} = 0.72$ sq ft/ft. Similarly the inside area would be 0.393 sq ft/ft, and the outside area would be 1.05 sq ft/ft.

The coefficient of heat transfer based on the inside area would be $7580/(200 \times 0.393) = 96.5$ Btu/(hr)(sq ft); on the outside area, 36.1 Btu/(sq ft)(hr); and on the average area, 52.7 Btu/(sq ft)(hr).

REFERENCES

Faires, V. M.: "Applied Thermodynamics," The Macmillan Company, New York, 1949.

Obert, E. F.: "Thermodynamics," McGraw-Hill Book Company, Inc., New York, 1948.

Mooney, D. A.: "Mechanical Engineering Thermodynamics," Prentice-Hall, Inc., Englewood Cliffs, N.J., 1953.

Mackey, C. O., W. N. Barnard, and F. O. Ellenwood: "Engineering Thermodynamics," John Wiley & Sons, Inc., New York, 1957.

Keenan, J. H.: "Thermodynamics," John Wiley & Sons, Inc., New York, 1941.

Zemansky, M. W.: "Heat and Thermodynamics," 4th ed., McGraw-Hill Book Company, Inc., New York, 1943.

Soo, S. L.: "Thermodynamics of Engineering Science," Prentice-Hall, Inc., Englewood Cliffs, N.J., 1958.

SAMPLE PROBLEMS SELECTED FROM PAST EXAMINATIONS

4-1. An engine operates on the Rankine cycle with complete expansion (Fig. 4-P-1). Steam, the working medium, is admitted to the engine at a pressure of 200 psia and a temperature of 600°F; it is exhausted at a pressure of 4-in. Hg.

a. Determine the ideal thermal efficiency of this cycle.

b. Determine the temperature of the exhaust steam leaving the engine.

c. Determine the theoretical horsepower which could be developed if the cycle consumes 1 lb of steam per second.

FIG. 4-P-1

d. Specify the volume in cubic feet per hour of the exhaust steam leaving the engine.

e. Sketch the *T-S* diagram.

4-2. Five pounds of a gas mixture is 30 per cent CO_2 and 70 per cent O_2 by weight. It is compressed from (1) a pressure of 15 psia to (2) a pressure of 150 psia by a process characterized by the equation $P_1 V_1^n = P_2 V_2^n$, where the value of n is 1.0. The temperature of the mixture is 60°F at the beginning of the process. Determine:

a. Volume V_1 of the mixture at the beginning of compression

b. Temperature t_2 of the mixture at the end of compression in °F

c. Work W in foot-pounds required to compress the 5 lb of mixture

d. Change in internal energy ΔE

The equation for work $W = \int_1^2 P \, dV$, and internal energy $E = c_v T$.

4-3. Saturated steam is used in a mixing tank to heat and mix 200 gal of solution. The solution is to be heated from 62 to 150°F by introducing steam directly into the solution. The specific heat of the solution is about 0.85 Btu/(lb)(°F) at 62°F and remains essentially constant over the temperature range stated. The specific weight of the solution is 8.40 lb/gal.

How many pounds of saturated steam at a

FIG. 4-P-3

gauge pressure of 20 psi will be required for heating if all the steam is condensed in the solution and the heat loss to the surroundings is assumed to be negligible?   (See Fig. 4-P-3.)

Absolute pressure, psi	Temper-ature, °F	Specific volume, cu ft/lb		Enthalpy or heat content, Btu/lb		Entropy, Btu/(°F)(lb)	
		Saturated liquid	Saturated vapor	Saturated liquid	Saturated vapor	Saturated liquid	Saturated vapor
5.3	165	0.0164	69.0	132	1131	0.238	1.839
14.7	212	0.0167	26.8	180	1150	0.312	1.756
20.0	228	0.0168	21.0	196	1156	0.335	1.732
34.7	259	0.0171	11.9	227	1167	0.381	1.687

4-4. The specific heat of a gas at constant pressure is 0.2025 [Btu/(lb)(°F)] and at constant volume is 0.1575 [Btu/(lb)(°F)].   What is the final volume of 10.0 cu ft of gas at an initial pressure of 25 in. Hg and a final pressure of 5 atm?   Assume the process to be adiabatic.   (Mercury weighs 0.49 lb/cu in.)

4-5. A system consisting of 1 lb of water initially at 70°F is heated at a constant pressure of 30 psia while confined inside a cylinder equipped with a piston.   If the addition of 1200 Btu of heat raises the temperature to 400°F, what is the change in the internal energy of the system?

4-6. A masonry wall has a 4-in.-thick brick facing wall bonded to an 8-in.-thick concrete backing.   On a day when the room temperature is 68°F and the outside temperature is 12°F, the inner-surface temperature of the concrete is 57°F and the outer-surface temperature of the brick is 19°F.   The thermal conductivity of the brick is 0.36 and of the concrete 0.68 Btu/(hr)(ft)(°F). Determine:

a. Over-all heat-transfer coefficient
b. Convection coefficients of the vertical concrete and brick walls

4-7. A small steam-generating plant burns oil as a fuel.   The oil has a specific gravity of 1.008 and costs $2.50 per barrel.   The heating value of the oil is 18,250 (Btu/lb).   The boiler operates at 75 per cent thermal efficiency when taking in feed water at 180°F and delivering dry saturated steam at 100 psig.   What is the fuel cost per 1,000 lb of steam on this basis? 1 bbl = 42 gal.

Absolute pressure, psi	Temperature, °F	Specific volume, cu ft/lb		Enthalpy or heat content, Btu/lb		Entropy, Btu/(lb)(°F)	
		Saturated liquid	Saturated vapor	Saturated liquid	Saturated vapor	Saturated liquid	Saturated vapor
14.7	212.0	0.0167	26.82	180.0	1150.2	0.312	1.756
85.3	316.5	0.01758	5.150	286.5	1183.6	0.459	1.615
100.0	327.8	0.01771	4.426	298.3	1186.6	0.474	1.602
114.7	337.8	0.01782	3.889	308.8	1189.0	0.487	1.591

4-8. The internal energy of a gas is given by $u = 0.08T + 0.002T^2$. If 1 lb of this gas expands without heat flow but with a temperature drop from 300 to 100°F, how much work is done?

4-9. The volumetric analysis for a gas mixture shows that it consists of 70 per cent nitrogen, 20 per cent carbon dioxide, and 10 per cent carbon monoxide. If the pressure and temperature for the mixture are 20 psia and 100°F, respectively, compute:

a. Partial pressures
b. Weight analysis

4-10. The relation between mass and energy as derived by Einstein is $E = MC^2$, where E = energy, M = mass, and C = speed of light. If 1 lb of uranium is caused to fission and there is a loss of one-tenth of 1 per cent of the mass in the process, how many kilowatthours of energy are liberated?

4-11. A steam turbine receives 3,600 lb of steam per hour at 110-fps velocity and 1525 Btu/lb. The steam leaves at 810 fps and 1300 Btu/lb. What is the horsepower output?

4-12. Atmosphere air has a dry-bulb temperature of 85°F and a wet-bulb temperature of 64°F. The barometric pressure is 14.0 psia. Determine:

a. Specific humidity in grains per pound of dry air
b. Relative humidity
c. Dew-point temperature

4-13. Air in the cylinder of a diesel engine is at 86°F and 20 psi in compression. If it is further compressed adiabatically to one-eighteenth of its original volume, find:

a. Final temperature and pressure

b. Work done in compression if the displacement volume of the cylinder is ½ cu ft

Assume $\gamma = 1.4$ for air.

4-14. A tank contains 10 cu ft of oxygen at 500 psia and 85°F. Part of the oxygen was used, and later the pressure was observed to be 300 psia and the temperature 73°F.

a. How many pounds of oxygen were used?

b. What volume would the used oxygen occupy at standard atmospheric pressure and 70°F?

4-15. An indicator card of a four-cycle automobile engine taken with a 420-lb spring is 3 in. long and has an area of 1.25 sq in. If the engine has 8 cylinders, 3.6-in. diameter by 3-in. stroke, and travels at 2,800 rpm, what is the developed horsepower?

4-16. A wall of 0.8-ft thickness is to be constructed from material which has an average thermal conductivity of 0.75 Btu/(hr)(ft)(°F). The wall is to be insulated with material having an average thermal conductivity of 0.2 Btu/(hr)(ft)(°F) so that the heat loss per square foot will not exceed 580 Btu/hr. Calculate the thickness of insulation required, if the surface temperatures of the walls are 2400 and 80°F, respectively.

4-17. There was 3 in. of ice on a pond when the atmospheric temperature was 2°F. Calculate the rate in inches per hour at which the ice was increasing in thickness.

Heat of fusion of ice = 144 Btu/lb
Thermal conductivity of ice = 12 Btu [in./(hr)(sq ft)(°F)].

4-18. A copper bar 15 cm long and of 6.0 sq cm cross section is placed with one end in a steam bath and the other in a mixture of ice and water at atmospheric pressure. The sides of the bar are thermally insulated. How much ice melts in 2 min? How much steam condenses in this time? The thermal conductivity of copper is 0.90 cal/(cm)(sec)(°C).

4-19. A steam turbine receives 3,600 lb of steam per hour at 1,100 fps velocity and 1525 Btu/lb enthalpy. The steam leaves at 810 fps and 1300 Btu/lb. Determine horsepower output.

4-20. One pound of nitrogen with initial volume of 6 cu ft and pressure of 300 psia expands according to the law $PV^n = $ constant, to a final volume of 30 cu ft and a pressure of 40 psia. Determine:

a. Value of n

b. Work done by gas in foot-pounds

c Heat received or rejected in Btu's

4-21. Three moles of nitrogen, $\gamma = 1.4$ $C_v = 4.6$ (g-cal/mole), are at atmospheric pressure and 20°C. The gas is then heated at constant volume to 40°C.

It then undergoes adiabatic expansion and returns to 20°C. Finally it is compressed isothermally to its original state.

   a. Draw the *P-V* diagram for this cycle, indicating the successive states $P_1V_1T_1$, $P_2V_2T_2$, $P_3V_3T_3$.

   b. Find P, V, and T of each state in terms of $P_1V_1T_1$.

   c. Find the joules of work done in adiabatic expansion.

   d. What is the value of the initial volume V_1?

   4-22. An automobile cooling system of 26 qt of water and antifreeze has a freezing point of −12°F. How much of the above mixture must be drained out in order to add sufficient antifreeze to protect the engine at −15°F? The table printed on the antifreeze can indicates that 2½ qt will protect a 13-qt cooling system to −12°F, and 4½ qt to −15°F.

   4-23. A steam turbine operating with steady-flow conditions produces 1,350 hp. All losses except exhaust amount to 144,000 Btu/hr. The steam flow is 150 lb/min. Inlet condition is 450 psia and 740°F, and exhaust occurs at a pressure of 0.8 psia. Determine the condition of the exhaust steam (quality if wet, or temperature if superheated).

   4-24. A gas has a constant-pressure specific heat of $C_p = 6.6 − 7.2 \times 10^{-4}T$ [Btu/(mole)(°R)]. Determine the entropy of this gas at 2000°R and 5 atm pressure if the base of zero entropy is taken as 520°R and 1 atm.

   4-25. A balloon weighs 425 lb and has a volume of 35,000 cu ft when filled with hydrogen gas weighing 0.0056 lb/cu ft. What load in pounds will the balloon support in air weighing 0.081 lb/cu ft?

   4-26. A gas company buys gas at 90 psig and 75°F and sells it at 3.80 in. of water pressure and 28°F. Disregard the losses in distribution and determine how many cubic feet are sold for each cubic foot purchased.

   4-27. An indicator card of a four-cycle automobile engine taken with a 425-lb spring is 2.80 in. long and has an area of 1.20 sq in. If the engine has six cylinders, 3.5 in. in diameter, and the stroke is 3 in. traveling at 3,000 rpm, determine the developed horsepower of this engine.

   4-28. The Btu's required to heat 1 lb of a certain substance is given by the equation $Q = 0.32t − 0.00008t^2$, where Q is expressed in Btu/lb and t is in Fahrenheit. What is the instantaneous specific heat of the substance at 150°F?

   4-29. *a.* How much heat is supplied and rejected in Btu/hr if a 100-hp heat engine operates on the ideal Carnot cycle between the temperatures of 540 and 140°F?

   b. What is the thermal efficiency?

   4-30. An air-speed indicator of a plane is operated on the same principle as the pitot tube. It is calibrated to read knots. If the indicator reads 200 knots at an altitude where the density of air is one-half the density at which it was calibrated, what is the true speed of the plane?

   4-31. A barometer tube 88 cm long contains some air above the mercury. It gives a reading of 68 cm when upright. When the tube is tilted to an angle of 45°, the length of the mercury column becomes 80 cm. What is the reading of an accurate barometer?

4-32. One mole of a monatomic ideal gas at 300° abs is subjected to three consecutive changes: (1) the gas is heated at constant volume until its temperature is 900° abs; (2) the gas is then allowed to expand isothermally until its pressure drops to its initial value; (3) the gas is then cooled at constant pressure until it returns to its original state.

a. Sketch a curve in the P-V diagram showing the above changes.

b. Calculate the total work done by the gas in the above changes, the total amount of heat transferred to or from the gas, and the total change in internal energy of the gas. (Express your answer in calories.)

$$C_v = 3 \text{ cal/(mole)(°K)} \qquad R = 2 \text{ cal/(mole)(°K)}$$

4-33. Find the physical state of a definite quantity of water in a vessel of known size.

a. 10 lb of water is injected into an evacuated vessel which is maintained at 350°F. The volume of the vessel is 10 cu ft. What will be the resulting pressure in the vessel? What percentage of the water will be evaporated?

b. Same as (*a*) except that only 1 lb of water is injected.

4-34. Steam expands behind a piston doing 50,000 ft-lb of work. If 12 Btu of heat is radiated to the surrounding atmosphere during the expansion, what is the change of internal energy?

4-35. Two pounds of dry and saturated steam is confined in a tank. A gauge on the tank indicates a pressure of 145 psi. Barometric pressure is 29 in. Hg. What is the temperature of the steam in the tank? Calculate its volume, enthalpy, entropy, and internal energy.

4-36. Fourteen hundred cubic feet of air at 85°F dry-bulb temperature and 50 per cent relative humidity is mixed with 200 cfm of air at 54°F dry-bulb temperature and 40 per cent relative humidity. On the basis of psychrometric chart values, find the resulting dry-bulb temperature, wet-bulb temperature, and relative humidity.

4-37. A boiler generates 3,000 lb of steam per hour at a pressure of 150 psig, steam temperature 465°F, feed-water temperature 180°F; what is the total equivalent evaporation from and at 212°F/hr?

4-38. Tests of a six-cylinder 4-in. bore and $3\frac{1}{8}$-in. stroke aircraft engine at full throttle show a brake horsepower of 79.5 at 3,400 rpm. The compression ratio is 8:1, the specific fuel consumption is 0.56 lb/bhp-hr. The higher heating value of the fuel is 19,800 Btu/lb. Determine (1) brake mean effective pressure; (2) brake torque; (3) brake thermal efficiency; (4) brake engine efficiency based on cold air standard if the ideal efficiency e is $e = 1 - (1/r_k{}^{k-1})$, where r_k = compression ratio.

4-39. Find the rated brake mean effective pressure of a 225-hp nine-cylinder diesel aircraft engine. It is a four-stroke cycle engine, rated at 1,950 rpm. Cylinder bore is $4\frac{13}{16}$ in.; stroke is 6 in.

4-40. Air is compressed in a diesel engine from an initial pressure of 13 psia and a temperature of 120°F to one-twelfth its initial volume. Calculate the final temperature and pressure, assuming the compression to be adiabatic.

4-41. A centrifugal compressor is to operate at 3,600 rpm and handle 20,000 cfm of free air. Compression is according to the law $PV^{1.35} = $ constant. Intake is atmospheric (14.4 psia at 70°F) and compression is to 25 psig.

 a. What is the final delivery in cubic feet per minute?

 b. Would final temperature be lower or higher if compression were (1) isothermal? (2) adiabatic?

4-42. A 100-hp engine is being tested by loading it with a water-cooled Prony brake. When the engine delivers the full-rated 100 hp to the shaft and the Prony brake being cooled with tap water absorbs and transfers to the cooling water 95 per cent of the 100 hp, determine:

 a. How many Btu's of heat are transferred to the cooling water per second?

 b. If the tap water is entering the Prony-brake shell at 65°F and leaves at 131°F, at what rate is tap water passing through the Prony-brake shell in cubic feet per second?

4-43. An open-cycle gas turbine receives air at 15 psia and 60°F. The compressor discharges at 75 psia. The temperature entering the turbine is 1250°F. Calculate:

 a. Heat added in the combuster, Btu/lb

 b. Efficiency of the cycle, per cent

4-44. The internal energy of a gas is given by

$$u = 0.08t + 0.002t^2 \qquad (t = °F)$$

If 1 lb of this gas expands without heat flow but with a temperature drop from 300 to 100°F, how much work is done?

4-45. A mixture of gases at 100°F consists by weight of 80 per cent nitrogen, 12 per cent carbon dioxide, 7 per cent oxygen, and 1 per cent water vapor. Total pressure is 14,696 psia.

 a. What is the dew point?

 b. How much heat would be removed in reducing the temperature of 1 lb of mixture to the dew point at constant total pressure?

4-46. Five cubic feet of a gas with $C_p = 0.55$, $R = 96.2$, expands polytropically from 140 psia and 120°F to a pressure of 50 psia and a volume of 10 cu ft. Find:

 a. t_2

 b. Change in internal energy

 c. Work done

 d. Change in entropy

 e. Heat added or given off

State in each answer, where it applies, the direction in which the change took place.

4-47. An Otto cycle engine has a compression ratio of 6:1. On test it uses 1 gal of gasoline in 15 min while developing 150 lb-ft torque at 1,500 rpm. The gasoline has a specific gravity of 0.70 and a higher heating value of 19,100 Btu/lb.

a. What is the thermal efficiency of the engine?

b. What is the ratio of the thermal efficiency to the air-standard ideal thermal efficiency?

c. What is the specific fuel consumption in pounds per horsepower-hour?

4-48. A gas made up of 5 lb methane and 10 lb ethane is placed in a tank at 60°F. If the volume of the tank is 19 cu ft,

a. What is the resulting pressure in the tank?

b. What is the mole per cent of the resulting mixture?

4-49. A throttling steam calorimeter has a pressure of 150 psia on the high-pressure side of its orifice and atmospheric pressure on the discharge side. The thermometer on the discharge side reads 280°F. Calculate the quality of the steam in the line.

4-50. Air is compressed in a diesel engine from an initial pressure of 13 psia and a temperature of 120°F to one-twelfth its initial volume. Calculate the final temperature and pressure, assuming the compression to be adiabatic.

4-51. Determine the heat-transfer coefficient of a wall consisting of 13 in. of brick and 1 in. of plaster. The specific conductivity for brick work and for plaster is 5.00. The surface resistances of brick and plaster are 4.02 and 1.40, respectively.

4-52. How many pounds of water can be evaporated from and at 212°F by the heat involved in the complete combustion of 1 lb of coal containing carbon, 65.2 per cent; hydrogen, 4.92 per cent; and oxygen, 8.6 per cent?

4-53. The atmospheric air has 87°F dry-bulb temperature and 65°F wet-bulb temperature. Calculate:

a. Specific humidity in grains per pound of dry air

b. Dew-point temperature

c. Relative humidity

barometric pressure is 14.7 psia.

4-54. Given a 500-kw generating set; efficiency of the engine and generator, 85 per cent. Steam pressure, 150 psia; feed-water temperature, 180°F. The engine uses 20 lb of steam per indicated horsepower per hour. Evaporation from and at 212°F is 10 lb of water per pound of dry coal. Coal contains 13,000 Btu/lb. What is the heat efficiency of the plant?

4-55. A steel tube 1.315 in. OD and 1.049 in. ID transmits 38,000 Btu/(hr)(sq ft) of outside-wall area to the surroundings. Calculate the outside-wall temperature if the inner wall is at 212°F. (k = 19.1 Btu/(hr)(°F)(ft) for tube metal.)

4-56. A jet-propelled plane has a fuel flow of 0.9 lb/sec with a heating value of 20,000 Btu/lb. Air inlet flow is 40 lb/sec. The plane is flying at a speed of 460 mph, and an absolute jet velocity of 2,100 fps occurs. Compute:

a. Propulsive force

b. Useful horsepower

c. Over-all thermal efficiency

4-57. Water at 200 psia and 300°F is introduced into an insulated chamber maintained at 50 psia. What percentage of the water so injected flashes into steam?

4-58. A tank contains air at 800 psia and 80°F. An amount of air measuring 700 cu ft at 14.7 psia and 60°F is removed. The pressure in the tank is now found to be 300 psia when the temperature is 80°F. What is the volume of the tank?

4-59. Steam is supplied to a nozzle at 100 psia and 400°F. The nozzle exhaust pressure is 20 psia.

a. What is the ideal exit velocity?

b. What would the ideal exit velocity have been if air were used under the same conditions?

4-60. A furnace fired with a hydrocarbon fuel oil has a dry-stack analysis of CO_2, 12 per cent; O_2, 7 per cent; N_2, 81 per cent. Calculate:

a. Composition of original fuel oil expressed as weight per cent

b. Percentage of excess air

c. Cubic feet of air at standard conditions per pound of fuel

4-61. A hollow steel cylinder having an internal volume of 4 cu ft contains air at the atmospheric pressure of 15 psi. How many cubic feet of the outside air must be pumped into the cylinder to raise the pressure to 45 psi? Assume that the temperature remains constant.

4-62. In an air cycle, process 1 to 2 is constant volume, 2 to 3 is adiabatic isentropic, and 3 to 1 is constant pressure. V_1 is 1 cu ft, V_3 is 2 cu ft, p_1 and p_3 are each 1 atm, and t_1 is 60°F (Fig. 4-P-62). Find each of the following:

a. Heat supplied, Btu

b. Heat rejected, Btu

c. Efficiency of cycle, per cent

d. Corresponding Carnot efficiency, per cent

Fig. 4-P-62

Fig. 4-P-63

4-63. At 1, Fig. 4-P-63, water is supplied at the rate of 500 lb/min at 3 psig and 60°F. At 2, steam is supplied at 3 psig and 95 per cent dry. At 3, mixture leaves at 212°F as saturated liquid. Assuming no heat loss from the chamber, answer each of the following:

a. How many pounds of steam per minute are required at 2?

b. Find the entropy change across the system.

4-64. An ammonia refrigerator plant is to operate between a saturated liquid at 120 psia at the condenser outlet and a saturated vapor at 15 psia at the evaporator outlet. If 30 tons' capacity is desired, compute on the basis of an ideal cycle only:

a. Coefficient of performance

b. Work of compression, Btu/lb

c. Refrigerating effect, Btu/lb

d. Pounds per minute of ammonia required for circulation

e. Ideal horsepower per ton of refrigeration

f. Pounds of condenser cooling water per minute, assuming a 150°F temperature rise

4-65. An ideally insulated tank of helium, pressure 3,000 psig, temperature 60°F, is connected to an empty weather balloon through a valve. The system is mounted on a weighing platform. The whole has a tare of 200 lb, including valve and weather balloon. The weather balloon is inflated to 4 ft in diameter, pressure 16 psia, average temperature 60°F in air at 14.7 psia, 60°F. If the tank pressure at the end of inflation is 200 psig, find the volume of the tank.

CHAPTER 5

Mechanics of Materials

The subject of mechanics of materials is an expansion of the more general subject of mechanics; it includes study of the effects of the elastic properties of structural materials. All materials deform when subjected to a stress. Fortunately, most of the important engineering materials exhibit unit deformations, or strains, which are very nearly proportional to the applied stresses within the working limits of the materials. This fact, expressed in the statement of Hooke's law that stress and strain are proportional, is the basis of the study of mechanics of materials.

The various phases of this subject which have been treated in past fundamentals examinations have included general considerations of stress and strain, effects of temperature on stress and strain, stresses resulting from torque loading, loaded beams, composite beams (principally reinforced concrete), shear and moment diagrams, riveted and welded joints, columns, and some consideration of compound stresses.

5-1. Modulus of Elasticity. The ratio of stress (in pounds per square inch) to strain (in inches per inch), called "Young's modulus" or the "modulus of elasticity," is constant for a given material up to the proportional limit. The modulus of elasticity, the proportional limit, the yield point, etc., are all determined experimentally for a given material. Curves illustrating these properties for some of the common engineering materials are shown in Fig. 5-1.

5-2. Creep Strength. Another phase of the general subject which should be mentioned here is the phenomenon known as "creep strength." When a metal deforms slowly under the long-time application of a stress which is well below its yield strength, the deformation is known as "creep." Creep is particularly important in high-temperature applications, as in turbine blades where the temperatures are high and the stresses are also high. A typical curve showing deformation of a material vs. time under load is given in Fig. 5-2.

5-3. Fatigue and Endurance Limit. It is also apropos to mention the subject of fatigue failure or endurance limit.   Fatigue is the term used to describe the failure or rupture of a metal part under repeated application of a load which is well below the permissible load as calculated from ordinary static stress considerations.   This is of particular importance in the design of parts which are to be subjected to cyclic loading.   Figure 5-3 shows some curves of stress vs. number of cycles to cause failure for a few engineering materials.   For most steels the endurance limit, or fatigue stress, is that stress which will withstand 10 million cycles without breaking.   For nonferrous metals it may be necessary to flex the metal through many more than 10 million cycles to determine the limiting stress at which rupture will occur, and some metals may fail to show any endurance limit at all, the value of stress at rupture constantly

FIG. 5-1. (a) Stress-strain diagram for mild steel; (b) typical stress-strain curves.

declining as the number of stress cycles is increased.   As a rough rule of thumb, the endurance limit for steels is generally considered to be about half the ultimate strength, though this will vary for different steels and may actually give stress values too high for the steel being considered.   For nonferrous metals, many of which have no endurance limit, the endurance strength may be as low as 20 per cent and is rarely more than 40 per cent of the tensile strength.

5-4. Stress Concentration. Notch sensitivity, or the stress concentration factor, is also extremely important in the design of members subject to cyclic loading. Any discontinuity or change of section, e.g., a hole, groove, notch, or bend, is a stress raiser. The localized stresses in some cases may reach three or more times the

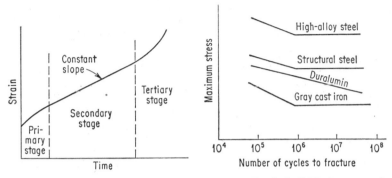

FIG. 5-2. Idealized creep curve.   FIG. 5-3. Typical S-N (stress-cycles) diagrams.

value of the calculated average stress in the member. Rough machining also produces localized stress concentrations, and the endurance limit of a hardened steel part with a rough file finish may be only 60 per cent of the endurance limit of a similar part of the same material with a polished finish.

The reader should be aware of these general considerations and should have some appreciation of their effects in a qualitative sense. The actual magnitude of the effects and the numerical values to be used in design are, however, beyond the scope of this text and will not be discussed here.

5-5. Stress and Strain. The general relationship of $E = S/\delta$ is all that is necessary to solve many of the simpler problems in mechanics of materials. To illustrate the use of this equation we can examine a few examples from past examinations. One such problem asked:

- A steel rod 10 ft long has a cross-sectional area of 0.40 sq in. and is carrying a load of 6,000 lb. Assume the modulus of elasticity for this steel to be 30,000,000 psi and determine:

a. Total elongation produced in the rod by this load

b. Load required to cause the steel rod to just reach its elastic limit of 82,000 psi.

For a 6,000-lb load the stress would be

$$\frac{6,000 \text{ lb}}{0.40 \text{ sq in.}} = 15,000 \text{ psi}$$

$$\delta = \frac{S}{E} = \frac{15,000}{30,000,000} = 5 \times 10^{-4} \text{ in./in.}$$

a. The total elongation would then equal

$$(10 \times 12) \text{ in.} \times (5 \times 10^{-4}) \text{ in./in.} = 0.060 \text{ in.}$$

b. The load to cause a stress of 82,000 psi would be

$$82,000 \text{ psi} \times 0.40 \text{ sq in.} = 32,800 \text{ lb}$$

Another, somewhat typical example is illustrated by the problem:

- A steel tape for measuring distance is 0.30 in. wide and 0.015 in. thick. It is exactly 100 ft long when supported throughout its length and pulled with a force of 15 lb. What will be its length if the chainmen pull with a force of 50 lb? E for steel $= 30 \times 10^6$ psi.

The cross-sectional area of the tape is $0.30 \times 0.015 = 0.0045$ sq in. If the chainmen pull with a force of 50 lb, this is $50 - 15$, or 35 lb more than the force required to stretch the tape to a length of 100 ft. Since the total applied load is still well within the proportional limit, the additional stretch is proportional to the additional load. The added load of 35 lb produces 35 lb/0.0045 sq in. $= 7,780$ psi additional stress.

$$\delta = \frac{S}{E} = \frac{7,780 \text{ psi}}{30 \times 10^6 \text{ psi}} = 2.59 \times 10^{-4} \text{ in./in.}$$

so the total length of the chain when subjected to a 50-lb pull will be $100 \text{ ft} + (100 \times 12) \text{ in.} \times (2.59 \times 10^{-4}) \text{ in./in.} = 100 \text{ ft} + 0.311 \text{ in.}$, or 100.0259 ft.

Another problem from a past example is:

- Two parallel wires 6 in. apart, one of copper and one of steel, are used to support a load P. The area of the copper wire is twice the area of the steel wire. Determine the distance x from the steel wire for applying the load so that the wires will remain equal in length (Fig. 5-4).

$$E_s = 30 \times 10^6 \text{ psi}$$
$$E_{cu} = 10 \times 10^6 \text{ psi}$$

Since $\delta = S/E$ and δ_s is to equal δ_{cu}, $S_s/E_s = S_{cu}/E_{cu}$, which means that the stress in the steel wire must be three times the stress in the

FIG. 5-4   FIG. 5-5

copper wire for the lengths of the two to remain equal. Since load equals stress times area of cross section, the load on the steel wire will equal $S_{cu} \times A_{cu}$. Applying the ratios given, $S_s = 3S_{cu}$ and $A_s = \frac{1}{2}A_{cu}$, we have that the steel wire must support $\frac{3}{2}$ as much load as the copper wire for the lengths of the two to remain the same. From $\Sigma F_y = 0$, we find that the copper wire will have to support $\frac{2}{5}$ of P and the steel wire $\frac{3}{5}$ of P. Taking moments about S gives $6 \times \frac{2}{5}P = Px$, or $x = 2.4$ in.

A slightly different type of example is illustrated in another past examination question:

- The lower chord in a panel of a bridge truss consists of three eyebars, each 8 by 1 in. in cross section. The two outside bars are each 20 ft 0 in. long, center to center of pinholes, and the middle bar is 20 ft $\frac{1}{8}$ in. long. The total tension in the three bars is 360,000 lb. Disregarding the bending of the pins, and assuming that they are parallel to each other and that they fit loosely in the pinholes before load is applied, calculate the unit stress in the bars. $E = 30 \times 10^6$ psi.

First, let us draw a figure (Fig. 5-5). Since the two outside bars are identical, the elongation in both will be the same. The inner bar is $\frac{1}{8}$ in. longer, so the total elongation of it will be $\frac{1}{8}$ in. less. The stress in the two outer bars will be $E\delta_1$, and the stress in the inner bar will be $E\delta_2$. The total load will equal the sum of the products of the stresses times the areas stressed, or

$$360,000 = (8 \times 1) \times E\delta_1 + (8 \times 1) \times E\delta_1 + (8 \times 1) \times E\delta_2$$

which gives $360,000/8E = 2\delta_1 + \delta_2$, where δ_1 and δ_2 are in in./in. or ft/ft. Because of the different lengths of the bars and since the total elongation equals length times δ_1, we have

$$20 + 20\delta_1 = 20.0104 + 20.0104\delta_2 \quad (20.0104 \text{ ft} = 20 \text{ ft } \frac{1}{8} \text{ in.})$$

which gives $\delta_1 = \delta_2 + 0.00052$. We then have

$$\frac{360,000}{8 \times 30 \times 10^6} = 0.0015 = 2\delta_1 + \delta_2$$

and $\delta_1 = 0.000673$ ft/ft or in./in.; $\delta_2 = 0.000153$ ft/ft or in./in. The stress in the two outer bars is

$$S = E\delta_1 = 0.000673 \times 30 \times 10^6 = 20,200 \text{ psi}$$

and the stress in the inner bar is $0.000153 \times 30 \times 10^6 = 4,600$ psi.
To check: load held by outer bars,

$$20,200 \text{ psi} \times 16 \text{ sq in.} = 323,000 \text{ lb}$$

load held by inner bar, 4,600 psi $\times$ 8 sq in. $= 37,000$ lb, and the sum equals the total applied load of 360,000 lb.

Another typical example is the following:

- A standard test specimen 0.506 in. in diameter by 2 in. gauge length shows an increase in length of 0.00067 in. when tension is increased from 500 to 2,500 lb. Calculate the modulus of elasticity.

The change in stress equals

$$\frac{2,500 - 500}{(0.506)^2 \times \pi/4} = 10,000 \text{ psi}$$

$$\frac{0.00667}{2} = 0.003335 \text{ in./in. change in strain}$$

$$E = S/\delta = \frac{10,000}{0.00333} = 30 \times 10^6 \text{ psi}$$

5-6. Thermal Stress. When the effects of temperature (thermal expansion) are included, the picture is changed a little. In most cases it will simplify the calculations if strain due to stress and the strain due to temperature are calculated separately and are then added algebraically to obtain the net or final result. This can best be illustrated by means of examples. One past examination problem was:

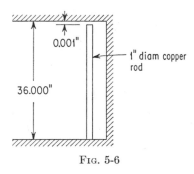

FIG. 5-6

- A 3-ft-long copper bar having a circular cross section 1 in. in diameter is arranged as shown in Fig. 5-6 with a 0.001-in. gap between its end and the rigid wall at room temperature. If the temperature increases 60°F, find the stress in the rod. (Assume the coefficient of thermal expansion for copper is 9.3×10^{-6} in./(in.)(°F) and its modulus of elasticity is 17×10^6 psi.) List the assumptions you had to make in order to arrive at your answer.

The unrestrained increase in length due to the increase in temperature would have been

$$[9.3 \times 10^{-6} \text{ in./(in.)(°F)}] \times 60°F \times 36 \text{ in.} = 0.0201 \text{ in.}$$

The bar can expand 0.001 in. and then will be restrained. This is the same (stresswise) as if it had been allowed to increase 0.0201 in. and was then compressed 0.0191 in. The resulting stress would be $S = E \times \delta$.

$$S = 17 \times 10^6 \text{ psi} \times 0.0191 \text{ in./36 in.} = 9,020 \text{ psi}$$

The assumptions that would have to be made are:

1. The walls must be perfectly rigid, i.e., undergo neither expansion nor deformation.

2. The bar (column) must remain straight.

3. The yield point of the copper was not exceeded.

Problems concerned with the effects of shrink fits are not uncom-

mon; two examples of this type will be reviewed.   The first example
is:

- A locomotive wheel is 48 in. in diameter.   A steel tire, with
  diameter 0.02 in. less than the wheel, is to be shrunk on.   The
  tire is at 20°C.   To what temperature must it be heated to
  make its diameter 0.02 in. oversize? α for steel $= 12 \times 10^{-6}$
  per °C.

Thermal expansion, or contraction, is linear and takes place in all
directions.   The diameter of the tire would then expand linearly
with a temperature increase.   Since it is 0.02 in. smaller than the
wheel and a clearance of 0.02 in. is desired to facilitate assembly, the
total diametral expansion would have to be $0.02 + 0.02 = 0.04$ in.
This would be a unit expansion of $0.04/48 = 8.33 \times 10^{-4}$ in./in.

$$\frac{8.33 \times 10^{-4} \text{ in./in.}}{12 \times 10^{-6} \text{ in./(in.)(°C)}} = 69.5°C \qquad \text{increase in temperature}$$

The tire must then be heated to a temperature of

$$20 + 69.5 = 89.5°C$$

The second example of this type is somewhat different and is as
follows:

- A steel liner is assembled in an aluminum pump housing by
  heating the housing and cooling the liner in dry ice.   At 70°F
  before assembly the liner outside diameter is 3.508 in. and
  the housing inside diameter is 3.500 in.   After assembly
  and inspection, several units were rejected because of poor
  liners.   It is desired to salvage the housing by heating the
  complete unit to a temperature which would cause a difference
  (clearance) in diameter of 0.002 in. between liner and housing
  and permit free removal of the liner.   Determine the temperature at which this may be possible.
  Thermal coefficient of linear expansion: steel, 0.0000065 in./
  (in.)(°F); aluminum, 0.000016 in./(in.)(°F).

At 70°F the interference is 0.008 in.   A clearance of 0.002 in.
is desired, so the expansion of the aluminum housing must be
0.010 in. more than the expansion of the steel liner, or the unit

expansion of the aluminum must be $0.010/3.5 = 0.00286$ in./in. greater than that of the steel. The differential expansion is $0.000016 - 0.0000065 = 9.5 \times 10^{-6}$ in./(in.)(°F). The required temperature increase would then be

$$\frac{0.00286 \text{ in./in.}}{9.5 \times 10^{-6} \text{ in./(in.)(°F)}} = 301°\text{F}$$

so the assembly would have to be heated to a temperature of 371°F.

A slightly different type of example is a problem which asked:

- A column is to be inserted next to an existing column to take up some of the load. The new column is to be 10 ft long and is to be stressed to 10,000 psi. The column will be shortened sufficiently to be inserted in place by cooling with dry ice. Assuming normal temperature of 70°F, to what temperature should the column be cooled to provide a clearance of $\frac{1}{32}$ in. before insertion and yet to take up its load when it is brought up to room temperature? Modulus of elasticity is 30,000,000 psi, and the temperature coefficient is 0.0000067.

To be stressed to 10,000 psi the column would have to be shortened a total of (10×12) in. $\times$ $(10,000 \text{ psi}/30,000,000 \text{ psi}) = 0.040$ in. The total shrinkage of the column length would then be

$$0.040 + \frac{1}{32} = 0.0713 \text{ in.}$$

The unit shrinkage would be $0.0713/120 = 5.94 \times 10^{-4}$ in./in. The change in temperature required would then be

$$\frac{5.94 \times 10^{-4} \text{ in./in.}}{6.7 \times 10^{-6} \text{ in./in.°F}} = 89°\text{F}$$

The column should be cooled to a temperature of $70 - 89 = -19°$F.

5-7. Torsion. Pure torsional loading (couple only, no bending) produces a shearing stress in a shaft with the magnitude of the stress, in any cross section, being proportional to the distance from the center of the shaft (Fig. 5-7). This follows from the fact that the deformation at any point equals $\rho \, d\theta$, and since stress is proportional to strain the stress increases from zero at the center to a maximum

at the outside.   Let S_s be the maximum shearing stress at the outer
fiber.   Then S_s/r will be the stress 1 in. from the center and $(\rho/r) \times$
S_s will be the stress at a distance ρ from the center.   Force equals
stress times area, so the force resisting the applied torque due to the
area dA equals $(\rho/r)S_s\,dA$; the resisting moment about the axis
of the bar due to this force is equal to $(\rho^2/r)S_s\,dA$, and $(S_s/r)\int\rho^2\,dA$
is the total moment about the axis due to all the internal shearing
forces.   The quantity $\int\rho^2\,dA$ is, we recall from Chap. 2, Mechanics,

FIG. 5-7   FIG. 5-8

the moment of inertia of the cross-sectional area about the axis
through its center or the polar moment of inertia of the area, which
quantity is ordinarily represented by the symbol J.   This gives us
the relationship that torque $= (S_s/r) \times J$, and the maximum stress
in the shaft due to the applied torque is $S_s = rT/J$.   The stress
at any other distance ρ from the center of the shaft equals

$$\frac{\rho}{r} \times \frac{rT}{J} = \frac{\rho T}{J}$$

Within the proportional limit, $\delta_s = S_s/E_s$, which gives the relationship $S_s = E_s\delta_s = (E_s r\theta)/l$, since, from Fig. 5-8, $\delta_s = r\theta/l$.   This
also gives us $T = (E_s J\theta)/l$.
    An example of the usefulness of these relationships is afforded by
a problem taken from a past examination:
- A solid round shaft $3\frac{1}{2}$ in. in diameter transmits 100 hp at
  200 rpm.   Determine:
  a. Torsional stress in the outer fibers
  b. Increase of stress if the shaft is made hollow with $1\frac{1}{2}$ in. ID
  c. Stress in the inner fibers of the hollow shaft

The power transmitted by a shaft equals $2\pi NT/33,000$ (Fig. 5-9), which means $T = (33,000 \times 100)/(2\pi \times 200) = 2,630$ ft-lb, or 31,500 in.-lb. The polar moment of inertia of a circle is $(\pi r^4)/2$, so $S_s = (r$ in. $\times T$ in.-lb$)/(J$ in.$^4) = 2T/(\pi r^3)$.

$$S_s = \frac{2 \times 31,500}{\pi \times (1.75)^3} = 3,740 \text{ psi}$$

For a hollow shaft of the same outer diameter but with an inner diameter of $1\frac{1}{2}$ in.,

$$J = \frac{\pi(r_{\text{OD}})^4}{2} - \frac{\pi(r_{\text{ID}})^4}{2} = \frac{\pi}{2}(1.75^4 - 0.75^4) = 14.25$$

$$S_s = \frac{1.75 \times 31,500}{14.25} = 3,870 \text{ psi} \quad \text{stress in outer fiber}$$

Increase of stress $= 3,870 - 3,740 = 130$ psia. The stress in the inner fibers of the hollow shaft will equal

$$\frac{r_{\text{inner}}}{r_{\text{outer}}} \times S_{\text{outer}} = \frac{0.75}{1.75} \times 3,870 = 1,660 \text{ psi}$$

FIG. 5-9. Torque = T × r = T ft-lb; constant velocity so peripheral speed = $2\pi N$ fpm (N = rpm); power = distance ×force/ time = $2\pi NT$ ft-lb/min.

One other past examination problem will be used as an example. Referring to Fig. 5-10, the problem asks:

- a. Determine the torque M_B such that the maximum unit shear stress is the same in both parts. Disregard stress concentrations.
- b. Determine the angle of twist in BC.

The torque $M_c = 3,000\pi$ in.-lb. The stress in the outer fibers of the shaft BC may be found from the equation:

$$S_s = \frac{rT}{J} = \frac{3 \times 3,000\pi}{(\pi/2)(3^4 - 2^4)} = 277 \text{ psi}$$

To produce the same stress in the solid portion of the shaft would require a torque of

$$T = \frac{JS_s}{r} = \frac{(\pi/2)(2^4)277}{2} = 1,110\pi \text{ in.-lb}$$

so torque in the amount of $(3,000\pi - 1,110\pi)$ or $1,890\pi$ in.-lb must be taken off at B, giving $M_B = 1,890\pi$ in.-lb.

Hollow shaft
4" ID
6" OD

Solid shaft
4" diam

FIG. 5-10

The angle of twist in length BC may be determined from the relationship $T = (E_s J \theta)/l$, or

$$\theta = \frac{T \times l}{J E_s} = \frac{3,000\pi \times (10 \times 12)}{(\pi/2)(3^4 - 2^4) \times 12 \times 10^6} \frac{\text{in.-lb} \times \text{in.}}{\text{in.}^4 \times \text{lb/in.}^2}$$
$$= 0.000923 \text{ radians}$$

0.000923 radians $\times 57.3°/\text{radian} = 0.0529°$.

5-8. Beams. The next topic is that of homogeneous beams, which have received, along with their corresponding shear and moment diagrams, far greater emphasis in past examinations than any other single facet of the general subject of mechanics of materials.

The general relationship for determining the stress in a beam due to bending is $S = (Mc)/I$, where M = moment, in.-lb, I = moment of inertia of the cross section, and c = distance from the neutral axis to the outermost fiber. The stress at any other point than the outer fiber is proportional to its distance from the center and would be $S = (y/c)(Mc/I) = (My)/I$.

The values of c and I can be determined from the geometry of the beam. The moment M depends upon the loading of the beam. As can be seen, the maximum stress will occur at the location of the greatest moment (for a beam of constant cross section).

The shear stress at any point is equal to the magnitude of the shearing force divided by the cross-sectional area at that point. It is seldom possible to determine by a glance just where the maximum shear and the maximum moment will occur in a loaded beam, so it is usually desirable to construct both the shear diagram and the moment diagram for the beam under consideration; then the points of maximum shear and maximum moment will be readily apparent.

5-9. Shear Diagram. The shear at any section of a beam is the algebraic sum of all the external forces on *either* side of the section; it is considered positive if the segment of the beam on the left of the cross section tends to move up with respect to the segment on the right. The algebraic sum of all the forces on *both* sides of the section will, of course, equal zero, since the system is in static equilibrium. It is usually simplest to add all the shearing forces to the left of the section being considered; this sum is equal to the shearing force acting at that point. If this process is repeated for different points over the length of the beam, a complete shear diagram may be constructed.

5-10. Moment Diagram. The moment diagram may be constructed in a similar manner; one must remember that the bending moment at any section of a beam is the algebraic sum of the moments of all the external forces on either side of the section. When calculating the bending moment, use the segment (or side) for which the arithmetic will be the simplest. A positive moment is one which tends to cause the beam to be concave on the upper side (top fibers in compression). An easy method of arriving at the correct sign in calculating bending moment is to give plus signs to the moments of upward forces and minus signs to the moments of downward forces. This method will give the correct sign to the algebraic sum of the moments, whether the forces to the right of the section or to the left of the section are used.

Examples of shear and moment diagrams for a few of the commoner types of loading are shown in Fig. 5-11.

For combined loadings the shear and moment diagrams may be constructed by adding (algebraically) the individual shear and moment diagrams due to the individual loadings. This will give the total values for shear and moment for all parts of the beams.

Each load will produce the same effect as if it had acted alone; it is unaffected by the other loads. Another method is to calculate the moments at different points on the beam and draw a smooth

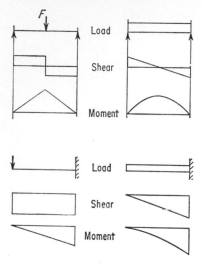

curve. Care must be taken, however, to make certain that the points of maximum total shear and maximum total moment are included. These points of maximum magnitude will be more easily determined by sketching the component shear and moment diagrams and determining the total shear and moment for all points of maximum magnitude (both positive and negative) on the component diagrams. This is illustrated in Fig. 5-12.

There are a few relationships which are of value in constructing and in checking shear and moment diagrams. One of these is that the derivative of the moment M with respect to distance is equal

Fig. 5-11. Shear and moment diagrams for some of the commoner types of loading.

to the shear V, or $V = (dM)/(dx)$. This means that the slope of the moment curve at any point is equal to the magnitude of the shear at that point. The relationship may also be written

$$\int_{M_1}^{M_2} dM = \int_{1}^{2} V\, dx \qquad \text{or} \qquad M_2 - M_1 = \int_{1}^{2} V\, dx$$

which means that the difference between the values of the moments at points 1 and 2 is equal to the area under the shear diagram between points 1 and 2. Similarly we have $W = (dV)/(dx)$ where

W is the load at any point and $V_2 - V_1 = \int_{1}^{2} W\, dx$. The use of

these relationships is illustrated in Fig. 5-12; the relationships themselves are illustrated in Fig. 5-13, along the relationships for determining the slope and deflection diagrams of the beam.

FIG. 5-12

A few examples are in order here; we shall start with the following past examination problem:

- What should be the width of a wooden joist 9 in. deep, if it has to carry a uniformly distributed load of 250 lb/ft over a span of 12 ft with a stress not exceeding 1,200 psi?

Load diagram: W = constant = w.

Shear diagram: $V = \int W\,dx = \int w\,dx = wx + C_1$; $V =$ 0 at $x = 0$, so $C_1 = 0$ and $V = wx$.

Moment diagram: $M = \int V\,dx = \int wx\,dx$; $M = [(wx^2)/2] + C_2$; $M = 0$ at $x = 0$, so $C_2 = 0$, $M = (wx^2)/2$.

Slope diagram: $\theta_x = \tan^{-1}\ (dy/dx) = dy/dx$, very nearly, for small angles. From $EI(d^2y/dx^2) = M$, $EI(dy/dx) = \int M\,dx$. $EI(dy/dx) = \int(wx^2/2)\,dx = (wx^3/6) + C_3$; $dy/dx = 0$ at $x = l$, so $C_3 = -wl^3/6$. $\theta = dy/dx = (l/EI)(wx^3/6 - wl^3/6)$.

Deflection diagram: $y = \int\theta\,dx$; $EI\,y = \int[(wx^3)/6 - (wl^3)/6]\,dx = [(wx^4)/24] - [(wl^3x)/6 + C_4]$; $y = 0$ at $x = 1$, so $C_4 = wl^4/8$; $y = [(wx_4)/24] - [(wl^3x)/6] - [(wl_4)/8]$.

FIG. 5-13

Since $S = (Mc)/I$, and the beam is rectangular, 9 in. deep, we have

$$I = \frac{bh^3}{12} = \frac{b \times 9^3}{12} = 60.8b$$

c will equal $9/2$, giving

$$S = 0.074M/b \quad \text{or} \quad b = 0.074M/S$$
$$\Sigma M_{R_1} = 0 = 12R_2 - (250 \times 12) \times 12\tfrac{2}{3}$$
$$R_2 = 1{,}500 \text{ lb}$$

Maximum moment = $1{,}500 \text{ lb} \times \dfrac{12}{2 \times 2} \text{ ft} \times 12 \text{ in./ft}$

$$= 54{,}000 \text{ in.-lb}$$

$$b = 0.074 \times \frac{54{,}000}{1{,}200} = 3.33 \text{ in. width required}$$

An example of a beam with an irregular cross section is afforded by this past examination problem:

- A wooden beam is made up of two timbers, one 4- by 6-in. and one 4- by 8-in., as shown in Fig. 5-14.
  a. Locate its horizontal neutral axis.
  b. Compute its moment of inertia about this axis.
  c. If this section is used as a uniformly loaded beam in a simple span 32 ft long, what maximum total load could it sustain, assuming a maximum bending stress of 1,200 psi?

FIG. 5-14

The location of the horizontal neutral axis can be obtained by taking moments about the lower edge.

$$\bar{y} = \frac{(4 \times 8) \times 2 + (6 \times 4)(4 + 3) + (4 \times 6)(4 + 6 + 2)}{(4 \times 8) + (6 \times 4) + (4 \times 6)}$$

$$\bar{y} = \frac{\text{moments of individual areas}}{\text{total area}}$$

$\bar{y} = 6.5$ in. from the bottom of the beam, 7.5 in. from the top.
Using the parallel-axis theorem and $I_{rect} = (bh^3)/12$,

$$I_{x-x} = 32 + (6 \times 4)5.5^2 + 72 + (6 \times 4)0.5^2 + 42.7 + 32 \times 4.5^2$$
$$= 1,527 \text{ in.}^4$$

$S = Mc/I$; $M_{max} = (wl^2)/8$; $c = 7.5$.

$$\text{Total load} = w \times l = \frac{S \times I}{c} \times \frac{8}{1} = \frac{1,200 \times 1,527 \times 8}{7.5(32 \times 12)} = 5,090 \text{ lb}$$

for a compressive stress in the topmost fibers of 1,200 psi.

If the tensile stress (or bending stress) in the lower fibers should control (1,200 psi tensile stress),

$$w \times l = \frac{1,200 \times 1,527 \times 8}{6.5(32 \times 12)} = 5,880 \text{ lb}$$

The allowable compressive stress in wood parallel to the grain is slightly less than the allowable tensile stress, however, and the smaller load would control.

Another past examination problem is as follows:

• For the loaded beam shown in Fig. 5-15,
   a. Calculate reactions R_1 and R_2.
   b. Draw shear and moment diagrams with the magnitude of maximum points indicated.
   c. Determine section modulus of beam if maximum allowable stress is 20,000 psi.

Referring to the figure, the reaction R_2 may be found by taking moments about R_1.

This gives $R_2 = \dfrac{5 \times 3,000 + 12(600 \times 14)}{11} = 10,530 \text{ lb}$

Taking moments about R_2 gives

$$R_1 = \frac{3,000 \times 6 - 1 \times (600 \times 14)}{11} = 870 \text{ lb}$$

Adding the forces in the y direction gives

$$10,530 + 870 - 3,000 - (600 \times 14) = 0$$

which checks.

The shear and moment diagrams are drawn directly below the given figure. From the moment diagram we see that the maximum moment is $-230,000$ lb-in.

$$S = \frac{Mc}{I} = \frac{M}{Z}$$

where $Z = I/c$, section modulus

$$Z = \frac{M}{S} = \frac{230,000 \text{ lb-in.}}{20,000 \text{ lb/sq in.}} = 11.5 \text{ cu in.}$$

The four important points on the beam have been labeled A, B, C, and D. Note in the shear diagram that the slope from A to B is zero since the load on the load diagram from A to B is zero. At B is a concentrated load, and the shear changes perpendicularly

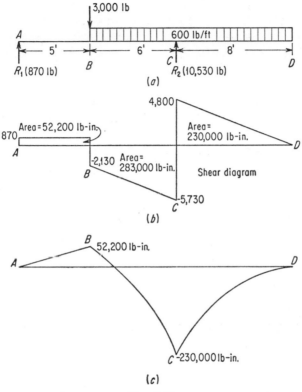

FIG. 5-15

at that point. From B to C the load is constant and the slope angle on the shear diagram is also constant. At point C the load changes abruptly because of the reaction R_2, and the shear also changes by the same amount. From C to D the load is constant, and the slope of the shear diagram is also constant. (Remember that loads on the *left* in an *upward* direction give a positive shear and loads *down* on the *right* give a positive shear.)

Looking at the moment diagram we see that the slope at any point equals the magnitude of the shear diagram at that point.   Thus the slope is constant from A to B and makes an abrupt change at B to a steadily increasing negative slope.   It makes another abrupt change at C from a large negative slope to a large positive slope which decreases to no slope (tangent to abscissa) at D.

Another example will help to illustrate these principles further. A past examination problem was as follows:

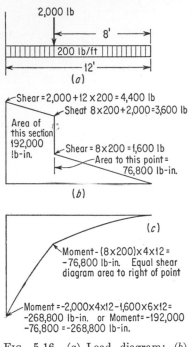

- A cantilever beam 12 ft long is fixed at the left end and carries a uniformly distributed weight of 200 lb/lin ft and a concentrated load of 2,000 lb at a point 8 ft from the right end. Draw the shear and moment diagrams and show the values of shear and moment at concentrated load and ends.   The diagrams must show the correct shapes.

FIG. 5-16. (a) Load diagram; (b) shear diagram; (c) moment diagram.

A figure must be drawn as the first step toward solution.   The figure and calculations are shown in Fig. 5-16.

5-11. Beam Slope and Deflection.   We have reviewed shear, bending moment, and stress in beams; this brings us to the problem of determining slopes and deflections.   The basic relationship for determining deflection or slope is $EI(d^2y/dx^2) = M$, to a close approximation.   The radius of curvature $R = EI/M$.

For a beam simply supported at the ends with a concentrated load at the center, this gives us the equation (see Fig. 5-17)

$$y_{max} = \frac{Fl^3}{48EI}$$

FIG. 5-17. Taking right half of beam and considering center point stationary, right end free to move up.

$$M_x = \frac{F}{2} x \qquad EI \frac{dy}{dx} = \int M \, dx = \int \frac{F}{2} \times dx = \frac{Fx^2}{4} + C_1$$

$$\frac{dy}{dx} = 0 \text{ at } x = \frac{l}{2} \qquad C_1 = \frac{-Fl^2}{16}$$

$$EIy = \int \frac{F}{4} x^2 \, dx - \int \frac{Fl^2}{16} \, dx = \left(\frac{Fx^3}{12}\right) - \left(\frac{Fl^2}{16}\right) x + C_2$$

$$y = 0 \text{ at } x = \frac{1}{2} \qquad C_2 = \frac{-Fl^3}{48}$$

$$y = \left(\frac{F}{EI}\right)\left(\frac{x^3}{12} - \frac{l^2 x}{16} - \frac{l^3}{48}\right) \qquad y_{max} = \frac{Fl^3}{48} EI \text{ at } x = 0$$

for the maximum deflection which occurs at the point of load (midpoint of beam). This relationship can be used to solve a past examination problem which asked:

- An I beam 14 in. deep on 20-ft span is simply supported at the ends. It has a moment of inertia of 440 (in.)[4].
  a. What load may be hung midway between the supports without producing a deflection of more than $\frac{1}{4}$ in.?
  b. What is the intensity of the stress produced?
  c. What total uniformly distributed load would produce the same deflection?
  d. What would then be the maximum bending stress?
     Use $E = 30,000,000$ psi.

First, draw a figure (Fig. 5-18). Disregarding the weight of the beam, we obtain for the load

$$F = \frac{48EIy}{l^3} = \frac{48 \times 30 \times 10 \times 440 \times 0.25}{(20 \times 12)^3} = 11,460 \text{ lb}$$

$$S = \frac{Mc}{I} \qquad M = \frac{11,460}{2} \times (10 \times 12) = 688,000 \text{ lb-in.}$$

$$c = \frac{14}{2} = 7 \text{ in.} \qquad S = \frac{688,000 \times 7}{440} = 10,950 \text{ psi}$$

For a uniformly distributed load, $y_{max} = (5wl^4)/(384EI)$, which gives

$$w = \frac{384EIy}{5l^4} = \frac{384 \times 30 \times 10^6 \times 440 \times 0.25}{5(20 \times 12)^4} = 76.4 \text{ lb/in.}$$

Unit algebra gives

$$\frac{\text{lb/in.}^2 \times \text{in.}^4 \times \text{in.}}{\text{in.}^4} = \text{lb/in.}$$

The total uniformly distributed load would then equal

$$76.4 \text{ lb/in.} \times (20 \times 12) \text{ in.} = 18,300 \text{ lb}$$

which could have been determined without the intermediate step by solving directly for $W = w \times l = \dfrac{384EIy}{5l^3}$. The maximum moment would occur at the mid-point of the beam and would equal

$$\frac{W}{2} \times \frac{l}{2} - \frac{W}{2} \times \frac{l}{4} = \frac{W \times l}{8}$$

$$S = \frac{Mc}{I} = \frac{18,300 \times (20 \times 12) \times 7}{8 \times 440} = 8,740 \text{ psi}$$

Another example which will help to illustrate a slightly different

Fig. 5-18   Fig. 5-19

aspect of the subject of beam deflection is the following past examination problem:

- A simply supported beam 10 ft long carries three equal concentrated loads located respectively 3, 5, and 7 ft from the left end. Calculate the ratio of the maximum deflection to the deflection under the load located 3 ft from the left end.

Again the first step is to construct a figure (Fig. 5-19). The loading is symmetrical about the center, so the maximum deflection will occur at the center. The maximum deflection will equal the sum of the deflections at the center of the beam due to each of the three individual loads. Each of these three deflections will be the same as if each load acted by itself; an easier solution is first to determine the deflection at the center due to the symmetrically placed loads P_1 and P_3, then to determine the deflection due to the load P_2, and then to add these two deflections to obtain the maximum deflection.

The deflection at the center due to loads P_1 and P_3 can be calculated from the equation

$$\Delta_{max} = \frac{Pa}{24EI}(3l^2 - 4a^2)$$

where $a = 36$ in.

$$l = 120 \text{ in.}$$

giving $\Delta_{max} = 57,000P/EI$.

The deflection at the center of the beam due to P_2

$$\Delta_{max} = \frac{Pl^3}{48EI} = 36,000\frac{P}{EI}$$

The total deflection at the center of the beam would then be equal to $93,000P/EI$, which is the sum of the partial deflections due to loads P_1, P_2, and P_3.

The deflection under the load located 3 ft from the left end would also be made up of two components. The deflection due to the two equal symmetrically applied loads P_1 and P_3 would equal

$$\frac{Pa}{6EI}(3la - 4a^2) = 46,600\frac{P}{EI}$$

The deflection at the same point due to the force P_2 would equal

$$\frac{Pa}{48EI}(3l^2 - 4a^2) = 38,000\frac{P}{EI}$$

The total deflection under the left load would then equal $84,600P/EI$, and the required ratio would be 1.10.

Another type of beam problem occasionally asked is illustrated by the example below:

FIG. 5-20. (c) Shear diagram; (d) moment diagram. The moment at the wall may also be calculated from the relationship $M = -[Fab(1 + a)]/(2l^2)$, which gives, for the two applied loads $-(240,000 + 300,000) = -540,000$ lb-in., which checks the values obtained by the other method.

• The beam illustrated in Fig. 5-20 has a 10 WF 54 section. Determine the reaction R and the maximum bending stress in the beam.

5-12. Statically Indeterminate Beams. This is an example of a statically indeterminate beam. It is called statically indeterminate because the number of unknown reactions exceeds those which may be determined by the static relationships alone. In this case there are three unknown reactions—the vertical reactions at the two ends and the couple at the left end. There being only vertical forces, we have only two equations based on the static relationships $\Sigma F_y = 0$ and $\Sigma M = 0$. To obtain the required answer we resort to a handbook for a method of determining the reaction R. For a single concentrated load, beam fixed at one end, supported at the other,

$$R = \frac{Fb^2}{2l^3}(a + 2l)$$

Applying this equation twice, once for each concentrated load, gives us the value for R.

$$R_1 = \frac{15{,}000 \times (6)^2}{2 \times (9)^3} (3 + 2 \times 9) = 7{,}780 \text{ lb}$$

$$R_2 = \frac{15{,}000 \times (3)^2}{2 \times 9^3} (6 + 2 \times 9) = 2{,}220 \text{ lb}$$

Note that the units of length cancel out, and it makes no difference whether we use lengths in feet or in inches, as long as we are consistent. $R = R_1 + R_2 = 10{,}000$ lb, where R_1 is due to the right-hand 15,000-lb load and R_2 is due to the left of the two loads.

With this value for R we can determine the upward reaction at the wall, $R_w = 15{,}000 + 15{,}000 - 10{,}000 = 20{,}000$ lb. Having the loading of the beam, we can construct the shear and moment diagrams. These are shown in Fig. 5-20 with the loading diagram. The direction of the beam has been reversed, with the free end placed at the left to simplify the analysis.

The shear diagram may be constructed in the manner which has been discussed previously. The moment diagram, however, is not quite so simple as those constructed previously. To construct the moment diagram, start at the left end of the beam where the moment is zero. We see from the shear diagram that the moment diagram will have a constant positive slope to the right to the point of application of the first load. Furthermore, the magnitude of the intercept of the moment curve at this point equals the algebraic sum of the areas under the shear diagram to the left of this point, which is 10,000 lb $\times$ 36 in. $= 36 \times 10^4$ lb-in. The moment curve then takes a constant negative slope to the point of application of the next load, at which point the moment equals

$$36 \times 10^4 - (5{,}000 \times 36) = 18 \times 10^4 \text{ lb-in.}$$

At this point the negative slope increases and remains constant to the end of the beam, where the moment equals

$$18 \times 10^4 - (20{,}000 \times 36) = -540{,}000 \text{ lb-in.}$$

which is the maximum moment along the length of the beam.

The section modulus of a 10 WF 54 beam is (from a table) 60.4 cu in.

Since stress $= (Mc)/I = M/Z$, where $Z = I/c$,

$$S = \frac{540,000}{60.4} = 8,950 \text{ psi}$$

The required answers are $S_{max} = 8,950$ psi and $R = 10,000$ lb.

Fig. 5-21

5-13. Composite Beams. The beams so far considered have all been of one homogeneous material. There are many beams, however, that are made of two materials, principally reinforced-concrete beams and steel-reinforced wood beams. Such beams are called "composite beams"; because of the difference in the moduli of elasticity of the two materials, they require a slightly different type of analysis than that used for homogeneous beams. One type of composite beam is shown in Fig. 5-21. It is made up of a 6- by 8-in. timber 10 ft in length, with a 6-in. wide strip of steel ⅛ in. thick attached to the bottom edge. To withstand the applied load the beam will deflect, the upper part of the wooden portion will compress, and the lower part of the wood and the steel will stretch. The stress in any part of the beam will equal the unit deformation in that particular portion times the modulus of elasticity of the material of which that portion is made. Since the steel on the bottom of the beam deforms the same amount as the wood fibers on the bottom of the beam, the steel will be stressed in the ratio E_s/E_w times the stress in the bottom-most wood fibers. Since $E_s = 30 \times 10^6$ and $E_w = 10^6$, the stress in the steel will be thirty times the stress in the wood. This means that the tensile load in the steel will be considerably greater than that in the wood, and the neutral axis will be below the geometric center of the beam.

Another way of looking at this problem is that since

$$\text{Force} = \text{stress} \times \text{area}$$

and Stress $= E \times \delta$, the steel strip could, theoretically, be replaced by a piece of wood with an area equal to $E_s/E_w \times$ area of steel, or thirty times the area of the steel, but with the same thickness. The equivalent wooden beam is shown in the figure, and the internal-force diagram showing the distribution of $S \times A$ over the cross section of the beam is also shown. To determine the stresses in the wood and in the steel we need to know the distance to the neutral axis y. This can be determined by taking moments about the upper edge of the beam; one must remember that a slice of the equivalent beam section would balance on a fulcrum placed at the neutral axis.

$$(6 \times 8) \times 4 + (\tfrac{1}{8} \times 180) \times 8\tfrac{1}{16} = (6 \times 8 + \tfrac{1}{8} \times 180) \times y$$
$$y = 5.36 \text{ in.}$$

$S = Mc/I$, where I is the moment of inertia of the equivalent beam about the neutral axis. Utilizing the parallel-axis theorem,

$$I_x = \frac{6 \times 8^3}{12} + 48 \times (1.36)^2 + \frac{180 \times (\tfrac{1}{8})^3}{12}$$
$$+ (180 \times \tfrac{1}{8})(2.64 + \tfrac{1}{16})^2$$
$$I_x = 256 + 88.8 + 0.0293 + 164 = 509 \text{ in.}^4$$
$$M_{max} = \frac{5,000}{2} \times (5 \times 12) = 150,000 \text{ lb-in.} \qquad c = 5.36$$

Maximum compressive stress in wood $S = \dfrac{150,000 \times 5.36}{509}$
$$= 1,580 \text{ psi}$$

The tensile stress in the bottom-most fibers of the equivalent beam would be

$$\frac{150,000 \times 2.77}{509} = \frac{2.77}{5.36} \times 1,580 = 816 \text{ psi}$$

and the stress in the steel would then equal $30 \times 816 = 24,500$ psi, since $\delta_{\text{wood}} = \delta_{\text{steel}}$ and $E_{\text{steel}} = 30 \times E_{\text{wood}}$.

The commonest type of composite beam is the reinforced-concrete beam, which can also be handled by the method described. One difference, however, is that the concrete is assumed to withstand no tensile stress and the portion of the concrete on the tension side of the neutral axis is disregarded in the stress calculations. A reinforced-concrete beam is shown in Fig. 5-22. It is required to determine the allowable concentrated load which the beam will hold if $n = 12$ and the maximum allowable stresses are 1,000 psi for the concrete and 20,000 psi for the steel. $n = E_{\text{steel}}/E_{\text{concrete}}$.

The equivalent beam cross section is drawn; as the concrete will take only compressive loading, the effective concrete area will extend only to the neutral axis. The location of the neutral axis is found as before.

$$10kd \times \frac{kd}{2} = (20 - kd) \times 24$$

$$(kd)^2 + 4.8kd - 96 = 0$$

$$kd = \frac{-4.8 + \sqrt{23 + 384}}{2}$$

$$= 7.7$$

The moment of inertia

$$I = \frac{10 \times (7.7)^3}{12} + (10 \times 7.7)\left(\frac{7.7}{2}\right)^2$$
$$+ 24(20 - 7.7)^2 = 5,150 \text{ in.}^4$$

(a)

(b) Beam cross section

(c)

(d) Equivalent beam cross section

Fig. 5-22

Note that the moment of inertia of the steel portion about its own neutral axis is disregarded since it is so small compared with the other components. $S = Mc/I$.

$$M_{concrete} = \frac{1,000 \times 5,150}{7.7} = 669,000 \text{ lb-in.} \qquad \text{for 1,000 psi stress}$$

$$M_{steel} = \frac{20,000 \times 5,150}{n \times 12.3} = 698,000 \text{ lb-in.} \qquad \text{for 20,000 psi stress}$$

Compressive stress in the concrete controls. Note the use of the n in the denominator for determining the allowable moment for the steel.

$$M_{max} = \frac{P}{2} \times \frac{L}{2} \qquad P = \frac{4 \times 669,000 \text{ lb-in.}}{10 \times 12 \text{ in.}} = 22,300 \text{ lb}$$

If a beam should be subjected to either tensile or compressive loading in addition to the bending moment caused by a transverse load, the maximum stress would equal $P/A \pm (Mc)/I$. The same would be true if the beam were upended and became a column, providing it was stiff enough so that the increase in eccentricity due to the applied load was negligible. This type of problem can be handled in the same fashion as the one above concerning beams. As an example, let us take a past examination problem which asked:

- In a solid masonry pier of circular cross section, what eccentricity of the vertical load will cause zero stress at the side away from the load? $I = (\pi r^4)/4$.

Fig. 5-23

The moment due to the eccentrically applied load equals $P \times e$ (Fig. 5-23), and the total stress will equal $\pm (P \times e \times c)/I \pm (P/A)$. When the tensile stress equals zero, we have

$$\frac{P \times e \times c}{I} = \frac{P}{A}$$

or

$$\frac{P \times e \times r}{(\pi r^4)/4} = \frac{P}{\pi r^2}$$

which gives $e = r/4$.

5-14. Columns.   The subject of slender columns has been touched upon only slightly in past examinations.   Since it is quite involved and since many empirical relationships are used, this subject would require far more space than could be justified here for its treatment. The interested reader is referred to one of the texts listed at the end of the chapter.

5-15. Compound Stresses.   The subject of compound stresses has also been touched upon lightly in a few of the past fundamentals examinations.   We shall restrict ourselves here to a brief discussion of one method of determining the principal stresses and the maximum shearing stress for a condition of combined loading.   The method we shall use is the one based on Mohr's circle, which is a graphical method and easier to apply and to remember than the purely analytical method.

As a basis for illustration let us use a problem from a past examination:

- The diagram of Fig. 5-24 (Mohr's circle) is used to find the maximum shearing stress in a member that is in combined tension, torsion, and circumferential tension, viz., a pipe under pressure with torsion and axial tension applied.

  a. Derive the equation for the maximum shearing stress from this diagram in terms of $S_{s\max}$ = maximum shearing stress; S_s = stress due to torsion; S_x = stress due to pure tension; S_y = stress due to circumferential tension.

  b. Draw a stress diagram for a unit area of the external pipe surface.

This problem has been given in a simplified manner.   Ordinarily the pressure, axial load, and torque would have been given.   Let us look at it in the more general sense to obtain maximum benefit from this illustration.

5-16. Mohr's Circle.   First determine the stresses acting at a section on the outer surface of the pipe. S_x = axial load divided by the cross-sectional area, $S_y = Pd/2t$ (assuming a thin-walled pipe), and $S_s = Tc/J$.   Having determined these stresses, we can construct Mohr's circle for the given case.   The general procedure is shown by means of Fig. 5-25.   First lay out the coordinate axes.

From the origin, point 0, lay off a distance $(S_x + S_y)/2$ along the abscissa. This gives the location of C, the center of the circle. Note here that $S_x + S_y$ is the algebraic sum of the two perpendicular stresses; if one of these stresses had been compressive we should have had the arithmetic difference instead of the arithmetic sum.

FIG. 5-24   FIG. 5-25

At a distance from the origin equal to S_y draw a vertical line and at a distance equal to S_s above the abscissa mark a point on this line. This point lies on the circumference of the circle. Now draw the circle.

The maximum shearing stress is equal to the radius of the circle. From the figure, the trigonometric relationship is

$$S_{smax} = \sqrt{S_s^2 + \left(\frac{S_y - S_x}{2}\right)^2}$$

or $\qquad S_{smax} = \tfrac{1}{2}\sqrt{(S_y - S_x)^2 + 4S_s^2}$

The principal stresses can also be quickly obtained and are shown on the figure as T_{min} and T_{max}. The directions of these principal stresses are also readily obtained from the figure. The lines drawn from the ends of the horizontal diameter to the construction point on the circumference give these angles, and the principal stresses act perpendicularly to these lines, i.e., T_{min} acts at an angle of β and T_{max} acts at an angle of α with the direction of S_y. The maximum shearing stress acts on a plane at an angle of 45° to these two principal planes.

The required stress diagram for a unit area of the external pipe surface shows the directions of the different stresses and would ordinarily be drawn before Mohr's circle was constructed. The diagram is shown in Fig. 5-26.

This discussion of Mohr's circle and compound stresses has been very brief but it provides an elementary working knowledge of the method which is adequate to handle successfully the bulk of this type of problem so far given in fundamentals examinations. For a more complete coverage the reader is referred to one of the references listed at the end of the chapter.

FIG. 5-26. (a) Sections of pipe surface showing applied stresses; (b) redrawn from Fig. 5-24 to show minimum and maximum stresses and angles α and β; (c) location of minimum and maximum stresses.

5-17. Riveted and Welded Joints. One other subject to be discussed is that of riveted and welded joints. These have also been touched upon, though lightly, in past examinations. Riveted joints can be lumped into two general classes—those in which the line of action of the applied load passes through the centroid of the rivet group and those which are subject to eccentric loading.

The simpler case, in which the line of action of the applied load passes through the centroid of the rivet group, may be illustrated by a past examination problem, illustrated in Fig. 5-27. The allowable load could be limited by tension in the plates, bearing stresses in the plates, or shearing stress in the bolts.

The controlling area in tension is the same for the left and right members and equals $\frac{3}{4}(5\frac{1}{2} - 2 \times \frac{3}{4}) = 3$ sq in. The maximum allowable load from tension considerations then equals

$$3 \times 20,000 = 60,000 \text{ lb}$$

The bearing area in single shear equals

$$4 \times 2(\tfrac{3}{4} \times \tfrac{3}{8}) = 2\tfrac{1}{4} \text{ sq in.}$$

This is the same as the bearing area in double shear, so the maximum allowable load as limited by bearing equals

$$2\tfrac{1}{4} \times 32{,}000 = 72{,}000 \text{ lb}$$

The shear area equals eight times the cross-sectional area of one bolt, or $8 \times \pi/4 \times (\tfrac{3}{4})^2 = 3.53$ sq in. The maximum allowable

Fig. 5-27. Allowable unit stresses, in pounds per square inch.

Tension, structural steel, net section.......... 20,000
Shearing, turned bolts in reamed holes........ 15,000
Bearing, turned bolts in reamed holes:
  Double shear............................. 40,000
  Single shear............................. 32,000

load as limited by shearing stress is then $3.53 \times 15{,}000 = 53{,}000$ lb.
  The allowable load is then limited by shear and equals 53,000 lb.
  In this case each of the four rivets has been assumed to withstand one-quarter of the applied load; the analysis is applicable only when the line of action of the applied force passes through the centroid of the rivet group. When the load is applied eccentrically, there will be a torque loading, as well as a portion of the applied load to be withstood by each rivet, and since different rivets will ordinarily be at different distances from the centroid of the rivet group, the stresses in the rivets will vary. This can best be illustrated by

means of another example selected from a past examination.   This problem asked:

• What is the maximum allowable load P if the allowable unit shearing stress in the rivets is 13,000 psi?   Assume that bearing stress does not govern.   All rivets are $\frac{3}{4}$ in. in diameter. The problem is illustrated in Fig. 5-28.

First we must determine the centroid of the rivet group.   This is just the centroid of the rivet areas and may be determined in the

FIG. 5-28   FIG. 5-29

same way that we have determined centroids of areas before.   In this case the rivet group is perfectly symmetrical about the center rivet, so the centroid of the group is at the center of the center rivet.

Next the length of the moment arm D must be calculated.   We recognize the familiar 3-4-5 right triangle, which means that $\alpha = 37°$ and $D = 8 \sin \alpha = 8 \times 0.6 = 4.8$ in.

As the eccentric force P is applied to the plate, the plate will turn and the rivets will deform slightly, since stress is proportional to strain and there can be no stress without a corresponding strain. Assuming that all rivets fill their holes completely, we know that the deformation of rivet (1) due to the twisting of the plate will equal $\frac{6}{3}$ times the deformation of rivet (2) (Fig. 5-29).   This means that the stress in rivet (1) due to the torque loading will be twice the stress in rivet (2).   Because of the symmetry of the joint, the stresses in rivets (1) and (5) due to resisting the applied torque will be equal, as will the stresses in rivets (2) and (4).   The stress in rivet (3) due to the torque will equal zero.   Since all rivets are the same size, the resisting forces will be proportional to the strains (or the stresses). This gives us

$$4.8P = 6 \times 2 \times TF_{(1)} + 3 \times 2 \times TF_{(2)}$$

where $TF_{(1)}$ and $TF_{(2)}$ are the forces exerted by rivets (1) and (2) resisting the applied torque. We know that $TF_{(1)}$ is twice $TF_{(2)}$, since the deformation of rivet (1) is just twice that of rivet (2). This gives us that $4.8P = 15TF_{(1)}$, or $TF_{(1)} = 0.32P$.

To this must be added, vectorially, $P/5$, since each rivet must withstand one-fifth of the applied force directly. The two resisting force vectors are shown in Fig. 5-30. The sum of the resisting horizontal

Fig. 5-30

force components is $0.32P + 0.12P = 0.44P$, and the vertical force component is $0.16P$. The total shearing force acting on rivets (1) and (5) is then $P \sqrt{0.44^2 + 0.16^2} = 0.468P$.

Since the total permissible shearing force in any one rivet is $13,000 \times \pi/4 \times (\frac{3}{4})^2 = 5,740$ lb, the maximum allowable value of $P = 5,740/0.468 = 12,300$ lb.

The majority of the controlling features discussed above also apply to welded joints, and it might be wise to review the important relationships here. We can then apply them to a sample problem covering a welded joint. First the minimum shearing stress will occur when the line of action of the force passes through the centroid of the rivet or weld area. If the load is applied eccentrically it will provide a moment about the centroid, and the centroidal point will act as a pivot point about which the riveted or welded joint will tend to rotate. Stress and strain are proportional; the greatest stress due to the applied moment will occur in the rivet or portion of weld farthest from the centroid, since the greatest strain will occur at that point.

To illustrate the application of these principles to the problem of a welded joint, let us look at a problem taken from a past fundamentals examination. This problem asked:

• A 3- by 3- by ½-in. angle is to be welded to each side of a gusset plate, as shown in Fig. 5-31. Design the size and length of welds necessary to hold safely a total tension force of 88,000 lb. The allowable shearing stress in the weld is 11,300 psi.

The shear area of a welded joint is taken as the smallest section of the joint, and the fillet weld is made the same thickness as the plate being welded. This is shown in Fig. 5-32. The effective thickness of the welds would then be ½ sin 45° = 0.354 in. The line of action of the force passes through the centroids of the angles; it

$$2\text{-}3\times3\times\tfrac{1}{2} \; L\text{s} \quad (b)$$

Properties of L section
$x = y = 0.98''$
$I = 2.2$ in.^{4}
Area = 2.75 in.^{2}

(c)

FIG. 5-31

FIG. 5-32

must also pass through the centroid of the weld area to provide a joint free from any torque effects. The welds will then be stressed in pure shear; since the moments of the two weld areas about the centroid must be equal in order to have no moment resulting from unequal strain we have

$$0.98W_u = 2.02W_L \quad \text{or} \quad W_u = 2.06W_L$$

From stress considerations,

$$88{,}000 \text{ lb} = 11{,}300 \text{ psi} \times \text{effective weld area}$$
Effective weld area = 7.8 sq in. = $(W_u + W_L) \times (0.500 \times 0.707)$
$$W_u + W_L = 22 \text{ in.}$$
$$W_L = 7.24 \text{ in.} \qquad W_u = 14.76 \text{ in.}$$

Make the welds 7½ in. and 15 in. long.

If the line of action of the force should not pass through the centroid of the weld area, the maximum stress will equal the vector sum of two component forces, as was the case for the eccentrically loaded riveted joint.

REFERENCES

The following texts are recommended as the easiest for review:

Seely, F. B., and J. O. Smith: "Resistance of Materials," John Wiley & Sons, Inc., New York, 1956.

Popov, E. P.: "Mechanics of Materials," Prentice-Hall, Inc., Englewood Cliffs, N.J., 1952.

Shanley, F. R.: "Strength of Materials," McGraw-Hill Book Company, Inc., New York, 1957.

SAMPLE PROBLEMS SELECTED FROM PAST EXAMINATIONS

5-1. See Fig. 5-P-1. A cast-iron punch-press frame is reinforced with a ¼- by 6-in. steel plate on the inner face, as shown. Allowable stresses, in pounds per square inch, are:

Cast-iron compression =	15,000
Cast-iron tension =	5,000
Steel tension =	20,000
$E_{cast-iron}$	= 18,000,000
E_{steel}	= 30,000,000

Find the maximum safe bending moment for the frame.

Fig. 5-P-1

5-2. The equation for the elastic curve of a simply supported beam of length L carrying a uniformly distributed load is $EI(d^2y/dx^2) = (wlx/2) - (wx^2/2)$. Find the equation for the slope of the beam at any point.

5-3. Three wires, each having a cross-sectional area of 0.20 sq in. and the same unstressed length of 200 in. at 60°F, hang side by side in the same plane. The outer wires are copper. The middle wire, equidistant from each of the others, is steel.

a. If a weight of 1,000 lb is gradually picked up by the three wires, what part of the load is carried by each?

b. What must the temperature become for the entire load to be carried by the steel wire?

E_{steel} $= 30 \times 10^6$ psi
E_{copper} $= 17 \times 10^6$ psi
Coefficient of expansion of steel $= 6.5 \times 10^{-6}$ psi*
Coefficient of expansion of copper $= 9.3 \times 10^{-6}$ psi*

* Psi given in problem.   Units should be in./(in.)(°F).

5-4. See Fig. 5-P-4.   What is the maximum tensile stress at section *A-A*?

Section *A-A*
Fig. 5-P-4   Fig. 5-P-6

5-5. In the space provided below, draw a shear and a moment diagram for a cantilever beam with a concentrated load at the end and a uniform load along its length. Explain the relation between the shear and moment diagram. What is the relation between the maximum and the average shearing stresses over a particular cross section?

5-6. *a.* Draw a moment diagram and a shear diagram for the 22 ft 0 in. beam loaded as shown in Fig. 5-P-6.

b. What is the magnitude of the maximum moment?   What is its location (in feet from the left end)?

5-7. A mine hoist weighing 5 tons empty is descending at a speed of 20 mph when the hoist mechanism jams and stops suddenly. If the cable is steel having a cross section of 1 sq in. and the hoist is 5,000 ft below the hoisting drum, what is the stress produced in the cable?

5-8. Locate the neutral axis by calculating the distance *y* on the reinforced-concrete beam section as shown in Fig. 5-P-8.

E_{steel} $= 30,000,000$ psi
$E_{concrete}$ $= 2,000,000$ psi
$A_s = $ area of steel $= 3.00$ sq in.

Fig. 5-P-8

Fig. 5-P-9

5-9. A select oak timber finished sized to 6 by 8 in. is 12 ft long and is employed as a properly embedded cantilever beam with a load P (Fig. 5-P-9). If $E = 1.8 \times 10^6$, compute:

a. Deflection y_2 of the free end of the beam

b. Maximum tensile stress at y–y.

Allowable stress — oak tensile = 1,000 psi; shear = 125 psi.

5-10. A steel column is an H section 50 ft long and supports a concentric load of 350,000 lb. The column section has the following dimensions: $A = 49.09$ sq in.; $I_{1-1} = 790.2$ in.^{4}; $d_{1-1} = 15\frac{1}{8}$ in.; $d_{2-2} = 15\frac{1}{8}$ in.; $I_{2-2} = 2{,}020.8$ in.^{4}. Employing the American Institute of Steel construction method, determine whether the column design is safe, when

$$\frac{P}{A} = \frac{18{,}000}{1 + (1/18{,}000)(l/r)^2}$$

5-11. See Fig. 5-P-11. Draw shear and moment diagrams, showing values at all breaks in diagrams.

Fɪɢ. 5-P-11

Fɪɢ. 5-P-12

5-12. The load deflection curve for a spring is shown in Fig. 5-P-12. When the load reaches 150 lb the spring is fully closed and no further deflection results. The load deflection curve can be represented by the equation

$$d = 4 - \frac{(L - 200)^2}{10{,}000}$$

where d = deflection, in.

L = load, lb

a. How much energy is stored in the spring when the load is 150 lb? When it is 300 lb?

b. At what load will the spring constant be 0.032 in./lb?

5-13. *a.* Draw a shear diagram and a moment diagram for the 10-ft 0-in. beam loaded as shown in Fig. 5-P-13.

b. Using a homogeneous steel beam with an allowable unit stress of 20,000 psi, compute the required section modulus.

Fɪɢ. 5-P-13

5-14. A beam 40 ft long is supported 10 ft from the left end and 5 ft from the right end. The beam is loaded as follows: a concentrated load of 6,000 lb at the left end and a uniform load of 600 lb/ft from the left end to the right end. What are the shear diagram, moment diagram, maximum shear, maximum moment, and location of maximum moment and shear with respect to the left end of the beam?

5-15. A 6-in. by 12-in. by 14 ft timber beam is supported at the left end and also at 4 ft from the right end. It has a load of 2,000 lb at the right end, a load of 2,000 lb 3 ft from the left end, and a load of 800 lb/ft between supports. Find the maximum moment in magnitude and position, and the maximum shear.

5-16. A beam 40 ft long rests on simple supports at the ends and has the following loads:

> Dead load—300 lb/lin ft
> Uniform live load—700 lb/ft
> Concentrated live load—10,000 lb

a. Find the maximum and the minimum bending moment that can be developed at a point 16 ft from the left support.

b. Find the maximum and the minimum shear that can be developed 16 ft from the left support.

5-17. A steel wire accurately graduated in feet was used to measure the depth of a deep well. The cross-sectional area of the wire was 0.03 sq in., and a 250-lb weight was attached to the wire to lower it into the well. According to the graduated scale, the measurement read 2,000 ft. What should the corrected measurement be? A steel bar 1 sq in. in cross-sectional area and 1 yd long weighs 10 lb.

5-18. Design a steel shaft of the proper size to transmit 40 hp at a speed of 240 rpm if the allowable working-unit stress in the shaft is $s = 9,000$ psi. Show all computations.

5-19. Concrete is to be mixed with a proportion by volume of 1:2:3 (1 cement, 2 sand, 3 aggregate, and 6 gal of water per sack of cement). The cement has 51.3 per cent voids and weighs 94 lb/cu ft, the sand has 35.4 per cent voids and weighs 111 lb/cu ft, the gravel has 32.0 per cent voids and weighs 108 lb/cu ft. Find the amount of each ingredient by weight necessary to make 1 cu yd of concrete. (The water necessary may be given in gallons or pounds.)

5-20. A beam 20 ft long carries a uniform load of 2,000 lb/lin ft, including its own weight, on two supports 14 ft apart. The right end of the beam cantilevers 2 ft; the left end cantilevers 4 ft. Draw the shear diagram and compute the positions and amounts of the maximum bending moments.

5-21. What uniform load W (lb/ft) will cause a simple beam 10 ft long to deflect 0.3 in. if it is also supported at mid-span by a spring whose modulus $K = 30,000$ lb/in. Assume $I = 100$ in.⁴, $E = 3 \times 10^7$ psi, $d = 10$ in. At no load the spring just touches the beam (Fig. 5-P-21).

Fig. 5-P-21

5-22. A 2-in. shaft is transmitting 30 hp at 200 rpm. A pulley which delivers the entire amount of power is keyed to the shaft by a $\frac{3}{8}$- by $\frac{1}{2}$- by 3-in. flat key. The shaft is in pure torsion. Determine the shear and crushing stresses in the key.

5-23. Find the shear just to the right of the left-hand reaction, and the bending moment under the 5,000-lb load (Fig. 5-P-23).

FIG. 5-P-23   FIG. 5-P-24

5-24. For the loaded beam shown in Fig. 5-P-24,

a. Plot shear diagram.

b. Plot moment diagram.

c. Find maximum tensile unit stress.

5-25. Where does the maximum bending moment occur in a beam with a 24-ft span that carries a load of 24,000 lb uniformly spread over its entire length and a further load of 12 tons uniformly spread over a section that starts 6 ft from the left support and extends 8 ft to the right? What is the maximum moment?

5-26. A steel gear is to be assembled on a steel motor shaft by heating the gear and cooling the shaft with dry ice. At 70°F the shaft measures 7.000 in. in diameter and the hole in the gear measures 6.996 in. in diameter. To what temperature must the shaft be cooled so that the gear may be assembled on the shaft with 0.005 in. clearance when the gear is warmed to 140°F? The coefficient of linear expansion for steel is 0.0000065 in./[(in.)(°F)].

5-27. *a.* Draw the shear and moment diagram for the load condition shown in Fig. 5-P-27.

b. On these diagrams give the location and amount of the critical values.

FIG. 5-P-27   FIG. 5-P-28

5-28. A machine part is loaded as a cantilever beam.   Two possibilities of design are being considered which would utilize different materials and different cross sections.   Show by your calculations which design will be the more rigid. Length of each = 6 in.   (Fig. 5-P-28).

5-29. A rigid horizontal bar 10 ft long, of uniform cross section and weighing 300 lb, is supported by two vertical wires, one of steel and one of copper.   Each wire is 5 ft long and $\frac{1}{100}$ sq in. in cross section.   The copper wire is attached 1 ft from one end of the bar, and the steel wire at such a distance X from the same end that both wires stretch by the same amount.   Find the tension in each wire and the distance X.

Young's modulus for steel = 30×10^6 psi; for copper = 15×10^6 psi.

5-30. A block of steel would increase its volume by 330 ppm when heated from 20 to 30°C at constant pressure.   What increase of pressure would be necessary to keep the block from expanding when its temperature is thus raised? The compressibility of steel is 4.4×10^{-8} sq in./lb.

5-31. A weight of 3,500 lb is supported by one piece of material A and two pieces of material B, as shown in Fig. 5-P-31.   Each of the three pieces has a

Fɪɢ. 5-P-31

cross section of 2 sq in. and a height of 6 in.   The weight is symmetrically placed on the supporting blocks.   Young's modulus for material A is 3×10^7 psi and for material B is 2×10^7 psi.

   a. What is the stress in the piece of material A?
   b. What is the stress in each piece of material B?

5-32. A solid circular shaft has a uniform diameter of 2 in. and is 10 ft long. At its mid-point 65 hp is delivered to the shaft by means of a belt passing over a pulley.   This power is used to drive two machines, one at the left end of the shaft consuming 25 hp, and one at the right end consuming the remaining 40 hp. Determine the maximum shearing stress in the shaft and also the relative angle of twist between the two extreme ends of the shaft if the steel shaft turns at 200 rpm.

5-33. An eccentrically loaded riveted joint is shown in Fig. 5-P-33. The applied load is 18,000 lb acting with an eccentricity of 8 in. from the geometric center of the group of six ¾-in. rivets. Determine the maximum shearing stress in the rivets.

FIG. 5-P-33   FIG. 5-P-34

5-34. A rectangular wooden beam is loaded as shown in Fig. 5-P-34.

a. If the allowable shearing stress parallel to the grain is 68 psi, is the maximum shearing stress in the beam within the allowable limit?

b. If the allowable bending stress is 720 psi, is the bending stress in the beam within the allowable limit?

5-35. A 4-in. diameter shaft transmits 1,000 hp at 2,000 rpm. If the same power is transmitted at 10,000 rpm,

a. What diameter of shaft is required to maintain the same maximum shearing stress?

b. Which shaft has the greatest angle of twist per unit length?

CHAPTER 6

Electricity and Electronics

The coverage of this subject in past examinations has been quite extensive, with occasional questions on many different facets of the over-all subject. The bulk of the questions have, however, been directed toward a few of the more important aspects. Alternating-current circuit analysis, including power factor and phase angle, has received the greatest amount of emphasis. Next in importance have been resistance and Ohm's law, followed by motor-generator theory, three-phase circuitry, transformers, batteries, electron tubes, capacitors, and voltmeters. The other facets have received less emphasis and may be lumped into the general category of miscellaneous.

6-1. Electron Theory. To start, we might recall that many of the various electrical phenomena can be explained by means of the electron theory. Current is the flow of electrons. Voltage differential between two points is the potential difference between those two points and is equal to the work done per unit charge against electrical forces when a charge is transported from one point to the other. We should also remember that like charges repel and unlike attract. The force of repulsion or attraction is proportional to the product of the two charges divided by the square of the distance between them. As an illustration of this, let us examine a past examination problem:

- Two electrons are stationary when 1 cm apart. They are allowed to move apart under the influence of their mutual repulsion. What is their relative velocity when they are 2 cm apart?

Charge of electron $= 1.6 \times 10^{-19}$ coulomb

$= 4.8 \times 10^{-10}$ statcoulomb

Mass of electron $= 9.11 \times 10^{-28}$ g

The force acting on one electron will equal the force acting on the other; action and reaction are equal and opposite.

$$F = \frac{kqq'}{S^2}$$

If q and q', the two charges, are in statcoulombs and the distance S is in centimeters, the force F will be in dynes for a proportionality constant of $k = 1$. This gives us that $F = e^2/S^2$, where e is the charge on an electron. Since $F = ma$, this gives us $a = e^2/(S^2 m)$. We also know that $v = dS/dt$ and $a = dv/dt$; since $1/dt = v/dS$, this gives $a = v(dv/dS)$. Combining the two relationships for a, we have $v(dv/dS) = e^2/(S^2 m)$, which reduces to $v \, dv = (e^2/m)(dS/S^2)$. Integrating both sides gives us

$$\frac{v^2}{2} = - \frac{e^2}{m} \left(\frac{1}{S} \right) \Big|_{S_1}^{S_2}$$

where $S_1 = 1$ cm

$S_2 = 2$ cm

We then have that

$$\frac{v^2}{2} = \frac{e^2}{m} \left(- \frac{1}{2} + 1 \right) = \frac{e^2}{2m} \qquad \text{or } v = \frac{e}{\sqrt{m}}$$

which gives

$$v = \frac{4.8 \times 10^{-10}}{\sqrt{9.11 \times 10^{-28}}} = 15,900 \text{ cm/sec} \qquad \text{or } 522 \text{ fps}$$

Similarly, an electrical charge is acted upon by a force equal to $E \times q$ in an electrical field, and a force $F = qvB$ in a magnetic field. These forces explain the action of electrons in electron tubes, cathode ray tubes, cyclotrons, and other electron devices. (q = charge, coulombs, v = velocity, B = flux density, and E = voltage differential.) A question in a past examination was:

- What are the three basic elements of a vacuum tube? What are their functions?

Any vacuum tube must have a cathode and a plate (Fig. 6-1). It must also generally have some provision for heating the cathode so that the free electrons may gain enough energy to leave the cathode (activation of the free electrons is achieved with light in a photoelectric tube). The third basic element may, then, be the heater. Most vacuum tubes (except for diodes and a few other types) possess a grid in addition to the cathode and the plate; this is probably the third element asked for.

FIG. 6-1

The cathode is electrically negative with respect to the plate; as it is heated it emits electrons which are attracted toward the plate and a current flows through the tube. The greater the potential difference, the greater the current. By adding the grid, which is negative with respect to the cathode, the flow of the electrons may be strongly retarded. A small change in the grid potential produces a large change in current flow.

6-2. Ohm's Law and Resistance. Whenever there is a flow of electrons through a conductor, there is a resistance to that flow. The resistance is described by Ohm's law, $V = IR$. The electrical resistance between two points is proportional to the distance and inversely proportional to the cross-sectional area of the conductor. As an illustration, let us review a past examination problem.

- A copper wire $\frac{1}{2}$ in. in diameter and 1,000 ft long has a resistance of 0.05 ohms at 20°C. What is the resistance of 500 ft of $\frac{1}{2}$-in. square wire of similar material?

$$\frac{R_{\text{square}}}{R_{\text{round}}} = \frac{A_r}{A_s} \times \frac{L_s}{L_r}$$

$$R_S = 0.05 \times \frac{0.196}{0.250} \times \frac{500}{1,000} = 0.0196 \text{ ohms}$$

It should also be remembered that the equivalent resistance for a group of resistances in series is equal to the sum of the individual resistances: $R = R_1 + R_2 + R_3 + \cdots$. The equivalent resistance for a group of resistances in parallel can be determined from the relationship $1/R = 1/R_1 + 1/R_2 + 1/R_3 + \cdots$.

For illustration, let us look at the past examination problem:

• Direct current flows through the circuit sketched in Fig. 6-2a. If the impressed voltage on terminals A and B is 25 volts, what is the line current?

We have a series-parallel circuit here, and the easiest way to determine the current is to determine the equivalent circuit resistance and apply Ohm's law. We can do this in steps. The first

(a)　　　　　　(b)　　　　　　(c)

Fig. 6-2

step is to calculate the equivalent resistance for the parallel circuit of 4 ohms and 8 ohms. $1/R = (\frac{1}{4}) + (\frac{1}{8})$; $R = 2.67$, which gives the equivalent circuit shown in Fig. 6-2b. Adding 2 plus 2.67 gives 4.67 ohms, series resistance in the branch. This gives another parallel circuit, for which the equivalent resistance is

$$\frac{1}{R_2} = \frac{1}{3} + \frac{1}{4.67}$$

$R_2 = 1.83$ ohms, and we have the equivalent circuit shown in Fig. 6-2c. The line current is $I = V/R_T = 25/6.83 = 3.66$ amp.

A somewhat more involved problem was:

• An electric traction line is 20 miles long and supplied with power from power stations at each end. The station at end A maintains a voltage of 580 volts, and the station at end B a voltage of 610 volts. The resistance of the trolley wire is 0.1 ohm/mile, and that of the rails is 0.05 ohm/mile. If a car taking 200 amp travels from A to B, at what distance from A will its voltage be a minimum, and what will this voltage be?

A sketch will help in understanding this problem. Referring to
Fig. 6-3 we see that the resistance to current flow from point A to

Fig. 6-3

the trolley and back to point
A will equal $(0.10 + 0.05)S$, or
$R_A = 0.15S$. The current draw
is 200 amp, so $I_A + I_B = 200$.

The voltage at the trolley will
be single-valued whether it is
supplied from A or from B. This gives us that

$$580 - I_A R_A = 610 - I_B R_B$$

We also know that $R_B = (20 - S) \times 0.15 = 3 - R_A$. To find
where the voltage is a minimum, we must find the point at which
the voltage drop is a maximum. This must be equated to the
distance S so that we may differentiate and find where $I_A R_A$ is a
maximum or $V_A - I_A R_A$ is a minimum. Starting with the relationship for equivalent voltages, we have:

$$I_B R_B = 30 + I_A R_A$$

Substituting for I_B and R_B gives

$$(200 - I_A)(3 - R_A) = 30 + I_A R_A$$

which reduces to

$$570 - 200 R_A - 3 I_A = 0$$

The variables we are interested in are $I_A R_A$ and S, so we multiply
by R_A, giving $570 R_A - 200(R_A)^2 - 3 I_A R_A = 0$, and then substitute for R_A its equivalent $(0.15S)$. This gives

$$28.5S - 1.5S^2 - I_A R_A = 0$$

Differentiating this equation gives $[d(I_A R_A)/dS] = 3S - 28.5$.
Setting this equal to zero gives $S = 9.5$ miles for maximum voltage
drop. At this point $I_A = 95$ amp, and the voltage at the trolley
equals $580 - (0.15 \times 9.5)95 = 444.7$ volts.

A very important application of resistance and Ohm's law is the
Wheatstone bridge. An example of this is afforded by a past
examination problem:

• In the circuit shown in Fig. 6-4, what is the required resistance of X so that $V_1 = 0$? With the value of X found above and $120V$ applied, what is the voltage V_2?

FIG. 6-4

First we add the letters A, B, C, and D to the figure to aid in identification of the points. For a general discussion we also label the resistances R_1, R_2, R_3, and R_4, and the currents I_1 and I_2.

For voltage V_1 to be zero, the voltage drops I_1R_1 and I_2R_2 must be equal. This means that I_1R_3 and I_2R_4 must also be equal, giving $I_1R_1 = I_2R_2$ and $I_1R_3 = I_2R_4$. Dividing one equation by the other gives $(R_1/R_3) = (R_2/R_4)$.

It is R_3 we are interested in.

$$R_3 = R_1 \frac{R_4}{R_2} = 1,500 \frac{600}{1,000} = 900 \text{ ohms}$$

To determine the voltage differential V_2, we must calculate either I_1 or I_2. Since the voltage difference between B and C is zero ($V_1 = 0$), there will be a drop of 120 volts across the branch ABD and across the branch ACD. Since $V = IR$,

$$I_1 = \frac{120}{1,500 + 900} = 0.05 \text{ amp}$$

and the voltage drop from A to B equals $0.05 \times 1,500 = 75$ volts.
To check, $I_2 = 120/(1,000 + 600) = 0.075$ amp, giving

$$V_2 = 0.075 \times 1,000 = 75 \text{ volts}$$

as before.

6-3. Battery Internal Resistance. Closely associated with the general subject of circuit resistance is the internal resistance of a battery. Any battery will have some internal resistance which will serve to reduce the effective potential as the current increases.

FIG. 6-5

A battery can be considered as consisting of a source of emf with a resistance, the internal resistance of the battery, in series. This equivalent circuit is shown in Fig. 6-5. The usefulness of this concept of an equivalent circuit may be illustrated by a past examination problem.

- A battery consists of 6 cells, each having an emf of 1.1 volts and a resistance of 4 ohms, connected in two parallel rows of three cells each in series. This battery is connected to a group of two resistances in parallel of 30 ohms and 6 ohms, respectively. The lead wire resistance is negligible. Using Ohm's law, calculate the current in the leads.

First draw the equivalent circuit (Fig. 6-6a). This circuit may be further simplified, as in Fig. 6-6b. We see that the no-load voltage of the cell is 3.3 volts. The current I will equal $I_1 + I_2$, and from Ohm's law we have that $3.3 - 12I_1 =$ voltage output of battery

FIG. 6-6

under load; since $V = IR$ and $V = 3.3 - 12I_1$, $I = (3.3 - 12I_1)/5$. But $I_1 + I_2 = I$, and $I_1 = I_2$, giving $2I_1 = (3.3 - 12I_1)/5$, or $I_1 = 0.15$ amp, $I = 0.30$ amp, which is the current in the leads.

Another past examination problem dealing with the internal resistance of a battery was:

- Two batteries, identical in every way, are connected in series across a 5-ohm resistor, and the current is found to be 0.2 amp. The same cells are then connected in parallel with the same 5-ohm resistor, and the current is found to be 0.16 amp across the 5-ohm resistor. What are the open-circuit voltage and the internal resistance of the batteries?

FIG. 6-7

First draw the equivalent circuits of the two hookups (Fig. 6-7). For the series circuit we have

$$2V - 2I_1R_i - 5I_1 = 0$$
$$2V = 0.4R_i + 1.00$$

For the parallel circuit

$$V - \tfrac{1}{2}I_2R_i - 5I_2 = 0$$
$$V = 0.08R_i + 0.80$$

Combining these two equations gives

$$0.2R_i + 0.50 = 0.08R_i + 0.80$$
$$R_i = 2.50 \text{ ohms}$$

which is the internal resistance of the batteries; $V = 1.00$ volt, open-circuit voltage.

6-4. Meter Internal Resistance. A closely associated subject is that of electrical metering and internal resistance of meters. For illustration let us review a past problem:

- An electrical milliameter, having an internal resistance of 500 ohms, reads full scale when 1 ma (milliampere—0.001 amp) of current is flowing.

a. If the meter is to be used as an ammeter reading 0.1 amp full scale, what size (ohms) resistor should be used in parallel with it?

b. If used as a voltmeter reading 100 volts full scale, what size (ohms) resistor should be used in series with the milliameter?

An ammeter is essentially a voltmeter which measures the voltage drop across a resistance or shunt. The milliameter in the problem reads full scale when measuring 0.5 volt differential;

$$V = 0.001 \times 500 = 0.5 \text{ volt}$$

To be used as an ammeter reading 0.1 amp full scale, it would be connected as shown in Fig. 6-8a. Since a current of 0.001 amp will

(a)   (b)

Fig. 6-8

flow through the meter when it reads full scale, 0.099 amp must flow through the shunt resistance. The voltage drop across the two parallel resistances must equal 0.5 volt. Then, by Ohm's law, $R_1 = 0.5/0.099 = 5.05$ ohms. Another way of looking at this is that the total resistance of the parallel circuit must equal 0.5 volt/0.1 amp = 5.0 ohms. Using the parallel-resistance rule, this gives $\frac{1}{5} = 1/R_1 + 1/500$, or $R_1 = 1/0.198 = 5.05$ ohms.

To use the milliammeter as a voltmeter reading 100 volts full scale it should be connected as shown in Fig. 6-8b. The total resistance in the meter circuit is $(500 + R_2)$ ohms. The current through the meter must be 0.001 amp for full-scale reading at 100 volts. $100 = 0.001R$; $R = 100,000$ ohms. The total resistance $R = 500 + R_2$; $R_2 = 99,500$ ohms required.

6-5. Inductance and Capacitance. In addition to resistance, a-c circuits usually contain inductance and/or capacitance. The analysis of this type of circuit has received the greatest emphasis in the electrical portion of the fundamentals examinations.

An illustrative problem is the following:

• A single-phase load takes 855 watts and 9.75 amp from a source when a 60-cycle voltage of 120 volts is applied. It is known that the current lags the voltage. Determine:

   a. Resistance of the load
   b. Impedance of the load
   c. Reactance of the load
   d. Power factor of the load
   e. Power-factor angle
   f. Inductance or capacitance, whichever predominates

6-6. Power Factor. The power taken by an electric load is measured in watts where watts = volts × amperes × power factor. The power factor equals the in-phase component of the current divided by the total current, or watts divided by volt-amperes. In this case the power factor pf = 855/(120 × 9.75) = 73 per cent. The impedance of the load $Z = E/I = 120/9.75 = 12.3$ ohms. The impedance also equals $\sqrt{(X_L - X_C)^2 + R^2}$, where X_L is the inductive reactance and X_C is the capacitive reactance. The power factor is equal to R/Z. The resistance of the load is then

$$0.73 \times 12.3 = 8.98 \text{ ohms}$$

and the impedance is 12.3 ohms. The reactance $X = X_L - X_C$ is equal to $X = \sqrt{Z^2 - R^2} = \sqrt{151.3 - 80.8} = 8.40$ ohms. The power factor, already determined, equals 0.73, or 73 per cent. The power-factor angle, more commonly called "phase angle," φ, equals the arc cosine of the power factor. In this case

$$\varphi = \cos^{-1} 0.73 = 43.1° \text{ lagging}$$

6-7. Phase Angles—Leading or Lagging. It is given that the current lags the voltage. From this we know that the inductance exceeds the capacitance. There are different methods of remembering this. One is by remembering that most industrial loads are inductive, because of induction motor loading, and for these the current lags, giving a lagging power factor. Another method is to remember the phrase, "*ELI* the *ICE*man." The *ELI* indicates that *E*, or voltage, comes before, or leads, *I* the current for an inductive load *L*. *ICE* indicates that current *I* comes before, or leads, the voltage *E* for a capacitive load *C*. We know that the current lags; therefore the voltage leads and the inductance predominates. $X_L = 2\pi f L$, or $L = X_L/(2\pi f)$, where L is in henrys.

$$L = \frac{8.40}{2\pi \times 60} = 0.0223 \text{ henry}$$

or 22.3 mh.   Capacitive impedance $X_C = 1/2\pi f C$, where C is in farads.

6-8. Vector Diagrams.   Figure 6-9a shows the vector diagram of the current and the phase angle.   Note that the in-phase component of the current will equal watts/volts = 855/120 = 7.12 amp, or it equals total current

$$I \times \cos \phi = 9.75 \times 0.73 = 7.12 \text{ amp}$$

The time diagram is shown in Fig. 6-9b.   Note that the current starts, or passes through zero, at a later time, $\omega t = \phi$, than the voltage, which passes through zero at $\omega t = 0$.   This indicates that the current lags, since it arrives at similar points (maximum, zero, minimum) after the voltage, or later than the voltage.

(b)

Fig. 6-9

6-9. Resonant Circuits.   The condition of resonance is important in LCR circuits; it occurs when the inductive impedance equals the capacitive impedance, or $X_L = X_C$.   For this condition $Z = R$, and the current through the circuit reaches its highest value.   For the case just considered, if the current had been limited only by the resistance, it would have been 120/8.98 = 13.36 amp, and the power would have equaled $W = I^2 R = 13.36^2 \times 8.98 = 1,605$ watts, instead of 855 watts as before.

As an example, a past problem asked:

- Find the resonant frequency of a series circuit consisting of a 0.005-μf capacitor and a 10-mh inductance.

$X_L = 2\pi f L$, and $X_C = 1/(2\pi f C)$.   For resonance, $X_L = X_C$,

$$f = \frac{1}{2\pi \sqrt{LC}} = \frac{1}{2\pi \sqrt{0.005 \times 10^{-6} \times 10 \times 10^{-3}}} = 22,500 \text{ cps}$$

Another problem was:

- • *a*. What is the magnitude of the impedance of the circuit shown in Fig. 6-10?
  - *b*. What is the magnitude of the line current?
  - *c*. What is the magnitude of the voltage across AB?
  - *d*. What is the power factor of the circuit?

First we must determine the capacitance of a single capacitor which will be equivalent to the capacitance of the three capacitors

FIG. 6-10   FIG. 6-11

in parallel. Since capacitance is proportional to area, capacitors in parallel are additive, as are resistances in series (see Sec. 6-10). The equivalent capacitance is, then, $5 + 10 + 5 = 20$ μf.

$$X_C = \frac{1}{2\pi \times 60 \times 20 \times 10^{-6}} = 132.6 \text{ ohms}$$
$$X_L = 2\pi \times 60 \times 0.25 = 94.2 \text{ ohms}$$
$$Z = \sqrt{(132.6 - 94.2)^2 + 10^2} = 39.7 \text{ ohms}$$

The line current $I = E/Z = 120/39.7 = 3.02$ amp. The voltage across AB is $E = IX_C = 3.02 \times 132.6 = 401$ volts. The power factor $pf = R/Z = 10/39.7 = 0.252$ leading, because the current leads the voltage when the reactive impedance exceeds the inductive impedance.

These are the answers requested, but we might examine this circuit a little further. The magnitude of the voltage across the inductance, from C to D, equals $IX_L = 3.02 \times 94.2 = 285$ volts, and the magnitude of the voltage across the resistance, from D to E, equals $IR = 3.02 \times 10 = 30.2$ volts. The vector impedance diagram showing this is sketched in Fig. 6-11. Since the current through all the components is the same, this diagram also serves as a voltage diagram. As a check,

$$E = \sqrt{(401 - 285)^2 + 30.2^2} = 120 \text{ volts}$$

The power consumed by the circuit equals volt-amperes times power factor, or $W = 120 \times 3.02 \times 0.252 = 91.2$ watts. The power also equals $I^2R = 3.02^2 \times 10 = 91.2$ watts.

6-10. Capacitors in Series and Parallel. We have noted that an equivalent capacitor to replace three capacitors in parallel is equal to the sum of the three capacitors. We might examine this a little

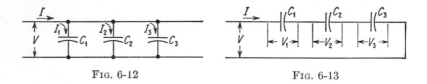

FIG. 6-12   FIG. 6-13

further. Looking at Fig. 6-12 we see that the voltage across the three capacitors is the same and equals V. The current is made up of the three branch currents: $I = I_1 + I_2 + I_3$. From $E = IX_C$, we get $I = V/X_C$; since $X_C = 1/(2\pi fC)$, $I = V \times 2\pi fC$. Similarly $I_1 = V \times 2\pi fC_1$, $I_2 = V \times 2\pi fC_2$, and $I_3 = V \times 2\pi fC_3$, which combine to give $C = C_1 + C_2 + C_3$.

The case of the series circuit is shown in Fig. 6-13. Here

$$V = V_1 + V_2 + V_3 = IX_{C1} + IX_{C2} + IX_{C3} = IX_C$$

Replacing the X_C's by their equivalents and canceling like terms gives

$$V = \frac{I}{C} = \frac{I}{C_1} + \frac{I}{C_2} + \frac{I}{C_3} \qquad \frac{1}{C} = \frac{1}{C_1} + \frac{1}{C_2} + \frac{1}{C_3}$$

6-11. Inductances in Series and Parallel. A circuit of inductances in series is shown in Fig. 6-14. Here $V = V_1 + V_2 + V_3$, or $IX_L = IX_{L_1} + IX_{L_2} + IX_{L_3}$; since $X_L = 2\pi fL$, this gives

$$L = L_1 + L_2 + L_3$$

for inductances in series, which we could reason from the fact that three (or more) coils connected end to end are equivalent to one coil divided into three (or more) sections.

FIG. 6-14   FIG. 6-15

Inductances in parallel (Fig. 6-15) give us $I = I_1 + I_2 + I_3$ and $V/X_L = V/X_{L_1} + V/X_{L_2} + V/X_{L_3}$, which reduces to

$$\frac{1}{L} = \frac{1}{L_1} + \frac{1}{L_2} + \frac{1}{L_3}$$

for inductances in parallel.

The relationships for resistances in series and parallel can be derived in the same way; as most engineers are familiar with these relationships, it will not be necessary to derive them.

6-12. Complex Number Notation. A word might be in order here about the complex number notation now commonly used to describe the electrical vector quantities. It might also be mentioned that electrical vectors are now frequently called "phasors" to differentiate them from force vectors. Since a phasor has either a leading component or a lagging component (Fig. 6-16), it is convenient to use the complex number notation to describe it. The out-of-phase component corresponds to the imaginary part, and the in-phase component corresponds to the real part of the complex number. Thus in Fig. 6-16 we have that $I_1 = 5 + j2$, $I_2 = 3 - j3$, $I_3 = 4$. $I = I_1 + I_2 + I_3 = 12 - j$. An example is afforded by a past examination problem:

FIG. 6-16

• The admittance of an a-c circuit is given as $Y = 4 - j3$.

  a. What is the simplified complex expression for the impedance?

  b. What is the magnitude of the pure resistance in the circuit?

The admittance of a circuit is defined as the reciprocal of the impedance, or $Y = 1/Z$. In this problem, then,

$$Z = \frac{1}{Y} = \frac{1}{4 - j3}$$

Simplification of this fraction, which is an example of division by a complex number, is effected by multiplying both numerator and denominator by the conjugate of the denominator. The conjugate of a complex number is formed by changing the sign of the complex term. For this case the conjugate of the denominator would be $4 + j3$. Simplification is achieved as follows:

$$Z = \frac{1}{4 - j3} \times \frac{4 + j3}{4 + j3} = \frac{4 + j3}{16 + 9} = 0.16 + j0.12$$

This is the answer to part (a). The answer to part (b) is $R = 0.16$ ohm. It might be further noted that the $+j0.12$ indicates a lagging phase angle (current lags voltage or voltage leads current) and a predominantly inductive circuit (ELI, voltage leads current in an inductive circuit). The phase angle $\phi = \tan^{-1} 0.12/0.16 = 36.9°$ (Fig. 6-17). The magnitude of the impedance equals

$$\sqrt{0.12^2 + 0.16^2} = 0.200 \text{ ohm}$$

Figure 6-17 shows the reactive component above the axis, which is in

FIG. 6-17

accordance with our convention. The voltage will equal current times impedance. This gives an identically shaped diagram for the voltage, shown also in Fig. 6-17, where the voltage leads the current, or the current lags the voltage.

The complex number notation serves to simplify many of the a-c circuit calculations. For a series circuit, the total impedance $Z = Z_1 + Z_2 + Z_3$, which follows directly from the fact that $Z = \sqrt{R^2 + (X_C - X_L)^2}$. Parallel-circuit analysis is much more troublesome, however; it can be handled more simply if one remembers that

FIG. 6-18

$$1/Z = 1/Z_1 + 1/Z_2 + 1/Z_3 \\ + \cdots$$

where all the Z's are in the complex number notation, than if one uses a step-by-step analysis. As an example of parallel-circuit analysis, let us review the past examination problem:

- Two parallel branches of an electrical circuit, one consisting of 5 ohms resistance and 0.023 henry inductance, and the other of 8.66 ohms resistance and 530 μf capacitance, take 30 amp from a 60-cycle main.

  a. What is the current in each branch?

  b. What are the instantaneous values of the currents in each branch when the current in the main has an instantaneous value of 36.7 amp?

First sketch the circuit (Fig. 6-18) and calculate the individual impedance.

$$X_L = 2\pi f L = 2\pi \times 60 \times 0.023 = 8.67 \text{ ohms}$$
$$X_C = \frac{1}{2\pi f C} = \frac{1}{2\pi \times 60 \times 530 \times 10^{-6}} = 5.00 \text{ ohms}$$

These give $Z_1 = 5 + j8.67$ and $Z_2 = 8.66 - j5.00$.

$$\frac{1}{Z} = \frac{1}{5 + j8.67} + \frac{1}{8.66 - j5.00} = \frac{5 - j8.67}{100} + \frac{8.66 + j5.00}{100}$$
$$= 0.1366 - j0.0366$$
$$Z = \frac{1}{0.1366 - j0.0366} = \frac{0.1366 + j0.0366}{0.02} = 6.83 + j1.83$$

or
$$Z = \sqrt{6.83^2 + 1.83^2} = 7.07 \text{ ohms}$$

The applied voltage $V = IZ = 30 \times 7.07 = 212$ volts. The same voltage acts across each branch, so

$$I_1 = \frac{V}{Z_1} = \frac{212}{5 + j8.67} = 10.6 - j18.36$$

or $\qquad I_1 = \sqrt{10.6^2 + 18.36^2} = 21.2$ amp

$$I_2 = \frac{V}{Z_2} = \frac{210}{8.66 - j5.00} = 18.36 + j10.6$$

or $\qquad I_2 = \sqrt{18.36^2 + 10.6^2} = 21.2$ amp

which are the values required for part (a).

The current in the main is given as 30 amp. This is the effective, or root mean square, current. The maximum current would equal

$$I_{\text{eff}} \times \sqrt{2} = 30 \times 1.414 = 42.4 \text{ amp}$$

The line current would equal the vector sum of the two branch currents $I = I_1 + I_2 = 28.96 - j7.76$. The phase angle would be $\tan^{-1} 0.268 = 15°$ lagging. Similarly for the two branch currents, $\phi_1 = 60°$ lagging and $\phi_2 = 30°$ leading. These three currents can then be plotted, since they are all of the form $I = I_{\max} \sin (\omega t + \phi)$. The main current will have an instantaneous value of 36.7 amp when

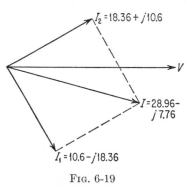

FIG. 6-19

$\sin (\omega t - 15) = 36.7/42.4 = 0.866$, or $\omega t - 15 = 60°$ and $\omega t = 75°$.

The instantaneous value of branch current

$$I_1 = 21.2 \sqrt{2} \sin (\omega t - 60°)$$

giving $I_1 = 30 \sin 15° = 7.76$ amp.

The instantaneous value of branch current

$$I_2 = 21.2 \sqrt{2} \sin (\omega t + 30°)$$

giving $I_2 = 30 \sin 105° = 29.0$ amp.

Taking the voltage as the reference phasor, we can plot the effective currents as in Fig. 6-19.

6-13. Transformers. There have been a few questions about transformers in the fundamentals examinations. Transformer analysis is relatively complex; we shall discuss it only briefly, trying to hit the high spots as indicated in past examinations.

Basically, a transformer is a device for increasing or decreasing an a-c voltage. The losses in a transformer are usually divided into two groups: iron losses, or core losses, and the I^2R losses due to the resistance of the windings. The iron losses are made up of the hysteresis loss and the eddy-current loss. The hysteresis loss is proportional to the frequency of the flux reversals and a power of the flux density. It can be expressed by the equation

$$P_h = k_1 f B^{1.6} \qquad \text{watts}$$

where the 1.6 power = a representative value. (The power of the flux density, called "the Steinmetz exponent," may vary from approximately 1.5 to over 2.0, with 1.6 being the value usually taken.)

f = frequency, cps

k_1 = a constant depending upon the characteristics of the core

B = flux density, lines or kilolines/sq in.

The eddy-current loss in the core may be represented by the equation:

$$P_e = k_2 f^2 B^2 \qquad \text{watts}$$

where the symbols have the same meaning as before except that k_2 is a different constant.

The copper loss equals $I_1^2 R_1 + I_2^2 R_2$, where I_1, R_1, I_2, and R_2 are the current and resistance in the primary and secondary windings. The resistances are usually small and can be approximated by a d-c test. The a-c resistance will, however, be several per cent higher, because of eddy-current losses in the copper.

The efficiency of a transformer is equal to

$$\frac{\text{output}}{\text{input}} \qquad \text{or} \qquad \frac{\text{input} - \text{losses}}{\text{input}}$$

The voltage regulation of a transformer in per cent equals (no-load secondary voltage minus full-load secondary voltage) divided by (full-load secondary voltage).

$$\text{Regulation} = \frac{V_2' - V_2}{V_2} \quad \%$$

Single-phase transformers are made with two windings and also with just one winding. When made with a single winding they are termed "autotransformers." Schematics of a single-winding transformer are shown in Fig. 6-20 connected for voltage step-down and step-up. In each case $E_2 = E_1(N_2/N_1)$.

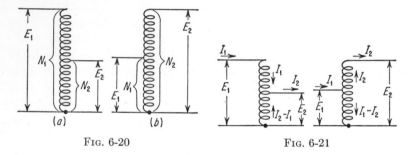

FIG. 6-20   FIG. 6-21

The common part of the winding carries both currents I_1 and I_2, but these currents buck each other, so this part of the winding is more lightly loaded than the other part. The current diagrams for the two cases are shown in Fig. 6-21 for an ideal autotransformer.

To illustrate, let us look at a past examination problem.

    • A 2,400/240-volt single-phase additive transformer is connected as shown in Fig. 6-22.

        a. What is the voltage at the load, i.e., is the transformer increasing or decreasing the voltage?

        b. At the instant the load current is 40 amp, what is the current in the supply circuit, assuming no transformer losses?

First we can redraw the diagram in the form of an autotransformer, as shown in Fig. 6-23. It is then immediately apparent that it is acting as a step-up transformer and is increasing the voltage. When the load current is 40 amp, the supply current will be (2,640/2,400) × 40 = 44 amp. It is interesting that in this case the current in the primary would be only 44 − 40 = 4 amp.

FIG. 6-22   FIG. 6-23

Another type of transformer problem sometimes given is illustrated by the following:

- A three-phase motor load totaling 325 kw at 0.75 power factor is carried by three transformers, each rated at 150 kva, and connected in Δ.

    a. If one transformer is disconnected, calculate the percentage of overload on the remaining two.

    b. What load, in kilowatts, at 0.75 power factor could two of these transformers carry without exceeding their rated load?

Let us examine this problem in a little more detail than is required to answer the questions. From 325 kw at 0.75 power factor we get 325/0.75 = 433 kva, or 433/3 = 144 kva per transformer. Let us assume that the secondary or motor voltage is 4,400 volts and the primary voltage is 13,200 volts. The voltage ratio would then be 13,200/4,400 = 3. The current on the secondary side due to one phase would be 144,000/4,400 = 32.7 amp, and the line current on the secondary side would equal 32.7 = $\sqrt{3}$ = 56.7 amp. The phase current on the primary side would equal 144,000/13,200 = 10.93 amp, and the line current on the primary side would be

$$10.93 \times \sqrt{3} = 18.95 \text{ amp}$$

The power in a balanced three-phase system equals line current times voltage differential between two lines times power factor times $\sqrt{3}$. For this case we have

$$P = 56.7 \times 4{,}400 \times 0.75 \times \sqrt{3} = 325 \text{ kw.}$$

The principal advantage of the Δ-Δ transformer connection is that if one transformer burns out or is removed, the three-phase system will still work, though under a reduced load. This connection of two transformers is known as the "open Δ" or "V connection." The basis of the operation of the open Δ is that the vector sum of any two of the line voltages in a balanced three-phase system equals the third line voltage. Thus we see that even though one of the transformers is removed, or burns out, the line voltages will remain constant. The line current, however, will now be only the current from one winding or it will equal the phase current. In the case being considered, the secondary line current would drop from 56.7 to 32.7 amp and the power would be only $1/\sqrt{3}$, or 57.7 per cent of the power if all three transformers were in use. If the load were maintained constant, the phase current, or current in the transformer winding, would have to increase in the ratio of $\sqrt{3}:1$. For this case the phase current would then have to increase to 56.7 amp and the load on each of the two transformers would be $56.7 \times 4{,}400 = 250$ kva, or a load of 167 per cent of rated capacity. This would be a 67 per cent overload.

We can also work this quite easily using only the information given. Since we have two transformers and a balanced load of 433 kva, the load on one of three transformers would be 433/3 and on one of two would be $(433/3) \sqrt{3} = 433/\sqrt{3} = 250$ kva, or an overload of 67 per cent on each of the two remaining transformers. This is the answer to part (a).

The total rated load which could be carried by the two transformers connected in an open-Δ arrangement would equal

$$150 \times \sqrt{3} = 260 \text{ kva}$$

which would be equivalent to $260 \times 0.75 = 195$ kw at a 0.75 power factor. This is the answer to part (b).

This might be clearer if we analyze it in a slightly different manner through the use of the phase current. Assuming the 4,400 volts secondary voltage, the rated phase current would be 150,000/4,400 = 34.1 amp. This would also be the line current for the open-Δ connection, and the total permissible load would then equal

$$34.1 \text{ amp} \times 4,400 \text{ volts} \times 0.75 \text{ power factor} \times \sqrt{3} = 195 \text{ kw}$$

When lines of flux are cut by a conductor, a voltage is produced which is proportional to the lines of flux cut per second. This is true for a transformer where the ratio of primary to secondary voltage equals the ratio of primary to secondary turns on the core. It is also true in a generator, and this phenomenon in large part governs electric-motor operation as well.

6-14. Generators. The generated voltage of the armature of a generator is:

$$E = \frac{N}{\text{paths}} \times \phi \times \text{poles} \times \frac{\text{rpm}}{60} \times 10^{-8}$$

where N = total number of inductors
ϕ = magnetic flux per pole

As an example, a past problem asked the following:

- It is desired to design a d-c generator which will generate an average electromotive force of 230 volts. The armature used has 180 series inductors between brushes. How many poles must be used if the flux per pole is 1.5×10^6 maxwells and the desired speed is 520 rpm?

A line of induction is called a maxwell, so $\phi = 1.5 \times 10^6$.

$$E = 180 \times 1.5 \times 10^6 \times \text{poles} \times \tfrac{520}{60} \times 10^{-8} = 230 \text{ volts}$$

giving $P = 9.82$, or 10 poles. The speed could be reduced slightly or, more probably, the flux lowered a small amount to give the voltage desired.

When the load exceeds the output of a generator it is sometimes necessary to parallel another generator to share the load. To perform the paralleling successfully,

1. The polarities of the two generators must be the same.
2. The voltage of the second generator must be the same as that of the first.

3. The load must be properly adjusted between the two after the connecting switch is closed.

In the case of shunt generators, balancing of the loads can be achieved by adjustment of the field rheostats. With compound generators it is necessary to provide an equalizer, or a connection between the two series fields, paralleling them. This is necessary

(a)   (b)

FIG. 6-24

to prevent instability in their operation. Since the current produced by the generator goes through the series fields, an increase in the load on one generator would increase the series field current, thus increasing the flux. This would, in turn, increase the voltage, which would tend to increase the current further, and unstable operation would result.

It might further be noted that since the voltage produced is proportional to the rate at which the lines of flux are cut, the voltage output of a generator will vary sinusoidally. This is illustrated in Fig. 6-24, where the instantaneous rate at which the lines of flux are being cut equals $v \sin \alpha$.

6-15. D-C Motors. The action of a motor is quite similar to the action of a generator, and the construction of a d-c motor is very nearly the same as the construction of a generator. As a matter of interest, some of the automobiles of the twenties were equipped with a generator which also served as the starter. The purpose of an electric motor is to convert electric power to mechanical power. It does this by utilizing the force exerted on a charge which lies in a magnetic field. The field is supplied by the field coils of the motor and the charge lies in the conductors wound on the armature. We recall, from earlier in this chapter, that the force on a charge $F = qvB$, where v is the velocity of the charge. The charge q that we are interested in here is due to the number of electrons affected by the magnetic field. The number of electrons in the conductor, which are also in the magnetic field, is proportional to the current in the conductor divided by the charge velocity. The equations describing this are:

$$i = nq_e vA$$
$$N = nlA$$
$$f = q_e vB$$
$$F = N \times f = nlAq_eBv = ilB$$

where i = current

n = number of moving charges per unit volume (number of electrons)

q_e = charge on an electron

v = velocity with which the electrons are moving

f = force on one electron

N = number of electrons

l = length of the conductor in the magnetic field

A = cross-sectional area of the conductor

B = magnetic-field flux density

Since the force on a conductor times the distance to the axis gives torque, it follows that motor torque is proportional to the armature current times the field. If we have a constant field, then the torque will be proportional to the armature current.

The static armature current in a d-c machine will equal the armature voltage divided by the resistance of the armature winding. Since the armature resistance is ordinarily low, this can mean a dangerously high current. The armature voltage during motor operation equals the applied voltage minus the back emf or the counter emf. The back emf is the voltage generated in the armature by virtue of the fact that as it rotates, the conductors in the armature winding cut the lines of force in the field. This generates a voltage in the armature winding which opposes the applied voltage and gives a net armature voltage equal to the difference of these two. This limits the armature current. The back emf equals speed times flux times a constant. $V = kNB$.

Applied voltage = back emf

+ (armature current $\times$ armature resistance)

This explains why reduced voltages are necessary to start large

motors.   When the armature is not rotating there is no back emf
and the current is limited by the applied voltage.   The positioning
of starting resistors for d-c motors is shown in Fig. 6-25.

6-16. Shunt Motors.   We might also note the effect of a reduction in load.   The field current of the shunt-wound motor is essentially constant.   If the load is reduced, the motor will tend to speed
up a little until the back emf has increased enough to balance the
loss in $I_a R_a$.

$$V = \text{back emf} + I_a R_a$$

As the load reduces, the required torque will reduce, thus reducing

Fig. 6-25

Fig. 6-26

the armature current, and the speed must increase to increase the
back emf enough to make up the difference.   This also explains
what happens when the field current of a shunt motor is reduced.
A reduction in field current will reduce the flux density and the rotor
must travel faster to generate an equivalent back emf.   If the field
current should be reduced to zero the speed would, theoretically,
become infinite.

6-17. Series Motors.   In the case of the series motor a reduction
in load would cause a reduction in torque and thus in armature
current.   Since the armature current is also the field current, this
would also cause a reduction in the flux density, and the increase
in speed required to maintain a balance between $I_a R_a$ and back
emf would rise as a power function.   The curves for series and
shunt motors are shown in Fig. 6-26.   Compound-wound motors

would have characteristics in between these two; a characteristic curve for this type is also shown in Fig. 6-26.

This explains why the load should never be removed from a series motor and why such a motor should be directly connected to its load or through gears and not through belts which might slip, come off, or break. It also explains why a shunt-wound motor should not be started or run with zero field current.

As an example of the application of some of these principles, a past examination problem was as follows:

- A d-c series-wound motor has a field resistance of $R_f = 0.80$ ohm and an armature resistance of $R_a = 0.50$ ohm. At 1,200 rpm the motor delivers 5 hp with a line voltage and line current of 100 volts and 46 amp, respectively.
  - a. What is the efficiency of the motor?
  - b. What is the counter emf generated by the armature at 1,200 rpm?
  - c. If the load is decreased so that the speed rises to 1,500 rpm, what is the line current?
  - d. What is the available torque for condition (c), assuming constant efficiency?

    Given the following relations: (1) torque varies directly as the armature current squared; (2) speed varies directly as the armature voltage; (3) flux varies directly as the armature current.

First we have the output of the motor, 5 hp, and the input, 100 volts × 46 amp. The efficiency is

$$\frac{5.00 \times 746}{46 \times 100} = 81 \text{ per cent}$$

since 746 watts equal 1 hp, which is the answer to part (a). This is a series-wound motor, so there is a drop through the field equal to 46 × 0.80 = 36.8 volts. The voltage across the armature is then 100 − 36.8 = 63.2 volts. The drop across the armature due to the armature resistance $I_a R_a = 23$ volts. The counter electromotive force must then equal 63.2 − 23 = 40.2 volts, which is the answer to part (b).

If the speed increases to 1,500 rpm, the counter emf must rise, and taking the second given relationship, armature voltage would rise to $(1,500/1,200) \times 40.2 = 50.2$ volts. As before, we have

$$iR_f + iR_a + \text{back emf} = 100 \text{ volts}$$

so $i = 49.8/1.3 = 38.3$ amp, line current (c).

Since for this case it is given that torque varies as the armature current squared, the torque would equal $(38.3/46)^2 = 0.695$ per cent of the original torque. The initial torque from hp $= 2\pi N Tq/33,000$ equals 21.9 ft-lb; so the torque for condition (c) is $0.695 \times 21.9 = 15.2$ ft-lb, answer to (d).

The relationship for horsepower is derived from the work done per revolution times rpm, N. Torque Tq is measured in foot-pounds or pounds force at a distance of 1 ft. The work done per revolution is then force acting times distance through which it acts 2π Tq ft-lb. This multiplied by rpm gives foot-pounds per minute, which, divided by 33,000 ft-lb/min hp, gives horsepower.

We might look at this problem a little further, since the second of the given relationships does not seem to be quite in accord with the theory. It states that speed varies directly as the armature voltage. This would imply that the armature voltage varies directly as the speed, but we know that while this is correct for a shunt motor with its constant field, it is not correct for a series motor where the flux is not constant but varies with the current. Since back emf is proportional to $N \times B$ and the field flux B is proportional to the field current (which is also the armature current), we have that back emf $= KNi$, and we can determine the constant K from the data given for the first case when $N = 1,200$ rpm, $i = 46$ amp, and the back emf was determined to be 40.2 volts.

This gives $K = 40.2/(1,200 \times 46) = 7.29 \times 10^{-4}$. When the speed increases to 1,500 rpm, the back emf will equal

$$7.29 \times 10^{-4} \times 1,500 \times I_2 = 1.093 \times I_2$$

The sum of the back emf and the IR drops must equal the line voltage of 100 volts. The IR drops equal $I_3(0.80 + 0.50)$, giving

$1.30I_2 + 1.093I_2 = 100$, or $I_2 = 41.7$ amp (c), instead of the 38.3 amp calculated previously. This is the correct current based on the theory of series-wound motors. The 38.3 amp would be correct for a shunt-wound motor. The back emf would then equal $1.093 \times 41.7 = 45.6$ volts, instead of 50.2 volts, as calculated previously.

The answer for part (d) would then be $(41.7/46)^2 \times 21.9 = 18$ ft-lb.

Let us examine the three given relationships in a little more detail.

The first states that torque varies directly as the armature current squared. Torque is proportional to the product of armature current times field flux. Since field flux is proportional to field current (which equals armature current in a series motor) this relationship is correct for a series motor. For a shunt motor the field current and flux are constant and the torque will be proportional to the armature current.

The second relationship, as we have already noted, is true for a shunt motor but not for a series motor.

The third relationship states that flux varies directly as the armature current. This we know to be correct for a series motor, since the armature current equals the field current for this type of motor. For a shunt motor the flux is essentially constant and does not vary as the armature current. This last relationship would appear to be at variance with the second given relationship; we must assume that a mistake was made in the statement of the problem, or that an attempt was made to simplify it and the simplification introduced a contradiction to motor theory.

6-18. Universal Motors. Series-wound motors will also operate on alternating current and are frequently used in the small sizes. Sparking is more of a problem, however, because of voltages induced by the alternating current, and a-c series motors have a greater number of armature coils and commutator segments than series motors constructed for use with direct current. Series motors built for use with alternating current will also operate satisfactorily with direct current; they are often called "universal" motors. The relationships for a-c series motors are the same as for d-c series motors.

6-19. Induction Motors. The commonest type of motor used on alternating current is the induction motor. Induction motors are made in two types, squirrel cage and wound rotor; they differ only in the construction of the rotor. The principle of operation of these two types is the same. The wound rotor is used to supply a higher starting torque and a limited amount of speed control. There is no electrical connection between the rotor circuits of an induction motor and the stator circuits of the supply line. The currents in the rotor are induced currents. The windings in the rotor are short-circuited and thus act like the secondary of a transformer, with the stator windings acting as the primary. When the rotor is stationary, the frequency of the induced current is the same as the line frequency. As the rotor gains speed, the frequency of the induced current will reduce, until the point at which if the rotor were to be turned at the synchronous speed, the frequency and the induced current would fall to zero, since no lines of flux would be cut. We recall that induced voltage is proportional to the rate at which the lines of flux are cut. If the rotor were to rotate at the synchronous speed, the conductors would be in phase with the alternating field and no lines of flux would be cut. Therefore an induction motor cannot operate at synchronous speed and there must be a certain amount of slip. This slip usually runs between 3 and 6 per cent, where slip equals 1 minus the ratio of actual speed to synchronous speed, or

$$\text{Slip} = 1 - \frac{\text{actual speed}}{\text{synchronous speed}}$$

The synchronous speed in rpm equals $120f/p$, where f is the frequency and p is the number of poles. This formula is primarily for single-phase current but can be generalized by dividing the number of poles by the number of phases, so that p should actually be poles per phase.

We have here the same sort of starting problem that we had with the d-c motors, viz., excessively high starting current. When the rotor is not moving, its conductors are being cut by the greatest number of lines of flux per second; thus, when the voltage is a maximum the current is also a maximum. The torque should also be a maximum, but in a single-phase motor, for instance, two equal and opposite forces act at the positive and negative poles; thus there is no operating torque. Various methods are used to start single-phase induction motors.

The basic torque equation Tq = KBI must be modified for alternating current to include the effects of phase angle. Since we are working with an inductive circuit, the current lags behind the voltage. The voltage is in phase with the flux, so there is a phase angle between the space distribution of the flux and the current that is equal to the phase angle between the voltage and the current. The torque is then proportional not only to the product of the flux and the current but to the cosine of the phase angle as well. In other words, torque is proportional to the product of voltage times the component of the current which is in phase with the voltage: Tq = KBI cos ϕ.

Under operating conditions, the slip is large enough to provide a frequency of the rotor voltage large enough to produce a reactance which cannot be neglected.

To illustrate some of these principles, let us look at a past examination problem which asked the following:

- The torque and slip of a 500-hp three-phase 60 cycle induction motor are 16,500 lb-ft and 2 per cent at full load. At a starting voltage of half-normal value, full-load torque was produced with 2.5 times normal full-load current.

  a. What was the full-load speed of the motor?

  b. How many poles did the motor have?

  c. What would be the starting current at rated voltage in terms of full-load current?

  d. What would be the starting torque at rated voltage?

Since it is a 500-hp motor and produces 16,500 lb-ft of torque, the full-load speed, from hp = $(2\pi N \text{ Tq})/33{,}000$, would equal 159.2 rpm. Since the full-load slip is 2 per cent and

$$\text{Slip} = 1 - \frac{\text{speed}}{\text{synchronous speed}}$$

159.2 must equal 98 per cent of the synchronous speed. Synchronous speed then equals 162.4 rpm. Actually, however, slip is given to the nearest percentage, and the actual slip then could be anywhere between 1½ and 2½ per cent, or the synchronous speed would lie somewhere between 161.5 and 163.2 rpm.

If this had been a single-phase motor, the number of poles would be $120f/S$, or $7,200/163.6 = 44$ poles, which is the nearest combination of a whole number of poles times speed of rotation to give 7,200. The speed is beyond the given range, however, and would correspond to a slip of 0.0276, or 3 per cent. Forty-five poles would correspond to a slip of 0.00502, or just barely 1 per cent. Taking the value of 44 poles for a single-phase motor would give a total of 132 poles for a three-phase motor, which seems a little out of reason. There is evidently a mistake in the statement of the problem, but what it is, is not apparent. If we take a torque of 16,500 lb-$in.$, we get a full-load speed of 1,910 rpm and a synchronous speed of 1,940 to 1,960 rpm, which does not make sense either, so we had better leave it as it stands. The full-load speed of the motor is 159.2 rpm (a) and the probable number of poles is 132 (b).

It is assumed that the impedance of the rotor is constant as long as it does not rotate. This means that rotor current would be proportional to the rotor voltage at the instant of starting. Since the rotor is, at standstill, the same as the secondary winding of a transformer, rotor voltage will be proportional to stator voltage and rotor current will also be proportional to stator current. At starting, then, stator voltage will be proportional to stator current; the answer to part (c) would be $\frac{2}{1} \times 2.5 = 5$ times full-load current.

Starting torque of an induction motor is given by the equation

$$\mathrm{Tq} = \frac{KBE_2R_2}{R_2{}^2 - X_2{}^2}$$

where $R_2{}^2 - X_2{}^2$ = the square of the rotor impedance, which is constant for zero rotor speed

K = a constant depending upon the physical characteristics of the motor

R_2 = resistance of the rotor

E_2 = rotor voltage

B = flux of the rotating field

This means that starting torque is proportional to $B \times E_2$. The flux is proportional to the stator voltage, and, of course, the stationary rotor voltage is also proportional to the stator voltage, so the starting torque is proportional to the square of the stator or applied voltage. The answer to part (d) is, then,

$$\left(\frac{1}{1\frac{1}{2}}\right)^2 \times 16{,}500 = 66{,}000 \text{ lb-ft}$$

6-20. Synchronous Motors. Synchronous motors operate on a different basis than induction motors. The rotor may be considered as a permanent magnet, and it follows the rotating field at synchronous speed. If the load is increased to the point where the torque required to maintain the speed exceeds the torque supplied by the motor, the rotor will slow down and stop. This is termed the breakdown, or pull-out, torque. If the load is maintained constant and the rotor field current is increased sufficiently, the current will lead the voltage and the synchronous motor will operate as a synchronous condenser.

6-21. Three-phase Current. There are occasional problems in balanced three-phase circuit network analysis. An example of this is the problem:

- A three-phase, 60-cps, 220-volts-between-wires, three-wire line supplies current to three single-phase heaters. Each heater has a resistance of 3 ohms and a reactance of 4 ohms. Determine:
  - *a.* The power supplied to the three heaters connected in three-phase Δ
  - *b.* The power which would be supplied by the same line if the heaters are connected in three-phase Y
  - *c.* The power factor of three-heater load in (a) and (b)

We might start by listing some of the important factors in balanced three-phase network analysis:

1. For a Y connection, line currents and phase currents are equal.
2. For a Y connection, the line voltages equal $\sqrt{3}$ times the phase voltages.
3. For a Δ connection, the line voltages and the phase voltages are equal.

4. For a Δ connection, the line currents equal $\sqrt{3}$ times the phase currents.

5. The instantaneous power for a three-phase system is constant and is equal to three times the average power per phase.

6. A balanced Δ connection may be replaced by a balanced Y connection if the circuit constants per phase obey the relation: Y impedance = ⅓Δ impedance.

X = 4Ω

R = 3Ω

R = 3Ω

R = 3Ω   X = 4Ω

X = 4Ω

Fig. 6-27

Let us solve part (b) first. We can draw an equivalent four-wire circuit (Fig. 6-27). Since this circuit is balanced, the neutral wire will carry no current and may be removed without affecting the circuit. We may simplify this circuit by sketching one branch (Fig. 6-28). The voltage from line to neutral, phase voltage, will equal $220/\sqrt{3}$ = 127 volts. The current will equal

$$\frac{V}{Z} = \frac{127}{3 + j4} = \frac{127}{3 + j4} \times \frac{3 - j4}{3 - j4} = \frac{381 - j508}{25} = 15.2 - j20.3$$

The line current would then equal $\sqrt{15.2^2 + 20.3^2}$ = 25.4 amp. The phase angle would equal $\tan^{-1}$ (20.3/15.2) = 53.1°. Since we do not know whether the impedance is reactive or inductive, we do not know whether the phase angle will be leading or lagging. The power per phase would equal 127 × 25.4 × cos 53.1° = 1,940 watts, or since $Z = \sqrt{3^2 + 4^2}$ = 5, line current equals $127/5$ = 25.4 amp; phase angle = $\tan^{-1}$ (X/R) = $\tan^{-1}$ (⅘) = 53.1°;

$$\text{Power} = I^2R = (25.4)^2 \times 3 = 1,940 \text{ watts per phase}$$

The total power supplied would be three times the power per phase, or 3 × 1,940 = 5,820 watts.

Total power can also be calculated from the relationship line-to-line voltage times line current times power factor times $\sqrt{3}$, which would be $220 \times 25.4 \times 0.60 \times 1.732 = 5,820$ watts, which is the answer to part (b).

Part (a) may be determined by taking a Y network with one-third the impedance per phase and calculating as above, or it may be determined directly. The Δ network is shown in Fig. 6-29. First let us solve the Δ network as shown. The phase voltage equals the line voltage, or 220 volts.

FIG. 6-28   FIG. 6-29

The phase impedance is again 5 ohms, so the phase current is $220/5 = 44$ amp. The phase angle is $\tan^{-1}(4/3) = 53.1°$, and the power per phase equals $220 \times 44 \times 0.60 = 5,820$ watts. The total power supplied is then $3 \times 5,820 = 17,460$ watts—the answer to part (a).

We can determine this also from the line current and line-to-line voltage. The line current for a Δ connection equals $\sqrt{3}$ times the phase current, or $44\sqrt{3} = 76.2$ amp. Total power would be $220 \times 76.2 \times 0.60 \times \sqrt{3} = 17,460$ watts.

The answer to part (c) is the cosine of the phase angle, which equals 0.60.

6-22. Three-phase Power Measurement. The measurement of three-phase power has also been touched upon in past examinations. Three-phase power can be measured with two single-phase wattmeters or with three single-phase wattmeters. Since the total power consumed in a three-phase circuit is equal to the sum of the powers consumed in the individual phases, the total power can easily be measured with three individual single-phase wattmeters. The connections for Y and Δ circuits are shown in Fig. 6-30. The total power equals the sum of the readings of the three wattmeters.

Three-phase power may also be measured with two single-phase wattmeters. The wiring diagram for this method is shown in Fig. 6-31. With this method the total power equals the sums of the

FIG. 6-30   FIG. 6-31

readings of the two wattmeters. This is true for both Y- and Δ-connected loads and for balanced and unbalanced circuits.

REFERENCES

The texts the author has found particularly helpful are:

Erickson, W. H., and N. H. Bryant: "Electrical Engineering, Theory and Practice," John Wiley & Sons, Inc., New York, 1952.
Fitzgerald, A. E., and D. E. Higginbotham: "Basic Electrical Engineering," 2d ed., McGraw-Hill Book Company, Inc., New York, 1957.

The following is also a good book on electricity and electronics:

Pumphrey, F. H.: "Fundamentals of Electrical Engineering," Prentice-Hall, Inc., Englewood Cliffs, N.J., 1951.

SAMPLE PROBLEMS SELECTED FROM PAST EXAMINATIONS

6-1. A 60-cycle 13,200-volt transformer has a core loss of 525 watts. When it is operated at the same maximum flux density of 50 kilolines/sq in. on 25 cycles, the core loss is 140 watts.

a. What was the test voltage on 25 cycles?

b. What was the normal hysteresis loss at 60 cycles?

$$P_h = k_1 f B_m^{1.6} \qquad P_e = k_2 f^2 B_m^2$$

6-2. A single-phase d-c motor delivers 5 hp and is 80 per cent efficient. It operates at 220 volts at a power factor of 0.707 lagging. What must be the reluctance of a condenser in parallel to bring the power factor to unity?

6-3. The power required by a three-phase 220-volt motor is measured by two wattmeters. One reads 2,000 watts and the other reads −400 watts. An ammeter in one of the lines reads 12 amp. Calculate the power factor.

6-4. Calculate the current in each of the four resistors shown in Fig. 6-P-4.

$A = 15\,\Omega$ $B = 60\,\Omega$

$C = 25\,\Omega$ $D = 200\,\Omega$

|←——— 120 volts ———→|

Fig. 6-P-4

6-5. A d-c shunt-connected motor is being supplied 220 volts and 54 amp. The armature has a resistance, at 75°C, of 0.08 ohm. The shunt field has a resistance of 55 ohms at 75°C. The stray power loss for this motor has been measured and is 180 watts. For this input, assume the motor to be operating continuously at a constant temperature of 75°C and determine:

 a. Shunt-field current
 b. Efficiency of the motor at this load
 c. Horsepower output for this load

6-6. Two condensers of 6 and 12 μf, respectively, are charged by a 120-volt battery. The condensers are in series. After being charged the condensers are connected by joining the two positive terminals to each other and doing the same with the negative terminals. What will be the final voltage of each condenser? What will be the charge on each?

6-7. A 110-volt 60-cps supply is connected to an unknown circuit. The circuit draws a current of 7.5 amp and uses 600 watts of power. The oscilloscope picture of current and voltage is shown in Fig. 6-P-7. Determine the following:

 a. Resistance in the circuit
 b. Impedance of the circuit
 c. Power factor of the circuit
 d. Phase angle of the circuit
 e. Whether the current leads or lags the voltage
 f. Reactance of the circuit
 g. Kind of reactance in the circuit

Current
Voltage

Fig. 6-P-7

6-8. A circuit consists of a 200-ohm resistor connected in series with the parallel combination of a coil and a 100-μf capacitor. The coil has a resistance of 10 ohms and an inductance of 1 henry. Calculate the voltage across the capacitor when this circuit is connected across a source of power delivering 125 volts at a frequency of $100/2\pi$ cps.

6-9. A group of small induction motors on a 230-volt 60-cps feeder in an industrial plant requires a total power of 25 kw at 0.707 power factor lagging. Determine the size of the capacitor to be connected in parallel with this load to correct the power factor to 0.90 lagging.

6-10. A load of 100 kva of induction motors on the three-phase 208-volt 60-cycle power supply to a shop is balanced and operates at a power factor of 80 per cent. It is proposed to bring the power factor to 90 per cent, lagging, by means of a Δ-connected bank of capacitors. Calculate the total kilovolt-amperes of capacitors required in this bank.

6-11. A 1,000-hp three-phase 2,200-volt induction motor is loaded to rated capacity. The efficiency is 92 per cent, and the power factor is 87 per cent lagging.

a. What is the current input to the motors?

b. What total kilovolt of capacitors is required connected in parallel with the motor to bring the power factor to 100 per cent?

6-12. A trouble lamp designed for plugging into the cigarette lighter receptacle on an automobile has a 50-ft cord of No. 18 copper wires. The lump is rated 60 watts at 10 volts. Assuming that 12 volts is maintained at the receptacle and that the resistance of the lamp does not change with temperature, what is the wattage input to the lamp?

6-13. Given the circuit shown in Fig. 6-P-13, determine V_L, V_{R_1}, and V_{R_2} when:

a. Switch A is open
b. Switch A is closed

Fig. 6-P-13

6-14. A coil has a reactance of 37.7 ohms and a resistance of 12 ohms. It is connected to a 110-volt 60-cycle line. Determine:

a. Impedance of the coil
b. Current through the coil
c. Phase angle with respect to the supply voltage as a reterence
d. Power factor of the circuit
e. Reading of a wattmeter connected to the circuit

6-15. A single-phase transmission line 12 miles long has a conductor with a resistance of 0.27 ohm/mile and a reactance of 0.62 ohm/mile. The voltage at the load end is 13,200 volts.

a. Calculate the voltage required at the powerhouse when the load is 1,500 kva at unity power factor.

b. Recalculate with a power factor of 0.8 lagging.

c. Recalculate with a power factor of 0.8 leading.

6-16. Find the current flowing through a series circuit consisting of a 10-mh inductor, a 10-μf capacitor, and a 10-ohm resistor when 120 volts, 60 cycles is applied across the combination.

6-17. A 2-μf capacitor has an air dielectric between plates separated 0.5 cm. If the capacitor plates have a potential difference of 1,000 volts, what will be the charge on the plates, the energy stored in it, and the voltage gradient? If a dielectric with a coefficient of 4 is placed between the plates with the same charge on them, what will be the voltage across the plates and the energy stored in the capacitor?

6-18. Calculate the three line currents and their phase angles. The loads are listed below. (See Fig. 6-P-18 for circuit.)

Load

A........ 1,200 watts, 0.8 power factor

B........ 1,200 watts, 1.0 power factor

C......... ½-hp motor, 80 per cent efficient at 0.6 power factor

Fig. 6-P-18

6-19. A storage battery for farm lighting produces 64 volts across its terminals on open circuit. The battery has 0.035 ohm internal resistance and is connected through a pair of copper wires, which have a resistance of 1.835 ohms per 1,000 ft, to a load 200 ft distant. The load draws 15 amp under the above conditions.

a. Determine the voltage at the load 200 ft from the battery.

b. Determine the voltage across the battery terminals when they are delivering this load.

c. Determine the voltage regulation at the load.

6-20. Two batteries, which are identical in every way, are connected in series across a 5-ohm resistor, and the current is found to be 0.2 amp. The same cells are then connected in parallel with the same 5-ohm resistor, and the current is found to be 0.16 amp across the 5-ohm resistor. What are the open-circuit voltage and the internal resistance of the batteries?

6-21. A 60-cycle single-phase motor draws 8.5 amp at 120 volts and has an inductive power factor of 87 per cent at this load.

a. How much power in watts is the motor using?

b. If a 150-μf capacitor is connected in parallel with the motor, what will the new power factor be?

6-22. A d-c generator has two poles, with each pole face having an area of 12 sq in. The flux density of the air gap is 40,000 lines/sq in.

a. Compute the average emf for one turn on the armature when the machine is running at 1,200 rpm. Assume that there is no stray flux outside the pole face area.

b. What is the relation between the average voltage, maximum voltage, and rms voltage?

6-23. The impedance of a series a-c circuit is $Z = 4 + j3$. The circuit consists of a resistor, capacitor, and inductor.

a. Which has the greater reactance, the capacitor or the inductor?

b. If a 200-volt 60-cycle source is connected to the circuit, what is the magnitude of the current flowing?

6-24. The resistance of the armature of a 50-hp 550-volt shunt-wound d-c motor is 0.35 ohm. The full-load armature current of this motor is 76 amp.

a. What should the resistance of the starter be for the initial armature current to be 150 per cent of the full-load armature current?

b. If the field current under full load is 3 amp, what is the over-all efficiency of the motor when it is delivering 50 hp?

c. Compute the stray power losses at 50-hp load.

6-25. It is necessary to measure the voltage across a line known to be about 220 volts. Two voltameters are available, (*a*) one with a 150-volt scale, internal resistance of 15,000 ohms, and (*b*) another with a 100-volt scale and internal resistance of 12,000 ohms. If the line voltage were actually 225 volts, what would be the reading of each meter if the two are connected in series across the line?

6-26. A slide-wire bridge is set up to measure an unknown resistance R_x (Fig. 6-P-26). The voltage E impressed on the circuit is 2.5 volts, and the resistance R_s is 50.5 ohms. The slide wire has a resistance of 12.92 ohms/ft at 70°F. When the slide is adjusted so that the galvanometer reads zero, $L_1 = 15.0$ in., and $L_2 = 25$ in.

a. What is the magnitude of the resistor R_x?

b. What is the magnitude of the current flowing through R_x?

c. What is the magnitude of the total current flowing through the battery?

Fig. 6-P-26

6-27. Specify the transformers required for a 500-hp 2,300-volt three-phase motor of 90 per cent power factor and 93 per cent efficiency supplied from a 6,600-volt three-phase line. If the above transformers are connected Δ and one of the three burns out, to what value must the load on the motor be decreased to prevent overloading the transformers?

6-28. The current in a certain circuit varies with time according to the relation $i = 4 + 2t^2$, where i is in amperes and t in seconds.

a. How many coulombs of charge pass a point in the circuit in the time interval between $t = 5$ sec and $t = 10$ sec?

b. What constant current would transport the same charge in the same time interval?

c. What constant current would produce the same heating effect in the wire during the same interval?

6-29. A cubical framework is put together as shown in Fig. 6-P-29. Each member is identical and has an electrical resistance of R. What is the equivalent resistance across the diagonal AB?

Fig. 6-P-29

6-30. Battery A has a no-load terminal voltage of 9 volts and an internal resistance of 2 ohms. Battery B has a no-load terminal voltage of 6.5 volts with an internal resistance of 1 ohm. When the positive terminals of the two batteries are connected together, the negative terminals are connected together, and a 3-ohm resistor is connected between positive and negative terminals, what current will flow through each battery?

6-31. An industrial plant has the following loads:

    25 kva at 0.85 power factor inductive
    50 kw at 1.0 power factor
    250 hp in motors at 0.90 power factor inductive and 86 per cent motor
        efficiency

a. Draw a complete vector diagram, with each plant load labeled, and indicate by a vector the reactance needed to correct the power factor to zero.

b. Calculate the magnitude of the reactance necessary to correct the plant power factor to zero. (This may be done graphically, if you wish.)

6-32. Three single-phase electric furnaces are each rated at 2,300 volts, 60 cps, 2,500 kva, and 80 per cent power factor lagging current. If these three furnaces were connected in Y to a three-phase 2,300-volt 60-cycle supply, determine:

   a. Total kilowatts which they would take from the circuit
   b. Approximate temperature which will be reached in terms of normal temperature when connected three-phase Δ

6-33. A small capacitor was connected in series with a 115-volt 200-watt Mazda lamp across a 220-volt 60-cycle supply. A voltmeter showed 115 volts across the lamp, an ammeter indicated 1.5 amp while the wattmeter read 200 watts. From these test data determine:

   a. Voltage across the capacitor
   b. Power factor for circuit
   c. Vector diagram for the circuit (label carefully)

6-34. Three dry cells, each of 1.5 volts emf and 0.1 ohm internal resistance, are connected in series through two external resistances of 0.5 ohm each. A resistance of 1.0 ohm is connected from a point between the two external resistances to a point between the first and second dry cells. Find the current flowing in each branch of the circuit shown in Fig. 6-P-34.

Fig. 6-P-34

6-35. An induction motor draws 25 amp from a 125-volt source and has a power factor of 0.8. What will be the line current when a condenser of 300 μf is connected across the terminals of the motor? The frequency is 60 cycles.

6-36. A circuit containing 0.1 henry inductance and 20 ohms resistance in series is connected across 100-volt 25-cycle mains. Find

   a. Circuit impedance
   b. Voltage across the inductance
   c. Power input
   d. Power factor

6-37. A series circuit consisting of a resistance of 50 ohms, a capacitance of 25 μf, and an inductance of 0.15 henry is connected across 120-volt 60-cycle mains. Find the line current.

6-38. A 30-hp 220-volt three-phase squirrel-cage induction motor with normal voltage applied to the stator has a starting torque of 1.25 times the full-load running torque.

   a. What would be the torque if 110 volts were applied for starting?
   b. What voltage should be applied to give full-load starting torque?

6-39. A 0.6 power factor inductive load takes 10 amp at 115 volts. What value of pure resistance in ohms may be placed in series with this load to make it operate normally from a 230-volt source?

6-40. A three-phase induction motor under test shows an input of 25 amp in each line. The voltage is 223 on each phase. The manufacturer's data show 85 per cent power factor and 90 per cent efficiency at this load. What is the motor output in horsepower?

6-41. *a.* In the circuit shown in Fig. 6-P-41, calculate the total current A_1 when 120 volts direct current has been applied for sufficient time for the current to have reached a steady value.

b. What will be the current A_1 if 120 volts, 60-cycle alternating voltage is applied?

FIG. 6-P-41

6-42. When a certain coil is connected to a 60-volt battery, 2 amp of current flows. When the same coil is connected to a 50-volt 60-cycle a-c source, only 1 amp flows. What is the inductance of the coil in henrys?

6-43. Three resistors, $R_1 = 0.2$ ohm, $R_2 = 0.3$ ohm, and $R_3 = 0.6$ ohm, are connected in parallel across the terminals of a storage battery having an internal resistance of 0.02 ohm and an emf of 6 volts on open circuit. With this circuit closed, determine:

a. Total current supplied by the battery to the three resistors
b. Terminal voltage of the battery to this load
c. Total power in watts supplied to the three resistors
d. Current in amperes through the 0.2-ohm resistor

6-44. A 200-hp three-phase four-pole 60-cycle 440-volt squirrel-cage induction motor operates at full load, with an efficiency of 85 per cent, a power factor of 91 per cent, and a slip of 3 per cent. For this full-load condition, determine the following:

a. Speed in rpm
b. Torque delivered in lb-ft
c. Line current fed to the motor

6-45. Three batteries have terminal voltages of 2.00, 1.95, and 1.84 volts, with internal resistances of 0.05, 0.075, and 0.064 ohm, respectively. The three batteries are connected in series with a 0.110-ohm resistance. (Assume the voltages and internal resistances remain constant.)

a. What is the voltage across the resistance?
b. What current is flowing through the resistance?

6-46. The wiring diagram for a d-c volt-meter is shown in Fig. 6-P-46. When 0.588 volt is applied across AB, the meter registers a full-scale deflection. The scale is graduated from 0 to 15. What should the meter read when 20 volts is applied across OP?

FIG. 6-P-46

6-47. A power company delivers 500 kw to factory A, 250 kva at 0.85 power factor lagging to factory B, and 750 kva at 0.97 power factor leading to factory C.

a. Draw a vector diagram showing the loads, power factor, and total kilovolt-amperes.

b. What is the total power load in kilowatts for the three companies?

6-48. A d-c shunt motor has the following constants:

Full-load speed, 1,200 rpm
Rated voltage, 230 volts
Full-load current, 58 amp
Armature resistance, 0.15 ohm

Calculate the speed of the motor when it is delivering one-half the rated torque. Assume that the field remains constant.

6-49. Show how to connect a 5-kva 2,300/230-volt transformer to give a 10 per cent boost on a 2,300-volt power line. What load can be safely supplied by this booster transformer?

6-50. In the series circuit, Fig. 6-P-50, consisting of three elements, the current is I and the voltages are as follows: $E_1 = 120$ volts leading 80°; $E_2 = 240$ volts lagging 70°; $E_3 = 150$ volts leading 30°.

a. Compute the voltage E which is imposed on the circuit.

b. Draw the vector diagram, clearly indicating E.

FIG. 6-P-50

6-51. An electrical series circuit has a resistance of 4.5 ohms and an inductive impedance of 15 ohms.

a. If 240 volts direct current is impressed across the system, how many amperes will flow?

b. If 240 volts alternating current is impressed across the system, how many amperes will flow?

c. Compute the apparent power measured in kilovolt-amperes for case (*b*).

d. Compute the real power measured in kilowatts for case (*b*).

6-52. An alternating current has a sine waveform which in turn has a maximum value of 200 volts (Fig. 6-P-52), and $e = E_m \sin \theta$.

a. Find for this waveform the instantaneous value of *e* when θ is $\pi/2$.

b. Find the effective voltage E_{eff}.

c. From 0 to π find the average voltage E_{avg} if the waveform is a true sine wave.

FIG. 6-P-52

d. What is the value of the form factor?

6-53. It is desired to supply a 250-watt 120-volt lamp 500 ft from the source of power with full 120 volts over a circuit of No. 14 copper wire. What voltage is required at the source? Disregard reactance.

6-54. Calculate the amperes in each of the four resistors shown in Fig. 6-P-54.

6-55. A load consists of three-phase motors and totals 750 kw at 80 per cent power factor lagging. A three-phase 300-kvar static capacitor is connected in parallel with the load. What is the resulting power factor?

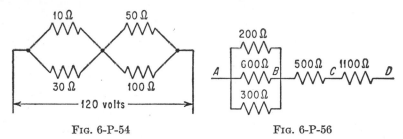

FIG. 6-P-54   FIG. 6-P-56

6-56. Referring to the sketch in Fig. 6-P-56, there is a difference in potential of 110 volts between *A* and *D*. Determine:

a. Drop in potential between *B* and *C*

b. Current in the resistance *CD*

c. Current flowing through the 200-ohm resistance between *A* and *B*.

CHAPTER 7

Chemistry

A general knowledge of chemistry is presupposed; discussion here is limited to those portions of the subject which have been emphasized in past examinations and to a few of the more general fundamental relationships applicable to many engineering problems. The reader who finds that he has retained little (or less) of his introductory college chemistry course, or who had no such course, will find it of value to read a beginning text, such as one of those listed at the end of this chapter.

A review of the questions in past fundamentals examinations concerning chemistry indicates that a complete coverage of this subject will be impossible in the space which can reasonably be allotted to it. On the other hand, the major emphasis has been on a relatively small (though very important) portion of the general subject, and this can be covered in some detail. The principal emphasis has been on the solution of problems embracing chemical reactions, including balancing of equations and calculation of the weights of the chemicals required or produced. Other subjects receiving lesser emphasis include water treatment, combustion, the universal gas law, Dalton's law of partial pressures, and relative humidity. From time to time questions have also been asked regarding electrolysis, battery reactions, specific heats of mixtures, chemical solutions, acidity and pH, molal quantities, etc.

7-1. Law of Le Chatelier. First let us review some of the generally applicable relationships of chemistry. One of these, the law of Le Chatelier, states, "When a system in equilibrium is subjected to a change (e.g., a change of temperature, concentration, or pressure), there is a shift in the point of equilibrium which tends to restore the original condition, or to relieve the strain." As an example, the combination of carbon and oxygen is exothermic and is represented by the equation $C + O_2 \rightarrow CO_2 + 97,000$ cal. If, after the reaction has reached a point of equilibrium, the system is heated, the point of equilibrium will shift to the left, using up heat and tending to lower the temperature of the system. The result will be a dissociation of some of the CO_2 which was previously formed and an increase in the concentrations of C and O_2.

An increase in the pressure acting on a system may also result in a shift in the point of equilibrium. For the reaction $N_2 + 3H_2 \rightarrow 2NH_3$, we have one volume of N_2 and three volumes of H_2 combining to form two volumes of NH_3, so an increase in pressure would cause the point of equilibrium to shift to the right. Such a shift would reduce the total equivalent volume of gas, as four volumes on the left combine to form two volumes on the right.

The shift in the point of equilibrium due to a change in concentration may be illustrated by means of the equilibrium constant, which is a constant for a given reaction at a given temperature and pressure. For a general chemical reaction $aA + bB \rightarrow cC + dD$, where we have a molecules of A reacting with b molecules of B, etc., the equilibrium constant $K = [(C)^c(D)^d]/[(A)^a(B)^b]$. For the previously used example, then, $K = (NH_3)^2/[(N_2)(H_2)^3]$, where $(NH_3)^2$ represents the concentration of NH_3 in the final mixture, in moles per liter, squared. Since K is a constant for a given temperature, we see that an increase in the concentration of either the N_2 or the H_2 must be followed by an increase in the concentration of the NH_3.

On the other hand, a chemical reaction will go to completion when one of the products is (1) insoluble, (2) volatile, or (3) only slightly ionized.
These conditions can be illustrated by the following chemical equations:

$$NaCl + AgNO_3 \rightarrow NaNO_3 + AgCl\downarrow$$
$$NH_4Cl + NaOH + heat \rightarrow NaCl + H_2O + NH_3\uparrow$$
$$HCl + NaOH \rightarrow NaCl + H_2O$$

In the last equation the water resulting is only slightly ionized so the reaction goes to the end.

7-2. Dalton's Law of Partial Pressures. Another general relationship of considerable importance is Dalton's law of partial pressures which states, "Each component of a mixture of gases exerts its pressure exactly as it would if the others were not present, and the sum of all their pressures makes up the total of the pressure exerted by the mixture of gases." The water-vapor pressure in gases collected over water is an example of a partial pressure. If oxygen is collected over water at a temperature of 64°F at a pressure of 780 mm Hg, the actual volume of oxygen at this temperature and pressure will be only 764.6/780 times the apparent volume, since the vapor pressure of water at 64°F is 15.4 mm Hg. This means that 15.4 mm of the measured pressure is due to water vapor, and the pressure of the oxygen is 780 − 15.4, or 764.6 mm. Then 15.4/780 × total volume is water vapor, and 764.6/780 × total volume is oxygen.

7-3. Avogadro's Law. Avogadro's hypothesis is an additional important relationship which should be kept in mind. It may be stated as follows: "Equal volumes of gases when subjected to the same conditions of temperature and pressure contain an equal number of molecules." This means that 1 liter of gas at 60°F and 14.7 psia will contain the same number of molecules regardless of the type of gas occupying that space—whether the gas is chlorine, hydrogen, or a mixture of gases, such as air. The number of molecules in 1 g mole of gas, which occupies 22.4 liters at 0°C and 1 atm of pressure, is 6.024×10^{23} and is known as Avogadro's number.

The application of some of these principles can be illustrated by means of an example taken from a past engineer-in-training examination.

- According to Avogadro's law, equal volumes of all gases at the same temperature and pressure contain the same number of molecules. Furthermore, 22.4 liters of a gas contain 6.06×10^{23} molecules at 0°C and 1 atm of pressure. How many molecules of nitrogen, N_2, are contained in 10 liters of nitrogen saturated with water vapor at 60°C and under a total absolute pressure of 2 atm? (Absolute zero may be taken as −273°C, and the vapor pressure for water is 3.1 psia at 60°C.)

7-4. Vapor Pressure. This introduces the concept of vapor pressure, which is the pressure (absolute) exerted by a vapor when it is in equilibrium with its liquid. The vapor pressure of a given liquid is dependent only upon the temperature; it is not affected by the total pressure acting on the system nor by the amount of space above the surface of the liquid. The boiling temperature of a liquid is the temperature at which the vapor pressure is equal to the local atmospheric pressure.

The vapor pressure of the water at the given temperature is 3.1 psia, and the total pressure is $2 \times 14.7 = 29.4$ psia. From Dalton's law of partial pressures we determine that the pressure due to the nitrogen equals $29.4 - 3.1 = 26.3$ psia. Application of the universal gas law (discussed in Chap. 4, Thermodynamics) gives the equivalent volume of nitrogen at 0°C and 14.7 psia.

$$\frac{P_1 V_1}{T_1} = R = \frac{P_2 V_2}{T_2} \qquad V_2 = V_1 \frac{P_1}{P_2} \times \frac{T_2}{T_1}$$

Note that the units of temperature and pressure cancel out and that as long as the same units are used for P_2 as for P_1 (and for T_2 as for T_1) they can be any units desired so long as they are absolute units

$$V_2 = 10 \times \frac{26.3 \text{ psia}}{14.7 \text{ psia}} \times \frac{273°\text{K}}{(273 + 60)°\text{K}} = 14.7 \text{ l}$$

of pure nitrogen at 0°C and 1 atm. The total number of molecules of nitrogen contained in the original 10 liters would then equal

$$\frac{14.7}{22.4} \times 6.06 \times 10^{23} = 3.98 \times 10^{23} \text{ molecules}$$

(NOTE: Avogadro's number is actually 6.024×10^{23}. The figure of 6.06×10^{23} was, however, the one given in the subject example.)

An additional example illustrating a more detailed application of Dalton's law of partial pressures is the following, taken from a past engineer-in-training examination:

- A tank having a capacity of 800 gal contains 500 gal of benzene at 35°F. Under these conditions the tank is sealed at atmospheric pressure. During storage the tank reaches 100°F. What is the gauge pressure in the tank? Assume that the air inside the tank is saturated with benzene vapor at the time the tank is sealed, and that the expansion of the tank due to the rise in temperature and pressure is negligible.

Coef of cubical expansion for liquid benzene
$$= 0.00077 \text{ cu ft/(cu ft)}(°F)$$
7.48 gal/cu ft
760 mm Hg = 1 atm

Temperature, °F	Vapor pressure, mm Hg
−9.5	10
71.2	100
109.4	200
141.9	400
163.7	600
176.2	760

Initially the pressure in the tank is equal to atmospheric pressure at 35°F. Assume this to be a standard atmosphere of 760 mm Hg. This is the total pressure in the tank

FIG. 7-1

at the time the tank is closed; it is made up of the pressure of the air in the tank and the pressure of the benzene vapor. To determine the amount of the pressure due to the benzene vapor at 35°F (and at the second temperature of 100°F) it is necessary to make a graph of vapor pressure vs. temperature from the data given. From the graph (Fig. 7-1) the vapor pressure of the benzene can be seen to equal 48 mm Hg at 35°F. The pressure due to the air at the time the tank is closed is then 760 − 48 = 712 mm Hg.

There are three things which affect the pressure: (1) The pressure of the air will increase because of the increase in the temperature. (2) The pressure of the air will increase because of the reduction in volume resulting from the expansion of the benzene. (3) The vapor pressure will increase as shown in Fig. 7-1. Dalton's law states that the change in the pressure of the air will be the same as if the air alone were occupying the space. Applying this reasoning, we can calculate what the final pressure of the air will be because of the change in temperature and volume, and then add the final vapor pressure of the benzene to the resulting air pressure; the sum will be the total pressure.

$$\text{Volume of air at start} = 800 \text{ gal} - 500 \text{ gal} = 300 \text{ gal}$$
$$\text{Final volume of air} = 800 \text{ gal} - 500(1 + 65 \times 0.00077) \text{ gal}$$
$$= 273 \text{ gal}$$

where 65 = change in temperature, °F

0.00077 = thermal coefficient of cubical expansion of the benzene

The change in absolute temperature is from $460 + 35 = 495°R$ to $460 + 100 = 560°R$.

From the universal gas law, $PV = WRT$, the relationship $(P_1V_1)/T_1 = WR = (P_2V_2)/T_2$ follows directly, which gives

$$P_2 = P_1 \frac{T_2}{T_1} \frac{V_1}{V_2}$$

The final air pressure would equal:

$$P_2 = 712 \times \frac{560}{495} \times \frac{300}{275} = 880 \text{ mm Hg}$$

The total pressure would then equal $880 + 170 = 1,050$ mm Hg, with the vapor pressure of the benzene added, and the gauge pressure would equal $1,050 - 760 = 290$ mm Hg, or

$$\frac{290}{760} \times 14.7 = 5.61 \text{ psig}$$

7-5. Chemical Reactions. The one phase of chemistry which has received the greatest emphasis in past examinations is the balancing of equations and the calculation of the weights of the products of the reaction.

A chemical equation is said to be balanced when the number of each of the different kinds of atoms on one side of the equation is exactly equal to the number of the same kinds of atoms on the other side of the equation.

$$C + O_2 \rightarrow CO_2$$
$$2H_2 + O_2 \rightarrow 2H_2O$$

are examples of balanced equations.

The weights of the different substances required for or produced by a chemical reaction will be in the same proportion as the molecular weights of the substances involved, as indicated by the balanced equation of the reaction. To illustrate this point, let us take as an example a problem from a past fundamentals examination:

• Hydrogen sulfide gas H_2S is used to precipitate lead sulfide PbS in a solution of hydrochloric acid.

   ___H_2S + ___$PbCl_2 \rightarrow$ ___PbS + ___HCl

   Formula weights: H = 1.008, Pb = 2.07.2, S = 32.06,

$$Cl = 35.46$$

   a. Balance the chemical equation and state how many moles of H_2S are required to produce 1 lb of PbS.
   b. How many pounds of H_2S are required to produce 1 lb of PbS?
   c. How many cubic feet of H_2S gas at 70°F and atmospheric pressure are required to produce 1 lb of PbS?
      The gas constant for H_2S is 23.7 ft-lb(lb)(°R).

To balance the equation we see that as it stands there are two atoms of hydrogen, two of chlorine, one of lead, and one of sulfur on the left, and only one of each on the right. The equation will be balanced if we put a 2 on the right-hand side, giving:

$$H_2S + PbCl_2 \rightarrow PbS + 2HCl$$

which shows that 1 mole of H_2S combines with 1 mole of $PbCl_2$ to give 1 mole of PbS and 2 moles of HCl.

The molecular weights can be determined from the formula weights given. $H_2S = 34$; $PbCl_2 = 278$; $PbS = 239$; $HCl = 36.5$.

To double check, $34 + 278 = 239 + 2(36.5)$.

The weight of H_2S to produce 1 lb of PbS can be determined by proportion: $x/34 = \frac{1}{239}$. $x = 0.142$ lb of H_2S.

The cubic feet of H_2S required can easily be determined by means of the universal gas law, $PV = RT$, which gives

$$V = \frac{23.7 \times (460 \times 70)}{14.7 \times 144} = 5.94 \text{ cu ft/lb}$$

The volume of H_2S required is then equal to

$$0.142 \text{ lb} \times 5.94 \text{ cu ft/lb} = 0.842 \text{ cu ft}$$

Another method of calculating the volume of gas involves the fact that 1 lb mole of gas occupies 359 cu ft at standard conditions. Since 1 lb mole of H_2S weighs 34.06 lb, this would give a volume of $0.142/34.06 \times 359 = 1.50$ std cu ft.

$$1.50 \times \frac{460 + 70}{460 + 32} = 1.615 \text{ cu ft}$$

at 70°F and 1 atm.

This answer is quite different from the 0.842 cu ft determined by the previous method, which indicates an error somewhere in the calculations.   Checking through the data, we find that the value for the gas constant for H_2S as given in the problem is obviously in error.   It should equal $1,544/\text{mol. wt} = 1,544/34.06 = 45.3$.   This value for R gives $V = (45.3 \times 530)/(14.7 \times 144) = 11.35$ cu ft/lb, and $(11.35 \text{ cu ft/lb}) \times (0.142 \text{ lb}) = 1.615$ cu ft, which is the correct answer for part (c).

Another example is afforded by a past examination problem which asked:

• A piece of plumber's solder weighing 3.0 g was dissolved in dilute nitric acid, then treated with dilute H_2SO_4.   This precipitated the lead as $PbSO_4$, which, after washing and drying, weighed 2.93 g.   The solution was then neutralized to precipitate stannic acid, which was decomposed by heating, yielding 1.27 g of SnO_2.   What is the analysis of the solder in terms of percentage of lead and tin?
Atomic weights: $Pb = 207.2$; $Sn = 118.7$; $O = 16.00$; $S = 32.07$; $H = 1.00$.

This is essentially a problem in ratio and proportion. The formula weight of $PbSO_4$ is 303.27 (207.2 + 32.07 + 64.0), which means that $(207.2/303.27) \times 2.93 = 2.00$, or that there is a total of 2 g of lead in the 2.93 g of $PbSo_4$.

The formula weight of SnO_2 is 150.7, which means that the SnO_2 contains $(118.7/150.7) \times 1.27 = 1.00$ g of tin.

The original 3 g of solder then contained 2.00 g of lead and 1.00 g of tin and therefore contained 66.7 per cent lead and 33.3 per cent tin.

A different type of problem is illustrated by the following example:

- An Orsat analysis of flue gases yields the following volumetric analysis: $CO_2 = 12.5$ per cent; $CO = 0.5$ per cent; $O_2 = 6.4$ per cent; $N_2 = 80.6$ per cent. Convert this analysis to an analysis by weight. Atomic weight: C = 12; O = 16; N = 14.

All that is needed here is to apply the universal gas law. Molecular weight of $CO_2 = 44$. $R = 1,544/\text{mol. wt} = 35.1$.

$$V = \frac{RT}{P} = \frac{35.1 \times (460 - 32)}{14.7 \times 144} = 8.16 \text{ cu ft/lb}$$

at standard conditions, or $w = 0.1227$ lb/cu ft.

For each cubic foot of flue gas there will be 0.125 cu ft of CO_2, which will weigh 0.125 cu ft $\times$ 0.1227 lb/cu ft = 0.01535 lb. Similarly, at standard conditions there will be

0.005 cu ft $\times$ 0.0781 lb/cu ft = 0.00039 lb CO/cu ft of flue gas
0.064 cu ft $\times$ 0.0893 lb/cu ft = 0.00572 lb O_2/cu ft of flue gas
0.806 cu ft $\times$ 0.0781 lb/cu ft = 0.0630 lb N_2/cu ft of flue gas

The weight of 1 cu ft of flue gas at 1 atm pressure and 32°F is then 0.08446 lb, and the weight percentages of the different constituent gases are $CO_2 = 18.1$ per cent; $CO = 0.5$ per cent; $O_2 = 6.8$ per cent; $N_2 = 74.6$ per cent.

The weight percentage may be calculated more easily by determining the weight of each gas in a mole volume of 359 cu ft. Since the volume per cent would also be the mole per cent, we would have, for 1 mole of flue gas:

Gas	Volume, %	Molecular weight	lb/mole of flue gas	Weight, %
CO_2	12.5	44	5.50	18.2
CO	0.5	28	0.14	0.44
O_2	6.4	32	2.05	6.76
N_2	80.6	28	22.57	74.6
Total.......	....	...	30.26	

One more somewhat similar type of example is afforded by a past examination problem which asked:

- Chlorination of municipal water supplies is common practice to destroy harmful bacteria. A common method for manufacture of chlorine is the electrolysis of sodium (NaCl) solutions.
  a. How many pounds of chlorine can be obtained from 1 ton of salt containing 97 per cent NaCl, assuming 30 per cent efficiency in the liberation of chlorine without concentrating the cell liquor?
  b. A steel cylinder contains 150 lb of dry chlorine. Calculate the volume in cubic feet that the chemical would occupy at 743 mm Hg pressure and at a temperature of 70°F. Use atomic weights Cl = 35.5; Na = 23.

The equation of the dissociation would be $2NaCl \rightarrow 2Na + Cl_2$, and $35.5/(35.5 + 23) = 0.607$ lb of Cl_2 from each pound of NaCl for complete dissociation. The process is only 30 per cent efficient, however, so only $0.30 \times 0.607 = 0.182$ lb of Cl_2 is actually obtained per pound of NaCl. Each ton of salt contains

$$0.97 \times 2,000 = 1,940 \text{ lb}$$

of NaCl, so $0.182 \times 1,940 = 353$ lb of Cl_2 can be obtained from 1 ton of salt.

From the universal gas law, $PV = RT$, we find the specific volume of chlorine gas at the given conditions.

$$V = \frac{RT}{P} = \frac{1,544}{35.5 \times 2} \times (460 + 70) \times \frac{1}{(743/760) \times 14.7 \times 144}$$
$$= \frac{21.8 \times 530}{2,070} = 5.58 \text{ cu ft/lb}$$

150 lb $\times$ 5.58 cu ft/lb = 838 cu ft of chlorine at the given conditions.

7-6. Combustion. There have also been a number of problems concerning combustion in past fundamentals examinations. These are essentially the same as other problems of chemical reactions. The only difference is that the fuel ordinarily combines with oxygen exothermically to produce heat and the products of the combustion. Combustion need not necessarily be an oxidation; there are many things that burn with intense heat without combining with oxygen (e.g., the reaction in an atomic hydrogen welding torch which produces a very high temperature, $H + H \rightarrow H_2$ + heat). Oxidation is the commonest type of burning, however, and is the one most frequently encountered in engineering and also in examinations. An example follows:

- One molecular weight of methyl alcohol, CH_4O, is burned in 10 per cent excess air. Write the combustion equation and determine the following:
  - *a.* Pounds of air required
  - *b.* The respective partial pressure of each of the products for a total pressure of 15 psia, assuming that the water vapor has not condensed
  - *c.* Volume occupied by the products at 240°F and 15 psia
  - *d.* Volume of air at 15 psia and 60°F needed to burn 1 ton of methyl alcohol per hour under the above conditions

First, write the equation:

$$\_CH_4O + \_O_2 \rightarrow \_CO_2 + \_H_2O$$

Since we are burning with 10 per cent excess air, we assume that the end products will be carbon dioxide and water vapor. Only the oxygen of the air will enter into the reaction; the nitrogen will not. Balancing the equation gives:

$$2CH_4O + 3O_2 \rightarrow 2CO_2 + 4H_2O$$

One pound mole of CH_4O weighs 32 lb and 32 lb of methyl alcohol combines with 48 lb of oxygen for complete combustion. Ten per cent excess air gives a total of 52.8 lb of oxygen. Since air consists of 23.2 per cent oxygen by weight, a total of

$$\frac{52.8}{0.232} = 228 \text{ lb}$$

of air would be required.

The products (of the combustion) would include CO_2, H_2O, the excess O_2, and the N_2, which took no part in the process. The complete equation, assuming the air to consist of 23.2 per cent O_2 and 76.8 per cent N_2 by weight (21 per cent O_2 and 79 per cent N_2 by volume), would be

$$CH_4O + O_2 + N_2 \rightarrow CO_2 + H_2O + N_2 + O_2$$

We are disregarding the approximately 1 per cent of CO_2 and inert gases present in the air, but this will not give any appreciable error, and their inclusion would multiply the complexity of the solution needlessly.

The weights of the different components would be:

$$CH_4O + O_2 \quad + N_2 \quad \rightarrow CO_2 + H_2O + N_2 \quad + O_2$$
$$32 \text{ lb} + 52.8 \text{ lb} + 175.2 \text{ lb} \rightarrow 44 \text{ lb} + 36 \text{ lb} + 175.2 \text{ lb} + 4.8 \text{ lb}$$

The partial pressures will be in the same ratios as the volumes, so let us calculate part (c) before part (b).

From $PV = RT$, the specific volume of the CO_2 is

$$V = \frac{RT}{P} = \frac{1{,}544}{44} \times (460 - 240) \times \frac{1}{15 \times 144}$$
$$= 11.37 \text{ cu ft/lb} \qquad \text{for } CO_2$$

Similarly for H_2O, $V = 27.8$ cu ft/lb; for N_2, $V = 17.85$ cu ft lb; for O_2, $V = 15.6$ cu ft/lb.

The volume occupied by all the products at 240°F and 15 psia would then equal

$$44 \times 11.37 + 36 \times 27.8 + 175.2 \times 17.85 + 4.8 \times 15.60$$
$$= 500 + 1{,}000 + 3{,}140 + 75 = 4{,}715 \text{ cu ft}$$

The answer to part (b) would then be, for CO_2,

$$P = \frac{500}{4{,}715} \times 15 = 1.59 \text{ psia}$$

for H_2O, $P = 3.18$ psia; for N_2, $P = 10$ psia; and for O_2, $P = 0.24$ psia.

Since it requires 228 lb of air to burn 32 lb of methyl alcohol, it would require $(2,000/32) \times 228 = 14,250$ lb of air to burn 1 ton. At 15 psia and 60°F, the specific volume of air would be

$$V = \frac{53.3 \times 520}{15 \times 144} = 12.83 \text{ cu ft/lb}$$

The required volume of air would then be

$$14,250 \times 12.83 = 183,000 \text{ cu ft/hr}$$

We could also have calculated these answers by using mole volumes.

Gas	Weight, lb	Molecular weight	Moles	Volume, %	Partial pressure, psia
CO_2	44	44	1	10.63	1.59
H_2O	36	18	2	21.26	3.19
N_2	175.2	28	6.26	66.52	9.98
O_2	4.8	32	0.15	1.59	0.24
Total.....	.....	...	9.41	100.00	15.00

Total volume $= 9.41$ moles.

$$9.41 \times 359 \times \frac{14.7}{15} \times \frac{460 + 240}{460 + 32} = 4,710 \text{ cu ft}$$

One mole of CH_4O requires 1.5 moles of O_2 for complete combustion. Air is 21 per cent O_2 by volume, so this would mean $1.5 \times 0.79/0.21 = 5.64$ moles of N_2. Adding 10 per cent gives 1.65 moles of O_2 plus 6.21 moles of N_2, or a total of 7.86 moles of air, which would occupy

$$7.86 \times 359 \times 14.7/15 \times {}^{520}\!/_{492} = 2,920 \text{ cu ft air/mole } CH_4O$$

One ton of CH_4O contains $2,000/32 = 62.5$ moles of CH_4O.

$$62.5 \times 2,920 = 182,500 \text{ cu ft/hr}$$

One other example of a combustion-process problem is the following:

• Assuming that air consists of 20 per cent O_2 and 80 per cent N_2 by volume, what will be the analysis in per cent by volume of the combustion gases if methane is burned at the rate of 1 g per 20 liters of air?

Reaction: $CH_4 + 2O_2 \rightarrow CO_2 + 2H_2O$.

The relative weights are

$$CH_4(16 \text{ g}) + 2O_2(64 \text{ g}) \rightarrow CO_2(44 \text{ g}) + 2H_2O(36 \text{ g})$$

so 1.0 g of CH_4 would require 4.0 g of O_2 for combustion, which would produce 2.75 g of CO_2 and 2.25 g of H_2O.

We know that 1 g mole of a gas occupies 22.4 liters at standard conditions. The 4.0 g of oxygen required to burn the 1.0 g of CH_4 would amount to $(4/32) \times 22.4 = 2.8$ liters, assuming that the air is supplied at standard conditions. Since 20 per cent of the 20 liters of air supplied is oxygen, this gives a surplus of $4.0 - 2.8 = 1.2$ liters of oxygen.

The 2.75 g of CO_2 produced by the combustion would occupy $(2.75/44) \times 22.4 = 1.4$ liters and the water vapor

$$\frac{2.25}{18} \times 22.4 = 2.8 \text{ liters}$$

It might be noted that there would be very little water vapor as such at 0°C, but the products of the combustion would be well above 100°C at some unknown temperatures. All the gases would expand in the same ratio (volume proportional to temperature for pressure constant), so any temperature may be selected as a reference point for determining volumetric ratios.

Volume-wise we should then have

1.0 g CH_4 + 4.0 liters O_2 + 16 liters N_2
  = 1.4 liters CO_2 + 2.8 liters H_2O + 1.2 liters O_2 + 16 liters N_2

which gives a percentage analysis of combustion gases of 6.5 per cent CO_2, 13.1 per cent H_2O, 5.6 per cent O_2, and 74.8 per cent N_2.

A slightly different type of problem concerning combustion is illustrated by another past examination problem:

• Assuming no heat loss in the process, calculate the weight of water in grams which could be raised in temperature from 25 to 100°C by the complete burning of 2.2 kg of carbon to carbon dioxide. The thermochemical equation for the combustion of carbon to carbon dioxide is

$$C + O_2 \rightarrow CO_2 + 95 \text{ kg-cal}$$

Use atomic weight C = 12.

The equation states that 1 mole of carbon (12 g) combines with 1 mole of oxygen (32 g) to produce 1 mole of carbon dioxide plus 95,000 cal. Therefore, 2.2 kg of carbon would produce

$$\frac{2,200}{12} \times 95,000 = 174 \times 10^5 \text{ cal}$$

It will require 75 cal to raise the temperature of 1 g of water from 25 to 100°C. It would, then, be possible to raise the temperature of $(174 \times 10^5)/75 = 2.32 \times 10^5$ g, or 232 kg of water, the required amount.

It probably should be noted that the calculations assume that the carbon and oxygen are at a temperature of 100°C before burning, and the products of combustion are cooled to 100°C after burning by the water being heated. Otherwise, allowance would have to be made for the heat used to raise the temperature of these substances. Should air be used to supply the oxygen and the products of combustion not be cooled to the supply temperature, an appreciable amount of heat would be utilized in raising the temperature of the air with its 79 per cent by volume of inert nitrogen.

7-7. Water Softening. The subject of hard water has also received a fair amount of emphasis in past examinations and so might be reviewed profitably. The degree of hardness is usually expressed in terms of the equivalent amount of $CaCO_3$ (calcium carbonate) in parts per million (ppm) by weight.

Hardness is caused by the presence in the water of bivalent ions of calcium, magnesium, or iron. These ions form insoluble precipitates when the water is boiled or when soap is added. Softening of the hard water may be accomplished by chemical precipitation of the undesirable ions before use or by replacing them with sodium ions which form soluble compounds. Softness may also be obtained by the formation of complex soluble ions.

An illustration of the substitution method of softening is afforded by the problem:

- A water-treating plant processes 2,000 gal of raw water per day. Analysis shows that the raw water contains 60 ppm (parts per million by weight) of calcium bicarbonate, $Ca(HCO_3)_2$. In passing through the zeolite softening process, the calcium ions are exchanged for the sodium ions, so that the softened water contains sodium bicarbonate, $NaHCO_3$, instead of $Ca(HCO_3)_2$. How many parts per million of $NaHCO_3$ does the softened water contain? Substituting Z for the zeolite radical, write the balanced chemical reaction. The formula for sodium zeolite is Na_2Z. Formula weights: Na, 23.0; H, 1.0; C, 12.0; Ca, 40.1; O, 16.0.

The equation of the process is $Na_2Z + Ca(HCO_3)_2 \rightarrow CaZ + 2NaHCO_3$. The formula weight of $Ca(HCO_3)_2$ is 162.1, and that of $NaHCO_3$ is 84, so 162.1 lb of calcium bicarbonate will form 168 lb of sodium bicarbonate. Then, 60 ppm of calcium bicarbonate would give $60 \times (168/162.1) = 62.2$ ppm of sodium bicarbonate. Actually, the 1,000,000 lb of water containing 60 lb of calcium bicarbonate theoretically becomes 1,000,002.2 lb of water containing 62.2 lb of sodium bicarbonate, but the slight change in total weight would have no effect on the calculations.

An example of the precipitation type of water softening is afforded by another past examination problem:

- A water supply for a chemical manufacturing plant contains 20 ppm (by weight) of CO_2 and considerable hardness in the form of $Ca(HCO_3)_2$. The hardness has been reported by the analyst as equivalent to 180 ppm of $CaCo_3$. Lime is to be added as a coagulant to remove the carbon dioxide and the calcium bicarbonate to render the supply more suitable for process water. The reactions, with the combining weights, are given below. If the process will require 3 mgd of water, determine the daily dosage of lime in pounds.

$$\underset{\substack{\text{Calcium}\\\text{hydroxide}}}{\overset{(56\text{CaO})}{\text{Ca(OH)}_2}} + \underset{\substack{\text{Carbonic}\\\text{acid}}}{\overset{(44\text{CO}_2)}{\text{H}_2\text{CO}_3}} \rightarrow \underset{\substack{\text{Calcium}\\\text{carbonate}}}{\overset{(100)}{\text{CaCO}_3}} + \underset{\text{Water}}{\overset{(2 \times 18)}{2\text{H}_2\text{O}}}$$

$$\text{Ca(OH)}_2 + \underset{\substack{\text{Calcium}\\\text{bicarbonate}}}{\overset{(100\ \text{CaCO}_3)}{\text{Ca(HCO}_3)_2}} \rightarrow 2\text{CaCO}_3 + 2\text{H}_2\text{O}$$

From the first equation it can be seen that 56 lb of CaO combines with 44 lb of CO_2 to give 100 lb of $CaCO_3$, which precipitates. An equal amount of H_2O (36 lb) is present on both sides of the equation. This gives us that $(20/44) \times 56 = 25.5$ lb of CaO required to remove 20 lb of CO_2 from the supply water.

From the second equation we see that 56 lb of CaO will precipitate 100 lb of $CaCO_3$, and since the hardness is equivalent to 180 ppm of $CaCO_3$, it will require $180/100 \times 56 = 101$ lb of CaO to precipitate the amount of $CaCO_3$ present in 1,000,000 lb of water.

There is also 20 lb of CO_2 present in 1,000,000 lb of water, so a total of $101 + 25.5 = 126.5$ lb of CaO will be required to soften 1 million lb of water.

Three million gallons per day of water would equal

$$3,000,000 \times 8.33 \text{ lb/gal} = 25 \times 10^6 \text{ lb}$$

of water per day. The total amount of lime which would be required would then equal $25 \times 126.5 = 3,160$ lb/day.

There may be some confusion regarding the calculation of the amount of CaO required to react with $CaCO_3$ when the compounds given in the equations are actually $Ca(OH)_2$ and $Ca(HCO_3)_2$.

$Ca(OH)_2$ is called "slaked lime" and forms when lime and water are brought together. $CaO + H_2O \rightarrow Ca(OH)_2 + heat$. It was required to determine the amount of lime before slaking.

$Ca(HCO_3)_2$ is calcium bicarbonate and is equivalent (in this instance) to $CaCO_3 + H_2CO_3$. Remember that it is the calcium which makes the water hard. Since the formula weight of $CaCO_3$

is 100 and the form weight of $Ca(HCO_3)_2$ is 162, a concentration of 162 ppm of $Ca(HCO_3)_2$ in water is actually equal to a hardness of 100 ppm.

REFERENCES

Frey, P. R.: "College Chemistry," Prentice-Hall, Inc., Englewood Cliffs, N.J., 1958.

Sienko, M. J., and R. A. Plane: "Chemistry," McGraw-Hill Book Company, Inc., New York, 1957.

SAMPLE PROBLEMS SELECTED FROM PAST EXAMINATIONS

7-1. A 5.82-g silver coin is dissolved in nitric acid. When sodium chloride is added to the solution all the silver is precipitated as AgCl. The AgCl precipitate weighs 7.20 g. Determine the percentage of silver in the coin. Atomic weights: H = 1.008; N = 14.008; O = 16.000; Ag = 107.88; Cl = 35.457.

7-2. In the electric-furnace method for producing phosphorus, the raw materials are phosphate rock, silica, and coke. The products are calcium silicate, phosphorus, and carbon monoxide.

a. Finish the following chemical equation:

$$?Ca_3(PO_4)_2 + ?SiO_2 + ?C = ?CaSiO_3 + 2P + ?CO$$

b. How many tons of $Ca_3(PO_4)_2$ are needed to make 1 ton of phosphorous? Atomic weight of P = 30.98; formula weight of $Ca_3(PO_4)_2$ = 310.2.

7-3. How much $PbSO_4$ is formed when a lead storage battery supplies 200 amp-hr of its capacity? Atomic weights: Pb = 207.2; S = 32; O = 16. One faraday of charge = 96,494 coulombs.

7-4. $N_2O_4(g) \rightleftharpoons 2NO_2(g)$. At 55°C for this reaction, $K = 0.66$. Calculate the percentage dissociation of N_2O_4 at 55°C and a total pressure of 380 mm. What are the partial pressures of N_2O_4 and NO_2 at equilibrium?

7-5. Caustic soda, NaOH, is an important commercial chemical. It is often prepared by the reaction of soda ash, Na_2CO_3, with slaked lime, $Ca(OH)_2$.

a. How many pounds of caustic soda can be obtained by treating 11.023 lb of soda ash with slaked lime?

b. What weight in pounds of lime, CaO, would be required? Assume complete reaction. Use approximate atomic weights: Ca = 40.1; C = 12; Na = 23; O = 16; H = 1.

7-6. In a certain chemical process two liquids enter a mixing chamber (Fig. 7-P-6) and are thoroughly mixed before being discharged at 80°F and 50 gpm.

Liquid (1) enters at 140°F and has a specific heat of 10 Btu/(gal)(°F). Liquid (2) enters at 65°F and has a specific heat of 8.33 Btu/(gal)(°F). Assume that

FIG. 7-P-6

there is no chemical reaction between liquid (1) and liquid (2), and that there is no heat lost or gained to the system.

a. What is the flow for liquid (1) and liquid (2)?

b. What is the specific heat of the mixed liquid?

7-7. A producer gas has the following percentage composition by volume at standard conditions of T and P: carbon dioxide = 5.8; carbon monoxide = 19.8; hydrogen = 15.1; methane = 1.3; oxygen = 1.3; and nitrogen = 56.7. Calculate the volume of dry air at the same conditions of T and P required for the complete combustion of 100 cu ft of this gas.

7-8. a. How many pounds of 93 per cent by weight H_2SO_4 can be obtained per ton of zinc sulfide, ZnS, ore of 50 per cent by weight purity?

b. For part (a), how many cubic feet of air at standard conditions, 1 atm and 32°F, will be required per ton of ore?

$$2ZnS + 3O_2 = 2ZnO + 2SO_2$$
$$2CO_2 + O_2 = 2SO_3$$
$$SO_3 + H_2O = H_2SO_4$$

7-9. What weight of calcium carbonate, $CaCO_3$, will react with excess hydrochloric acid, HCl, to produce 10 liters of carbon dioxide, CO_2, at 25°C and 770 mm pressure? Atomic weights: Ca = 40; C = 120; O = 16; Cl = 35.

7-10. Iron pyrite, FeS_2, is roasted in the presence of air so that sulfur dioxide, SO_2, is driven off in the form of a gas. The SO_2 is collected and combined with water to form sulfuric acid, H_2SO_4. How many pounds of 60 per cent sulfuric acid (60 per cent H_2SO_4 and 40 per cent H_2O) can be produced per ton of iron pyrite, assuming no losses in the process?

7-11. The following is the equation for the disintegration of uranium 238. Explain the significance of this equation with respect to both superscripts and subscripts.

$$_{92}U^{238} = _{90}Th^{234} + _2He^4$$

7-12. Pure silver, Ag, is combined with nitric acid, HNO_3, to yield silver nitrate, $AgNO_3$, nitric oxide, NO, and water, H_2O.

a. Write the balanced chemical equation for this reaction.

b. How many pounds of silver would be required to liberate 100 cu ft of nitric oxide at 60°F and 1 atm pressure? The gas constant for nitric oxide is 49.5 ft-lb/(lb)(°F). Formula weights: Ag = 107.9; N = 14.0; H = 1.01; O = 16.0.

7-13. Soda ash, Na_2CO_3, is produced commercially by the Solvay process, which may be represented by the following chemical equations:

$$CO_2 + NH_3 + NaCl + H_2O \rightarrow NaHCO_3 + NH_4Cl$$
$$2NaHCO_3 + heat \rightarrow Na_2CO_3 + H_2O + CO_2$$

In order to produce 2.2 kg of soda ash, how many grams of salt, NaCl, are required? Use atomic weights: Na = 23; C = 12; O = 16; Cl = 35.5.

7-14. Limestone containing 60 per cent by weight of $CaCO_3$, and 40 per cent of $MgCO_3$, when heated in a kiln, undergoes the following reactions:

$$CaCO_3 \rightarrow CaO + CO_2$$
$$MgCO_3 \rightarrow MgO + CO_2$$

Given that 1 mol. wt of a gas occupies 380 cu ft at the conditions of production from 1 ton of limestone,

a. How many pounds of MgO are produced?

b. How many cubic feet of CO_2 are produced?

The atomic weights are Ca = 40.1; Mg = 24.3; C = 12; O = 16.

7-15. If a current of 1 amp passes through a solution of NaCl for 1 hr, what are the products and what are the weights of the products formed at the cathode?

7-16. The complete combustion of propane gas is represented by the following skeleton equation:

$$C_3H_8 + O_2 = CO_2 + H_2O$$

a. Balance the equation.

b. How many cubic feet of air (air is 21 per cent O_2 by volume and 79 per cent N_2 by volume) measured at 25°C and a pressure of 760 mm Hg would be required to burn 10,500 cu ft of propane gas measured at the same conditions of temperature and pressure?

7-17. A high-grade phosphate rock containing phosphate equivalent to 85 per cent "bone-dry phosphate," $Ca_3(PO_4)_2$, is treated with an excess of sulfuric acid which converts 95 per cent of the phosphate to phosphoric acid. How much phosphoric acid would be produced from 100 tons of rock? Assume the reaction involved is given by the following equation:

$$Ca_3(PO_4)_2 + H_2SO_4 \rightarrow H_3PO_4 + CaSO_4$$

Atomic weights: Ca = 40; P = 31; O = 16; H = 1; S = 32.

7-18. One of the principal scale-forming constituents of water is calcium carbonate, $Ca(HCO_3)_2$. Explain how this substance may be removed from water:

   a. By boiling
   b. By adding calcium hydroxide, $Ca(OH)_2$

Write the chemical equations.

7-19. A gas analysis by volume gives the following: CO_2, 12 per cent; H, 4 per cent; CH_4, 5 per cent; CO, 23 per cent; N_2, 56 per cent.
   a. Find the percentages by weight.
   b. Write the combustion equation.
   c. How much air is required for complete combustion?
Atomic weights: $C = 12$; $O = 16$; $H = 1$; $N = 14$.

7-20. For preparation of ferrous sulfide, FeS, three parts by weight of iron fillings are heated with two parts by weight of sulfur. The product from such a process is found to contain 60 per cent by weight of FeS.

Calculate the complete analysis of the product in per cent by weight, assuming that no sulfur is lost and no other sulfides are formed.

7-21. What is the composition in volume per cent of the gases obtained from burning FeS_2 with 50 per cent excess air, assuming that all the iron goes to Fe_2O_3 and all the sulfur to SO_2?

7-22. In a gaseous mixture collected over water at 14°C, the partial pressures of the components are hydrogen, 300 mm; ethane, 100 mm; oxygen, 50 mm; ethylene, 189 mm. The aqueous tension at 14°C is 12 mm.
   a. What is the total pressure of the mixture?
   b. What is the volume per cent of hydrogen?

7-23. In the electric-furnace method of producing phosphorus, the raw materials are phosphate rock, silica, and coke. The products are calcium silicate, phosphorus, and carbon monoxide. Balance the following chemical equation:

$$Ca_3(PO_4)_2 + SiO_2 + C \rightarrow CaSiO_3 + P + CO$$

7-24. One of the principal scale-forming constituents of water is calcium bicarbonate, $Ca(HCO_3)_2$. This substance may be removed by treating the water with lime, $Ca(OH)_2$, in accordance with the following reactions:

$$?Ca(HCO_3)_2 + Ca(OH)_2 \rightarrow ?CaCO_3 + ?H_2O$$

   a. Determine the number of pounds of lime required to remove 1 lb of calcium bicarbonate.
   b. Determine the pounds of each of the products of the reaction per pound of calcium bicarbonate.

7-25. Gasoline may be represented approximately by the formula C_8H_{18}.
   a. Write the reaction for the complete combustion of C_8H_{18} with oxygen.
   b. Determine the weight of oxygen required per pound of fuel, and the weight of each of the products of combustion.

7-26. *a.* Chlorine may be prepared by the electrolysis of an aqueous solution of sodium chloride. If the decomposition efficiency of NaCl in the electrolytic cell is 50 per cent, what weight of chlorine would be obtained per ton of salt electrolyzed?

b. What would be the volume in cubic feet of the chlorine gas at standard conditions of temperature and pressure?

c. Explain how application of chlorine to a municipal water supply makes the water bacteriologically safe for drinking.

7-27. A pound of cane sugar, $C_{12}H_{22}O_{11}$, is burned with the theoretical amount of air to give complete combustion. What is the composition of the products of combustion expressed as per cent by volume?

7-28. An ultimate analysis of a Southern coal is as follows:

$$
\begin{array}{lr}
\text{Carbon} & 0.7161 \\
\text{Hydrogen} & 0.0526 \\
\text{Oxygen} & 0.0979 \\
\text{Nitrogen} & 0.0123 \\
\text{Sulfur} & 0.0074 \\
\text{Ash} & \underline{0.1137} \\
& 1.0000
\end{array}
$$

Atomic weights: $C = 12$; $H = 1$; $O = 16$; $N = 28$; $S = 32$.

a. Compute pounds of air per pound of fuel theoretically required for combustion.

b. Compute the flue gas weight per pound of fuel at theoretically perfect combustion.

c. What is the percentage of CO_2 in the wet gas?

7-29. Write the chemical formula for and calculate the weight of water and copper formed by the reaction of hydrogen with 10 g of cupric oxide.

CHAPTER 8

Engineering Economics

Economics, primarily as applied to investment, is another subject which has received a fair amount of attention in almost all the past fundamentals examinations. The principal emphasis has been on comparing the costs of alternate types of equipment purchase, pay-out periods, and costs of replacement of existing equipment. Included with these general subjects have been the complementary subjects of depreciation, interest, sinking funds, etc.

8-1. Interest. It would probably be best to start with a discussion of interest. The simplest form of interest is termed, appropriately enough, "simple interest." This is the amount charged in dollars per year for the use of $100 of capital; it is similar to yearly rental. Thus, if someone charged $3 interest for a loan of $60 for a period of 8 months, the simple interest rate would be $(\frac{3}{60}) \times (1\frac{2}{8}) = 7.5$ per cent. Simple interest is seldom used for periods of longer than 1 year except when the interest is paid in cash to the owner of the capital instead of being added to the capital. If the money is deposited in an account of some type the interest is ordinarily added to the account when it is due, and for the next period interest is calculated on the total amount, principal plus accrued interest. This is known as compound interest.

By this method the amount in the account at the end of the first interest period would be $S_1 = \text{principal} + i \times \text{principal} = P(1 - i)$; at the end of the second interest period the sum would equal $S_2 = S_1 + i \times S_1 = S_1(1 - i) = P(1 + i)^2$. Similarly

$$S_3 = S_2 + i \times S_2 = S_2(1 + i) = P(1 + i)^3$$

For n periods, $S_n = P(1 + i)^n$, which is known as the compound interest law.   Restating this we have, "The total amount of money at the end of n periods resulting from the investment of a principal P at an interest rate of i per period can be determined from the equation $S_n = P(1 + i)^n$."   Note that n is the number of investment periods and i is the interest rate per period.   If interest should be compounded quarterly, the number of periods would be four times the number of years and the interest rate i would be one-quarter the yearly or nominal rate.   Similarly, n would equal twice the number of years the money was invested if the interest were compounded semiannually, and i would be one-half the nominal or yearly rate.

8-2. Nominal and Effective Interest.   This leads to the distinction between nominal and effective rates of interest.   Interest rates are usually quoted on an annual, or yearly, basis, and such an annually based rate is termed the "nominal" interest rate.   Interest payments (or charges) are, however, frequently made semiannually, quarter-annually, or monthly.   In such a case part of the yearly interest can also earn interest during part of the year; the equivalent total yearly interest is termed the "effective" interest rate.   Thus an interest rate of 5 per cent compounded semiannually would give a nominal interest rate of 5 per cent but an effective interest rate equal to $(1 + 0.025)^2 - 1 = 0.0506$, or 5.06 per cent.   Similarly, 5 per cent compounded quarterly would give an effective rate of interest of 5.09 per cent, though the nominal rate would still be 5 per cent.

A past examination problem illustrating this point was as follows:

- You may purchase government bonds at \$750 each which mature in 10 years and have a face value of \$1,000 at the end of 10 years.   Determine:
  a. The average nominal interest rate earned by the purchase price of \$750, assuming annual compounding.
  b. Compare the "nominal" rate of interest with the "effective" rate.   Under what conditions will the "nominal" and "effective" rates of interest differ?

Annual compounding would mean ten interest periods, so $1,000 = 750(1 + i)^{10}$, giving $i = 2.92$ per cent nominal interest rate.   The effective rate would be the same in this case, since the nominal and the effective rates will be different only when the interest periods are shorter than a year.

Effective annual interest rate $= [1 + (i/m)]^m - 1$, where i is the nominal interest rate and m is the number of interest periods per year.

The actual rate of interest paid (or earned) is an important factor in comparing alternate investments or methods of borrowing money. A slightly more complex interest problem is illustrated by the following:

- A household finance company lends a young engineer $120 cash for which he agrees to pay the company $8.72 per month for 18 months. He receives the $120 cash, begins payments at the end of the first month, and continues the monthly payments until 18 payments have been made to complete the contract. For this particular capital-recovery-with-return schedule, determine:

  a. The nominal annual rate of interest earned by the company's capital.

  b. The effective annual rate of interest earned by the company's capital.

The nominal yearly rate of interest is that equivalent rate which would have been charged on a yearly basis had not the payments been required monthly.

The total amount paid by the young engineer was

$$18 \times \$8.72 = \$157$$

The simple interest rate was then $(157 - 120)/120 = 30.8$ per cent, but the young engineer had use of only half the money for the whole period, so the true simple interest was twice this, or 61.6 per cent for a period of 18 months, or $1\frac{1}{2}$ years. The nominal or equivalent yearly rate i can be determined from the compound interest law: $0.616 = (1 + i)^{3/2} - 1$, which gives $i = 37.7$ per cent.

When the young engineer pays $8.72 at the end of each month for 18 months, he is actually setting up a sinking fund, the present value of which is $120, since that is the amount he received in return for his agreement to pay $8.72 per month for 18 months. Theoretically the company can reinvest the $8.72 as it is received from the young engineer and receive interest on each payment from then on.

Assuming 18 interest periods, each of 1 month's time, with a payment at the end of each period, the sum of money which would be available at the end of the 18 months would equal

$$S = 8.72(1 + i)^{17} + 8.72(1 + i)^{16} + \cdots + 8.72$$

since the first payment would earn interest for the 17 remaining periods, the second payment for the 16 remaining periods, etc. The last payment would be made at the end of the 18 periods and would earn no interest.

If we multiply both sides of the equation by $(1 + i)$ and then subtract the original equation from the new one, we obtain

$$S(1 + i) = 8.72(1 + i)^{18} + 8.72(1 + i)^{17} \cdots + 8.72(1 + i)$$
$$(-)S = \qquad\qquad 8.72(1 + i)^{17} \cdots + 8.72(1 + i) + 8.72$$
$$S \times i = 8.72(1 + i)^{18} - 8.72$$

which can be generalized to give

$$S \times i = R[(1 + i)^n - 1]$$

where n = number of periods

i = interest rate per period

R = amount invested at the end of each period

S = total amount in the sinking fund at the end of n periods

If the young engineer had invested the $120 for the 18 periods of 1 month each at an interest rate of i per period, he would have had a total of $S = 120(1 + i)^{18}$ at the end of the 18 months. The more general relationship is $S = P(1 + i)^n$, where S is the amount at the end of n periods and P the amount initially invested. Substituting this equivalence for S in the previous equation and solving for R gives

$$R = P\,\frac{i(1 + i)^n}{(1 + i)^n - 1}$$

where R = amount to be invested in the sinking fund at the end of each period

P = present worth of the sinking fund, or the amount which could be invested in a lump sum now to give an amount equal to that in the sinking fund at the end of n periods

The amount at the end of the n periods would be S, where $S = P(1 + i)^n$, or $S = R[(1 + i)^n - 1]/i$.

In the problem being considered, $R = \$8.72$, $P = \$120$, and $n = 18$. This problem cannot be solved directly for i; it would have to be solved by trial and error, assuming an i, solving the relationship $[i(1 + i)^n]/[(1 + i)^{n-1}]$, and plotting the results against the value of i until the desired value of R/P was obtained. This expression, however, has already been calculated for many values of i and n and is listed in interest tables as the capital recovery factor. $R/P = 8.72/120 = 0.0727$, for the example being considered. From a capital recovery factor table with $n = 18$, the CRF $= 0.0727$ for $i = 3$ per cent and 0.0697 for $i = 2\frac{1}{2}$ per cent. The interest rate per period would then be 3 per cent, and the effective annual rate of interest earned by the company's capital would equal $(1 + 0.03)^{12} - 1 = 1.426 - 1$, or 42.06 per cent. Using the equation given previously, Effective annual interest $= [1 + (i/m)]^m - 1$, we can again calculate the nominal rate i from the effective rate.

$$0.426 = \left(1 + \frac{i}{12}\right)^{12} - 1$$

$$1.426^{1/12} = 1.031 = 1 + \frac{i}{12}$$

$i = 12 \times 0.031 = 0.371$ or 37.1 per cent nominal interest

which is approximately the same as the value calculated previously by a different method.

8-3. Present Worth. Another interest concept which should be discussed is that of the present worth of an amount of money required at some future date. This can be illustrated by means of an example:

> • A young man is about to purchase a new car. A roadster just right for his needs now costs $1,000. The addition of a rumble seat for his prospective in-laws will cost $150 at some future date. A roadster with a rumble seat costs $1,100 now. With interest at 8 per cent, determine how soon he must get married to justify the purchase of the $1,100 car.

Since the $1,000 would be invested anyway, the question is, "When would $100 invested now be worth $150 if interest is at

8 per cent?" The only question is whether to spend the $100 now or, theoretically, to invest it at 8 per cent compounded annually. We have, then, that $150 = 100(1 + 0.08)^n$, which gives $n = 5.27$, or $100 invested today at 8 per cent compounded annually would amount to $150 in 5.27 years. This means that the young man would have to get married before a lapse of 5.27 years to gain by the investment now in the rumble seat.

8-4. Cost Factors. As we can see from the foregoing, interest is an expense. It is an expense charged to us if we borrow, and it is an expense if we purchase a piece of equipment, in that we do not receive the interest we would otherwise get if we invested the money in an interest-producing enterprise. This loss of interest due to investment in a machine is a cost attributable to the machine and must be taken into account in any consideration of the advisability of purchasing a given machine. There are, of course, other cost factors involved, and any final decision as to whether to purchase must be based on a consideration of all the contributing factors. These can best be reviewed with the aid of a few examples.

Let us examine first the question:

- A company may furnish a car for use of its salesman, or the company may pay him for the use of his car at the rate of 11 cents per mile. The following estimated data apply to company-furnished cars: A car costs $1,800; it has a life of 4 years and a trade-in value of $700 at the end of that time. Monthly storage cost for the car is $3 and the cost of fuel, tires, and maintenance is $0.028 per mile. What annual mileage must a salesman travel by car for the costs of the two methods to be equal if the interest rate is 8 per cent?

The best way to handle such a problem is to itemize all the individual expenses of each of the alternative methods and add them to determine the total costs of the two possibilities. One method is a flat 11 cents per mile. The other method includes costs of operation, storage, depreciation, and loss of interest due to the invested capital. Oddly enough, the problem does not mention the costs of insurance, taxes, and license, which are appreciable today, but since these were not included we shall not consider them in our solution.

The type of depreciation has not been specified, so we shall use straight-line depreciation and average interest. This would give an annual depreciation cost of $(1,800 - 700)/4 = \$275$. The calculation of average interest often causes confusion, so we shall discuss it in some detail. The cost of depreciation is assessed at the end of each year; the amount invested throughout the first year is $1,800. Similarly, the amount invested throughout the second year is $1,525, the third year $1,250, and the fourth year $975. The average interest lost would then be $(144 + 122 + 100 + 78)/4 = \$111$ per year. This could also have been calculated by adding the first year's interest loss to the last year's and dividing by two, or

$$i_{\text{avg}} = \frac{144 + 78}{2} = \$111$$

per year. This can be generalized to give:

$$i_{\text{avg}} = \frac{\text{first cost} + \text{salvage value} + \text{yearly depreciation}}{2} \times i$$

We should then tabulate all the yearly costs and add them to obtain total yearly cost.

Depreciation...............	$275
Loss of interest............	111
Storage ($12 \times \$3$)...........	36
Operating costs.............	$0.028 \times$ miles
Total yearly costs........	$422 + 0.028 \times$ mileage

The problem asks when this would be equal to a unit cost of 11 cents per mile, so we have $0.11 \times m = 422 + 0.028 \times m$, giving a yearly mileage of 5,146 miles.

8-5. Costs of Nonoperation. Using this problem we can illustrate another concept which causes considerable misunderstanding, that is, the cost of not operating something that is already owned. In this case, using the above figures and assuming that the salesman owns his own car, our salesman is confronted with the need of deciding, on a purely economic basis, whether he should drive to a town 400 miles distant or whether he should take the train. The ticket agent tells him that the ticket for the trip will cost only $14, which is considerably less than the $44 it would cost to drive his car at a cost of 11 cents/mile. We must recognize, however, that our salesman already owns his car. The question is not whether he should buy a car, but rather, whether he should use a car he now possesses. The costs of depreciation, loss of interest, and storage go right on whether he drives the car or not. We might, then, say that it costs him $(275 + 111 + 36)/5{,}146 = \$0.082$ per mile to not drive the car, so the total cost of train trip would be $\$14 + 400 \times 0.082 = \$46.80$, which is more expensive than driving. Another, and perhaps more realistic, way of looking at this question is to compare the additional out-of-pocket cost of driving vs. the cost of the train ride. Depreciation, loss of interest, and storage are what might be termed "fixed costs." A fixed cost is one which does not vary over the operational life span of the equipment being considered. The yearly operating cost of the car varies, depending upon how many miles the car is driven. The fixed costs might be considered costs of owning a car; the operating cost is only the cost of driving a car. The actual cost of driving the car on the proposed trip would be $400 \times 0.028 = \$11.20$, which again is $\$2.80$ less than the cost of the train ride.

It might be mentioned here that this is not a discussion of the pros and cons of car vs. train. These items are only incidental to the concept of fixed costs, which continue whether the equipment is operated or not; they help to illustrate the costs of nonoperation. It should be easy to see, with the aid of the illustration, why it is often more profitable—at least for a while—to operate a plant at a loss than to shut it down altogether.

As another example, let us consider the problem:

- Machine A cost $\$4,400$ five years ago. The book value of the machine today is $\$2,400$. The highest offer for it today is $\$1,000$. In five more years the salvage value will be $\$4,000$. The annual operational costs have been $\$1,300$ and are expected to continue in that amount for the next 5 years. Machine B costs $\$7,200$ and has a life of 10 years, at which time it will be worth $\$900$. Estimated annual cost is $\$300$. With money worth 8 per cent, what is the annual cost of each?

This problem evidently has an error in it. Salvage values do not ordinarily increase unless the antique value becomes a factor, and what is junk today is not an antique 5 years hence.   Therefore we must assume that the typist forgot a period and that the salvage value in 5 years will be $40 rather than $4,000.

8-6. Book Value.   We note that the book value of the machine is $2,400, while the best price it can be sold for is $1,000.   The concept of book value is confusing to many persons and causes many errors in investment judgment.   Book value is a fictitious value and depends upon the accuracy of the estimated depreciation. It has no real significance and should be ignored when considering the cost of replacement.   Regardless of what the book value may be, the machine is worth only what it can be sold for, and that is $1,000.   It may help to consider the case in which the book value is less than the salvage value.   In this case you would certainly not dispose of the machine for the book value, you would sell it for the best price you could get, and that is the figure you would use in estimating replacement cost, not the lower book value.   The same is true when the book value is higher than the salvage value; you would still use the sale price and not the book value in the determination of replacement cost.

The yearly costs of the machines will be depreciation, loss of interest on the capital invested, and the operating costs.   Let us tabulate these and compare them:

Machine A now represents a capital investment of $1,000 and at the end of 5 years will be worth only $40.   The average yearly depreciation would then be $(1,000 - 40)/5 = \$192$.   The yearly operating cost would be $1,300, and the average interest loss would equal $(1,000 + 40 + 192)/2 \times 0.08 = \$49.28$.   The comparative costs would be:

Cost item	Average yearly cost over next 5 years, machine A	Average yearly cost over next 10 years, machine B
Depreciation (straight-line)......	$ 192.00	$ 630.00
Operating cost..................	1,300.00	300.00
Average interest...............	49.28	349.20
Total annual cost.............	$1,531.28	$1,279.20

It would pay to replace machine A with the new machine B. The average costs for machine B have been calculated for a 10-year period. If the average interest had been calculated for a 5-year period, the estimated costs would have been higher, as would the depreciation costs. The best information available, however, indicates that the new machine will last 10 years, so the average annual cost of operation has been estimated on a 10-year basis.

Another problem in an examination was:

- An asset has a first cost of $13,000, an estimated life of 15 years, and a salvage of $1,000. For depreciation, use the sinking-fund method, with interest at 5 per cent compounded annually, and find:
  a. The annual sinking-fund annuity or depreciation charge.
  b. The balance in the sinking fund, i.e., the amount accumulated toward depreciation of the asset at the end of 9 years.
  c. If the asset were to be sold for $4,000 at the end of 9 years, what would be the net *book-value gain or loss?*

Since the salvage value at the end of 15 years is $1,000 and $13,000 will be required for replacement, there must be a total of $12,000 in the sinking fund at the end of the 15-year period. We need to determine, then, what amount we must deposit at the end of each year to amount to $12,000 at the end of 15 years with interest at 5 per cent.

The sinking-fund formula previously derived is

$$R = \frac{Si}{(1 + i)^n - 1} = \frac{12,000 \times 0.05}{(1.05)^{15} - 1} = \$556$$

to be deposited at the end of each year for 15 years.

This could also have been determined with the aid of compound interest tables. Under the heading of "Sinking-fund Factor" we find a value of 0.04634 for 5 per cent compound interest and 15 periods. This is equal to $i/[(1 + i)^n - 1]$ and need only be multiplied by the value of S to give R. $R = 12,000 \times 0.04634 = \$556$.

We could also obtain the same value from the column headed "Compound Amount Factor" or "Amount of Annuity." This column gives the amount in a sinking fund at the end of n periods for a sinking-fund deposit amount of $1, or $R = 1$. The value in this column corresponding to $i = 5$ per cent and $n = 15$ is 21.5785, or $1 deposited at the end of each year for 15 years would provide an amount equal to $21.5785 at the end of that time. Since we need $12,000, $R = 12,000/21.5785 = \$556$.

The annual sinking fund or annuity charge (a) is $556. This is also called the "sinking-fund deposit factor."

At the end of 9 years there would be an amount equal to

$$S = R\frac{(1 + i)^9 - 1}{i} = 556\frac{1.05^9 - 1}{0.05} = \$6,130$$

The answer to part (b) is $6,130.

If the asset were sold at this time for $4,000, this would give a total of $6,130 + 4,000 = \$10,130$ available to balance the replacement cost of $13,000. The book value at this time equals

$$13,000 - 6,130 = \$6,870$$

or the first cost less the amount in the sinking fund. The actual value is only the market value of $4,000, so there is a "book-value loss" of $2,870.

This brings up another interesting point. If we had used straight-line depreciation, the book value at the end of 9 years would have been

$$13,000 - 9 \times \frac{13,000 - 1,000}{15} = \$5,800$$

which would have given a book-value loss of $1,800.

8-7. Depreciation. If we had used the "fixed-percentage-on-diminishing-balance" method of depreciation, the book value at the end of 9 years would be $2,790, giving a "book-value gain" of $1,210. The three types of depreciation curves are shown in Fig. 8-1.

The fixed-percentage-on-diminishing-balance method depreciates an asset by a fixed percentage of its value at the beginning of the year. The book value at the end of the first year is equal to Cost $\times (1 - D)$; at the end of the second year,

$$C(1 - D)(1 - D) = C(1 - D)^2$$

at the end of the third year, $C(1 - D)^2(1 - D) = C(1 - D)^3$; at the end of nth year, $C(1 - D)^n$.

For the case considered, $C = \$13,000$, and the book value at the end of the fifteenth year is $\$1,000$, so $13,000(1 - D)^{15} = \$1,000$;

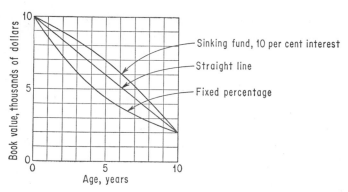

First cost... $\$10,000$
Salvage value at end of ten years...................... $\$2,000$
Straight-line depreciation............ $(10,000 - 2,000)/10 = \$800$ per year
Book value.. $\$10,000 - 800n$
Fixed percentage............................. $10,000(1 - D)^{10} = 2,000$
$$1 - D = 0.852$$
Book value.. $10,000 \times 0.852^n$
Sinking fund, interest at 10 per cent

Amount in sinking fund........................... $S = R\dfrac{(1 + i)^n - 1}{i}$

Book value................................. $10,000 - 502 \times \dfrac{1.10^n - 1}{0.10}$

FIG. 8-1

$D = 0.1572$, and the depreciation allowance each year is 15.72 per cent of the book value of the asset at the beginning of that year. The book value at the end of the first year would then be

$$13,000 \times 0.8428 = \$10,950$$

at the end of the second year, $13,000 \times 0.8428^2 = \$9,230$, or $10,950 \times 0.8428$; at the end of the fifth year,

$$13,000 \times 0.8428^5 = \$5,530$$

at the end of the ninth year, $13,000 \times 0.8428^9 = \$2,800$; at the end of the fifteenth year, $13,000 \times 0.8428^{15} = \$1,000$.

The only difference in these three cases is the method of keeping the books. Since sinking funds are seldom if ever actually set up in practice and exist only as accounts in the books of the organization, these three cases would be just the same in so far as the actual investment procedure and recommendations were concerned.

Depreciation schedules are set up primarily for purposes of taxation and rate setting. They also give an estimate of the capital which may be required for replacement at any given time, but since replacement capital is ordinarily borrowed, long-term forecasts of this factor are seldom of any value. The tax picture is important however, and for this particular expense it can be seen that the fixed-percentage method will give the greatest benefit if the asset has to be sold before the end of its expected useful life. The book-value loss reflects a tax loss but should not enter into any investment decision.

Another example dealing with present value is afforded by the problem:

- An engineer is currently paying \$125 per month house rent. He can build a house for \$12,000 which should have a life of 30 years. Taxes, insurance, and repairs will amount to \$550 per year. This engineer has capital which is currently earning 6 per cent on a mortgage which will be coming due very soon. Assuming that the capital can be reinvested at 6 per cent and using straight-line method for depreciation, allowing \$3,000 salvage, calculate:
  - *a.* The equivalent present worth of 30 years' rent at \$125 per month using 6 per cent interest.
  - *b.* The equivalent present worth of 30 years' owning the house.
  - *c.* Comparing present-worth values, which plan is more economical?

Part (*a*) asks, What is the present value of an annuity in which \$125 is deposited at the end of each period with interest at ½ per cent per period, for 360 periods.

The annuity, or sinking-fund, formula used previously is

$$R = P \frac{i(1 + i)^n}{(1 + i)^n - 1}$$

which gives as the answer to (a)

$$P = 125 \frac{(1.005)^{360} - 1}{0.005(1.005)^{360}} = 125 \times 166.8 = \$20,850$$

This can also be calculated with the aid of a compound interest table, but we shall have to finagle a bit since most tables do not go beyond 100 periods ($n = 100$), and we have 360 periods. Let us split the total number of periods into four sets of 90 periods each. From the "Present Worth Factor" column we see that the present worth of a 90-term annuity for \$1 deposits with interest at $\frac{1}{2}$ per cent per period is \$72.33. In the "Compound Interest" column we see that the present value of \$1 invested at $\frac{1}{2}$ per cent for 90 periods is \$0.6383. If we invested \$1 per period for 90 periods with interest at $\frac{1}{2}$ per cent per period, the present value of the future sum is \$72.33. However, the present value of the second annuity, \$1 invested at the end of each period from period 91 through period 180, is $72.33 \times 0.6383 = \$46.17$, etc. We can build up a table to show this.

Period	Present value of annuity		
1–90.........	72.33×1	=	\$ 72.33
91–180........	72.33×0.6383	=	46.17
181–270........	72.33×0.6383^2	=	29.47
271–360........	72.33×0.6383^3	=	18.81
Present value of all four annuities..			\$166.78

This is the same as the value obtained with the formula.

The equivalent present worth of 30 years' rent at \$125 per month is, then, \$20,850 with interest at $\frac{1}{2}$ per cent per month.

This is the same as saying that if we invested \$20,850 at an interest rate of $\frac{1}{2}$ per cent per month, at the end of 30 years (360 months) it would equal the same amount that we should have if we

invested \$125 per month for 360 months (30 years) in an annuity
with interest at $\frac{1}{2}$ per cent per month.

$$\$20,850 \times 1.005^{360} = \$125,500$$
$$\$125 \times \frac{1.005^{360} - 1}{0.005} = \$125,500$$

This is not quite the true case, however, since interest is actually
6 per cent per year and not $\frac{1}{2}$ per cent per month. We could
assume that each monthly deposit of \$125 would draw interest at
6 per cent per annum until the end of the fiscal year in which it was
invested and then at 6 per cent compounded annually till the end
of the 30-year period. This would give an annuity in which the
amount deposited at the end of each year would equal \$1,541.

$$(125 \times 12 + ^{11}\!/_{12} \times 0.06 \times 125 + ^{10}\!/_{12} \times 0.06 \times 125 + \cdots$$
$$+ \, ^{1}\!/_{12} \times 0.06 \times 125)$$

This is cutting things a little too fine, however, and it would be
better to figure the annuity based on 30 end-of-the-year payments of
\$1,500 (12 $\times$ 125).   The present worth of such an annuity would be

$$\$1,500 \times \frac{1.06^{30} - 1}{0.06 \times 1.06^{30}} = 1,500 \times 13.76 = \$20,640$$

which is a better answer to part (a).

If the house were owned, \$550 would have to be spent every year
for taxes, insurance, and repairs.   This would amount to an annuity
with a present value of

$$\$550 \times 13.76 = \$7,570$$

This means that of the \$20,640 present worth of the rent annuity,
\$7,570 would have to be used to set up a fund to return \$550 each
year for 30 years for expenses.

Another way of looking at this is to say that of the \$1,500 per year
rental income \$550 would have to be used for expenses, leaving a
net of \$950 to be deposited in the annuity at the end of each year.
Either method will give the same value.

$$\$20,640 - \$7,570 = \$13,076$$
$$\$950 \times 13.76 = \$13,076$$

In addition to the present worth of the net rental income annuity, there is also the estimated $3,000 value of the house 30 years hence. The present worth of $3,000 is

$$\frac{\$3,000}{1.06^{30}} = \$522$$

The equivalent present worth of 30 years' owning the house—the answer to (b)—is then

$$\$13,076 + \$522 = \$13,598$$

The present worth of $12,000 is, of course, $12,000. Comparing these two figures we can see that the answer to part (c) is that it would be beneficial to build the house.

We can also determine this by calculating the values of the two alternatives at the end of 30 years. For the $12,000 invested at 6 per cent we should have

$$\$12,000 \times 1.06^{30} = \$68,920$$

The rent money less expenses which could be invested in an annuity at the end of each year would equal $950. At the end of 30 years this would amount to

$$\$950 \times \frac{1.06^{30} - 1}{0.06} = 950 \times 79.058 = \$75,100$$

To this should be added the $3,000 which the house will be worth in 30 years giving a total of $78,100. This is $9,180 more than the value of $12,000 thirty years hence. This should also equal the value of the difference of the present worths 30 years hence, or $1,598 \times 1.06^{30} = \$9,180$, which checks.

Another facet of engineering economics is illustrated by the past problem:

- A contract is let for $10,000. It is to be completed in 4 weeks' time, subject to a penalty of $240 per day if that time is exceeded. At the end of 3 weeks the work is 60 per cent complete. Labor costs were initially estimated to come to $4,000 on the basis of 40 hr/week. If overtime labor must be compensated at double time:

a. Would it be cheaper to take the penalty or to complete the job by working overtime? (Give cost figures.)

b. By what percentage would the estimated labor cost be increased by the cheaper plan?

Since the work is 60 per cent complete there is 40 per cent to go. Working at the present rate will then require

$$(^{40}\!\!/_{60}) \times (3 \times 40) = 80 \text{ hr}$$

or 10 more days. With 1 week left this would mean 16 hr-days, but the problem implies that this would be all right. The cost of labor is 4,000/4 = $1,000 per week, or $200 per day. Let us figure costs of each method.

Penalty Method:

10 days' labor @ $200....................	$2,000
5 days' penalty @ $240..................	1,200
Total cost labor plus penalty...........	$3,200

Overtime Method:

5 days' straight time @ $200....................	$1,000
5 equivalent days' double time @ $400..........	2,000
Total cost................................	$3,000

It would be cheaper to complete the job by working overtime.

With the cheaper plan the total labor cost would be the $3,000 spent during the first 3 weeks plus the $3,000 spent the last week, giving a total labor cost of $6,000 as compared with the $4,000 estimate, or a 50 per cent increase.

REFERENCES

The texts the author has found of most help in the phases of engineering economy emphasized in the examinations reviewed are:

Grant, E. L., and W. G. Ireson: "Principles of Engineering Economy," The Ronald Press Company, New York, 1960.

Thuesen, H. G.: "Engineering Economy," Prentice-Hall, Inc., Englewood Cliffs, N.J., 1957.

SAMPLE PROBLEMS SELECTED FROM PAST EXAMINATIONS

8-1. To obtain a certain service two plans are being considered. (1) Plan A will require the purchasing of certain special equipment costing $12,000. The salvage for this special equipment will be $500 regardless of the length of time it may have been used. Annual labor costs will average $3,500. (2) Plan B simply involves $5,000 labor cost per year. All other incomes and expenses under the two plans will be the same. Allow 5 per cent interest on capital, 5 per cent compounded annually on amortization or sinking fund for depreciation, and determine how many years it will take for the special equipment of Plan A to pay for itself. (HINT: annual cost tabulation and a final interpolation give an exact answer.)

8-2. A young engineer has estimated that his annual earnings should average $6,000, $10,000, and $15,000 per year in succeeding decades from the time he takes his first job after graduation. Allow 3 per cent interest compounded annually each for cost of money and return, and determine:

a. Present worth (at graduation) in cash of the 30 years' earnings
b. Equivalent uniform annual value of the 30 years' estimated income

8-3. A piece of earth-moving equipment was purchased at a cash price of $25,000. The life of this equipment was estimated at 6 years with no salvage. However, at the end of 4 years the machine had become so inefficient, because of wearing of parts, that it was replaced. Depreciation was allowed on the company books by the sinking-fund method with 4 per cent interest. Determine:

a. Estimated annual depreciation
b. Balance in the depreciation sinking fund at the end of the 4 years
c. Sunk cost at the time of replacement

8-4. A certain type of automatic milling machine can be purchased for $6,500. Expert estimates indicate a life of 10 years and $500 salvage for this particular machine. Use the sinking-fund method for depreciation charges and calculate total *annual capital recovery* charges, which include return on capital on this machine, when interest is (*a*) 4 per cent, (*b*) 6 per cent.

8-5. An old light-capacity highway bridge may be strengthened at a cost of $9,000, or it may be replaced by a new bridge of sufficient capacity at a cost of $40,000. The present net salvage value of the old bridge is $13,000. It is estimated that the old bridge, when reinforced, will last for 20 years, with a maintenance cost of $500 per year and a salvage value of $10,000 at the end of 20 years. The estimated salvage value of the new bridge after 20 years of service is $15,000. The maintenance on the new bridge will be $100 per year. If the interest is 6 per cent, determine whether it is more economical to reinforce the old bridge or replace it. Use straight-line depreciation, plus average interest.

8-6. A lathe costs $10,000 now. It has a life expectancy of 20 years and an estimated salvage value of $2,000 at the end of 20 years.

At 7 per cent interest, what is the annual "capital-recovery-with-a-return" cost of the lathe on the basis of the above estimates? Use straight-line depreciation plus average interest in your calculations.

8-7. A company buys a machine for $12,000, which it agrees to pay in five equal annual payments, beginning 1 year after the date of purchase, at an interest rate of 4 per cent per annum. Immediately after the second payment, the terms of the agreement are changed to allow the balance due to be paid off in a single payment the next year.

a. What is the yearly payment for the first 2 years?

b. What is the final payment?

8-8. A manufacturing plant has been purchasing the energy required for plant operation. It is considering building a power plant to supply a load estimated at 1,000 kw (24 hr/day, 365 days per year). Purchased power will cost $0.023 per kwhr. The cost of the required plant is $1,000,000, and total operating expense including interest on investment is estimated at $95,000 per annum. Assuming 8 per cent sinking-fund depreciation, 15-year life, and zero scrap value, determine whether energy should be purchased or supplied by the new power plant.

8-9. A manufacturer is planning to produce a new line of products which will require the buying or renting of new machinery. A new machine will cost $17,000 and have an estimated value of $14,000 at the end of 5 years. Special tools for the new machine will cost $5,000 and have an estimated value of $2,500 at the end of 5 years. Maintenance costs for the machine and tools are estimated to be $200 per year. What will be the average annual cost of ownership during the next 5 years if interest is 6 per cent? Assume that the annual cost is equal to the straight-line depreciation, plus average interest.

8-10. How much would the owner of a building be justified in paying for a sprinkler system that will save $500 per year in insurance premiums? The system will have to be renewed every 20 years and has a salvage value of 10 per cent of its initial cost. Interest is at 5 per cent.

8-11. The owners of a concrete batching plant have in use a power steam shovel, which, if repaired at a cost of $2,000, would last another 10 years. Maintenance costs, operating costs, taxes, and insurance would be $2,500 per year. The present salvage value of the power steam shovel is $6,000; if it is repaired and used for 10 years, the estimated salvage value at the end of that time is estimated to be $500. A new power shovel could be purchased at a cost of $30,000, and its estimated salvage value at the end of 10 years would be $20,000. The maintenance costs, operating costs, taxes, and insurance would be $1,500 per year. If the interest rate is 6 per cent, determine whether it is more economical to repair and use the old steam shovel or to buy the new one. Use straight-line depreciation, plus average interest.

8-12. A debt of $10,000 with interest compounded annually at the rate of 4 per cent is to be paid in a lump sum at the end of 5 years. To create a fund with which to pay the debt, the debtor decides to deposit equal sums at the end of each 6 months with a savings association where the interest is compounded semiannually at an annual rate of 3 per cent. What should be the amount of the semiannual deposit?

8-13. The state will furnish an automobile to certain employees or will permit them to use their personal car and will pay 10 cents per mile. A car costs $2,350 and has a life of 5 years, with a trade-in value of $600; it costs $10 per month for incidentals, the cost of tires and repairs is $4 per month, and fuel and oil cost 2 cents per mile.

a. It is necessary for an employee to travel how many miles per year in order that the cost of the two methods be equal? Interest is computed at 6 per cent; depreciation is computed by the straight-line formula.

b. If the individual travels 10,000 miles per year, what will be the financial advantage or disadvantage?

Answers to Sample Problems

1-1. 0.5 radians/min, or 28.7°/min
1-2. $x = 0.526D$, $y = 0.850D$
1-3. 433 ft
1-4. $y = 2x^2 + x - 1$
1-5. 13 sq in./sec
1-6. $3y = 14x + 18$
1-7. $dr/dt = -0.1193$ in./sec
1-8. 40,100 sq ft
1-9. 44.4°
1-10. 8.58 gal
1-11. -1
1-12. *a.* 5.34 mph closing the gap
    b. 10.7 mph separating
    c. 1.30 hr, 20.0 miles apart
1-13. $wl/4 - w/6$
1-14. $\sin^{-1}(0.25l - 0.75) - 3.989$
    radians
1-15. *a.* $x = 8.12$, $y = 3.42$; and
    $x = -3.50$, $y = -4.34$;
    angle between line and tan-
    gents is 85.5°
    b. $2 \tan x$
1-16. 1,842 ft
1-17. $3y = 4x + 8$
1-18. *a.* slope = 0, -1
    b. $x = 4a$, $y = 2.67a + 1.25$,
    and $x = 0$, $y = \frac{5}{4}$
    c. $x = 4.83a$,
    $y = -2.27a + 1.25$, and
    $x = -0.83a$,
    $y = -0.393a + 1.25$
1-19. 453 cu units
1-20. 500 ft

1-21. *a.* 100 ft $\times$ 100 ft, and
    50 ft $\times$ 50 ft
    b. 10,000 sq ft, and 2,500 sq ft
1-23. $\pi/4$
1-24. $a/2(e^{x_{1/a}} - e^{-x_{1/a}})$
1-25. *a.* 45°
    b. 68.3 yd
1-26. 1.194 fpm
1-27. *a.* $x = 0$
    b. $x = -\pi/2$
1-28. 21.4 miles
1-31. *a.* $34x^2/15$
    b. $\frac{1}{16}y^8z^{12}$
    c. $1/(a + x)$
    d. $2.5^{1/6}$
    e. $x = 7$
1-32. 18.3°; 128.37°; 119.8 ft
1-33. 111.5°
1-34. 5.043
1-35. 1.605 hr
1-36. y increases as x increases, no
    maximum. y approaches infin-
    ity as x approaches infinity.
    $y_{min} = -10\frac{1}{3}$ at $x = \frac{1}{3}$
1-37. *b.* $y = -0.50x - 2.5$
    c. 18.75 sq units
1-38. $D = 23.4$ ft; $L = 23.3$ ft
1-39. 374 ft
1-40. $\frac{1}{2}$
1-41. $\frac{1}{2}$

2-1. 1.868 sec
2-2. 0.446 in.

2-3. 0

2-4. 500 lb, 300 lb (coefficient of friction, 0.50)

2-5. 5.44 lb/ft

2-6. 13.33 ft; 4,170 lb

2-7. 35 fps

2-8. 4.33 in.

2-9. 20.3 fps

2-10. *a.* 2 lb
  b. 2.67 lb

2-11. U_3U_4, 15,400 lb compression;
  U_4L_4, 13,330 lb tension

2-12. 4.73 ft

2-13. 0.795 radians/sec

2-14. AB, 618 lb compression
  AC, 425 lb tension
  AD, 816 lb tension

2-15. *a.* $v = t^3 - 6t^2 + 8t$;
  $a = 3t^2 - 12t + 8$
  b. At $t = 0.844$ sec
  c. $t = 2$ to $t = 4$ sec

2-16. 10.15 lb

2-17. *a.* 732 lb
  b. 250 lb
  c. 688 lb
  $R = 518$ lb

2-18. 0.530 ft; 126 mph

2-19. 15.7 hp

2-20. $\bar{x} = 3.45$ in.; $\bar{y} = 3.46$ in. from lower left corner

2-21. 6.4 in.

2-22. $CH = 1,020$ lb tension;
  $CD = 4,160$ lb compression

2-23. 56,500 lb

2-24. 3.52 fps

2-25. 56,600 ft high; 227,000 ft horizontally

2-26. *b.* 213.7 mph
  c. N7.6°W

2-27. *a.* 20,900 rpm
  b. 2,390,000 ft/sec²

2-28. $d = -(V_1 - V_2)^2/2a$

2-29. $v = (46.2e^{4t} + 32)/(1.445e^{4t} - 1)$

2-30. 19.7 lb

2-31. *a.* $\omega = 0.00117$ radians/sec
  b. 5.86×10^8 ft-lb

2-32. $AC = 840$ lb tension;
  $BC = 840$ lb tension;
  $CD = 2,500$ lb compression

2-33. $A_y = 96.4$ lb, $B_y = 103.6$ lb,
  $P = 82.2$ lb
  $A_x = 32.1$ lb, $B_x = 0$

2-34. *a.* 14.2 ft
  b. Maximum moment = 269,000 lb-ft at rear wheels

2-35. *a.* $v = 6.15$ fps
  b. $h = 369$ ft

2-36. $\mu = 0.433$

2-37. 1.74 in.

2-38. *a.* $F = W \tan \alpha$
  b. Vertical row, force $= F$
  horizontal row, force $= W$
  slanting row, force $= W/\cos \alpha = F/\sin \alpha$
  c. $\alpha = 5.7°$

2-39. *a.* $L_1U_2 = 2.23k$ compression
  b. $U_0U_1 = 5.98k$ compression

2-40. *a.* 11.48 ft
  b. $\theta = 50.4°$
  c. $F_x = 1,657$ lb
  d. $BN = 6.93$ ft

2-41. *a.* $T = 4,520$ lb
  b. $M = 75,000$ lb-ft

2-42. *a.* $\bar{x} = 5.84$ in., $\bar{y} = 2.00$ in.
  b. Required $I = 225.3$ in.⁴

2-43. *a.* $I_{x-x} = 1,551$ in.⁴
  b. $P = 8,620$ lb

2-44. $a = 16,500$ lb tension;
  $b = 10,000$ lb tension

2-45. $A = 20,000$ lb tension;
  $B = 30,000$ lb compression

2-46. *a.* $X = 2 \times$ weight of tractor
  b. $X = 0.966 \times$ weight of tractor

2-47. *a.* $A_x = -1.06P$;
  $B_x = -1.06P$
  $A_y = 0.353P$; $B_y = 0.353P$

b. $AE = 0$;
$AD = 0.707P$ tension;
$BF = 0,750P$ compression;
$BD = 0.350P$ compression

2-48. $P = (W/r) \sqrt{2rh - h^2}$;
$\alpha = \sin^{-1} (1/r) \sqrt{2rh - h^2}$

2-49. a. 3.22 fps
b. 1.93 ft from edge

2-50. 81.7 rpm

2-51. 5.7 in. up from base;
$I = 380$ in.^{4}

2-52. 4.25 in.

2-53. 47.4 mph, 13.5°

2-54. 17 fps; 25 ft-lb

2-55. 19.1 in.

2-56. a. 160 lb in 9-ft length, 120 lb
in 12-ft length
b. 124 lb in cable

2-57. 19.1 lb to right, 47.1° down
from horizontal; from lower left
corner, $x = 30.9$ in.,
$y = 2.77$ in.

2-58. $L_0U_2 = 11,440$ lb compression;
$L_0L_2 = 22,860$ lb tension;
$U_2U_4 = 20,000$ lb compression;
$U_2L_4 = 4,050$ lb compression

2-59. 5.5 revolutions

2-60. 379 ft

2-61. 25.0 psi

2-62. 2.67 ft to left and 4.0 ft below

2-63. 17.67 lb

2-64. 303 lb

2-65. a. 115.08 ft; $a = 7.5$ ft/sec^2 at
time $t = 2$ sec; at $t = 5$ sec,
$a = 9.2$ ft/sec^2, $v = 46$ fps

2-66. a. 322 lb
b. 0.0394 ft/ft

2-67. $I = 327$ in.^{4}

2-68. 140 lb

2-69. 3,500 fps

2-70. 635 fps

2-71. b. 20 in.

2-72. 13.0 fps to right, 15° down from
horizontal

2-73. 9,100 ft-lb

2-74. a. 2.73 lb/in.
b. 3.33 in.

2-75. a. 256 ft-lb
b. 240 ft-lb
c. 16 ft-lb

2-76. a. 16.1 ft/sec^2
b. 193.2 ft

2-77. 31.6 fps; 31,000 ft-lb

2-78. 1.90 sec; 5,220 ft-lb

2-79. a. 48.9 sec, 3,230 ft
b. 6,610 ft
c. 1 hr 56 min

2-80. It is not possible to lose 50 per
cent energy and retain momen-
tum. If 25 per cent of the
kinetic energy is lost, the velocities after impact would be 2.10
fps and 5.65 fps.

2-81. 10.18 ft

2-82. $v = 1.96 \sqrt{R - r}$

2-83. a. 15.1 fps
b. 13.55 in.

2-84. $v = 25.5$ fps to right at angle of
45° up from horizontal;
$a = 134$ ft/sec^2 to right, 10.3°
above horizontal

2-85. a. 0.875 fpm
b. 11.8 min from start of movement

2-86. 9.85 in.

2-87. $F_1 = 4$ lb; $F_2 = 117.6$ lb

2-88. $b/c = 2.13$

2-89. a. 6.44 ft/sec^2
b. 9.84 fps
c. 153 lb-sec
d. 600 lb

2-90. a. 40.4 lb
b. 63.2°
c. 44.8 lb

2-91. The given distances are not
compatible. If $ae = 21$, then

$ef = 10.5$ and $af = 31.5$, from the geometry of the figure.

   a. 16,000 lb tension

   b. 16,000 lb compression

   c. 8,000 lb tension

3-1. 561 lb

3-2. 40.7 fps

3-3. 40,400 gal/hr

3-4. 0.66 sp gr

3-5. 7.13 ft

3-6. *a.* 250 psig

   b. 3.47 cfs

3-7. With the figures given, the suction pressure is calculated to be -316 psig, which is impossible. If the flow rate is taken as 60 gpm, the suction pressure is -7.92 psig.

3-8. 41.6 ft

3-9. 9.54 ft from the toe

3-10. 361.9 hp

3-11. 231 gpm

3-12. 18,750 lb

3-13. *a.* 99.1 ft

   b. 67.5 ft

   c. 39 gpm

   d. 78.0 per cent

3-14. *a.* 13.5 ft from toe

   b. 5,250 psf at toe, 2,850 psf at heel

   c. 19.8 ft from toe

   d. Yes

3-15. 87.0 lb

3-16. Problem not solvable with data given. If 10.5 psig changed to 8.0 psig, the discharge would be 335 gpm.

3-17. *a.* 4.11 kw

   b. 5.20 hp

   c. 2.72 hp

   d. 52.4 per cent

3-18. 51,400 lb to right, 60° down from horizontal, if flow is to right

3-19. *a.* $x = 2.11$ ft

   b. $F = 12,000$ lb

3-20. 275 cfs

3-21. *a.* 1,180 lb force

   b. 56.4 hp

3-22. *a.* 1.96 ft

   b. 590 cfs

3-23. 608 lb lift

3-24. 875 lb

3-25. *a.* 6.9 cm

   b. Above

3-26. 1.37 cfs

3-27. *a.* 147.5 ft

   b. 137.5 ft

   c. 10 ft

3-28. *a.* 7,660 lb force

   b. 0.187 in. below horizontal center line

3-29. 3.25 ft

3-30. 6.50 min

3-31. 790 psig (assuming $f = 0.017$)

3-32. 194 ft/1,000 ft

3-33. *a.* 3.82 fps

   b. 42.2 per cent efficiency

   c. 0.0299

3-34. 28.2 lb/ft

3-35. 3,210 centipoises

3-36. Assuming free discharge at 3 and taking $p_3 = 0$,

   $p_1 = 43.7$ psig, $v_1 = 46.6$ fps

   $p_2 = 10.7$ psig, $v_2 = 62.1$ fps

   $p_3 = 0$, $v_3 = 93.2$ fps

3-37. Schedule 40 ¾-in. pipe

3-38. *a.* 5 cm

   b. 4,900 dynes/sq cm

3-39. 42 min, assuming a discharge coefficient of 0.60

3-40. 115.7 psig; 102.5 hp

3-41. *a.* 16.0 fps

   b. 2.40 fps

3-42. 40 psi

3-43. 32.9 g

3-44. 1.8 ft

3-45. 6.54 ft

3-46. 0.166b

3-47. 16.9 cu cm

3-48. *a.* 77.2 lb to right, 85.9° down
from horizontal
  b. 870 lb to right, 32.1° down
from horizontal
  c. 916 lb to right, 36.0° down
from horizontal

3-49. −290 psf at upstream edge of
base (in tension)

3-50. 3,540 lb

3-51. 17.8 psi

3-52. 53.4 cfs through 24-in. diameter
line
6.6 cfs through 12-in. diameter
line

3-53. *a.* 1.385 cfs
  b. 4.46 psi

4-1. *a.* 28.5 per cent
  b. 125.4°F
  c. 494 hp
  d. 548,000

4-2. *a.* 53.4 cu ft
  b. 60°F
  c. −266,000 ft-lb
  d. zero

4-3. 120 lb

4-4. 1.018 cu ft

4-5. 1106 Btu

4-6. *a.* U = 0.356 Btu/
(hr)(sq ft)(°F)
  b. Brick face h = 2.85 Btu/
(hr)(sq ft)(°F); concrete face
h = 1.815 Btu/
(hr)(sq ft)(°F)

4-7. 54 cents

4-8. 42,300 ft-lb

4-9. Partial pressures:
N_2 = 14.0 psia, CO_2 = 4.0 psia,
CO = 2.0 psia
Weight analysis: N_2 = 62.8 per
cent, CO_2 = 28.2 per cent,
CO = 9.0 per cent

4-10. 1.13 × 10⁸ kwhr

4-11. 300 hp

4-12. *a.* 59 grains/lb dry air
  b. 31.9 per cent
  c. 51.7°F

4-13. *a.* (Assuming 20 psig) 1270°F,
1,965 psig
  b. 7,800 ft-lb

4-14. *a.* 10.6 lb
  b. 128 cu ft

4-15. 151.3 hp

4-16. 7.05 in.

4-17. 0.179 in./hr

4-18. 54 g of ice; 8 g of steam

4-19. 334 hp

4-20. *a.* n = 1.25
  b. 345,600 ft-lb
  c. 172 Btu added to gas

4-21. *b.* State 2: p = 1.069p_1,
V = V_1, T = 1.069T_1
State 3: p = 0.848p_1,
V = 1.18V_1, T = T_1
State 4: p = p_1, V = V_1,
T = T_1
  c. 1,265 joules
  d. 72 liters

4-22. 4.95 qt

4-23. 88.6 per cent quality

4-24. 7.83 Btu/(mole)(°R)

4-25. 2,215 lb

4-26. 6.46 cu ft/cu ft

4-27. 119.7 hp

4-28. 0.344 Btu/(lb)(°F)

4-29. *a.* 636,000 Btu/hr supplied;
382,000 Btu/hr rejected
  b. 40 per cent

4-30. 282.4 knots

4-31. 75.62 cm

4-32. *b.* 780 cal added.   No change
in internal energy over a complete cycle.

4-33. *a.* 134.63 psia; 29.6 per cent
  b. 47.21 psia; 100 per cent
4-34. 76.3 Btu (nonflow process)
4-35. $t = 363.13°F$; $v = 5.696$ cu ft;
  $h = 1195.0$ Btu/lb;
  $s = 1.5646$ Btu/(lb)(°F);
  $u = 1111.1$ Btu/lb
4-36. $DB = 81°F$; $WB = 60°F$;
  52 per cent relative humidity
4-37. 3,000 lb/hr
4-38. bmep = 236 psi;
  brake torque = 123 lb-ft;
  brake thermal efficiency = 23
  per cent;
  efficiency based on cold-air
  standard = 40.7 per cent
4-39. 92.9 psi
4-40. 388 psia; 1110°F
4-41. *a.* 9,480 cfm
  b. isothermal, lower; adiabatic,
  higher
4-42. *a.* 67.2 Btu/sec
  b. 0.0163 cfs
4-43. *a.* 234 Btu/lb
  b. Efficiency = (usable work
  out of turbine)/(heat added
  in combuster)
4-44. 176 Btu
4-45. *a.* 58°F
  b. 10.025 Btu
4-46. *a.* −46°F
  b. −127.7 Btu
  c. 59,400 ft-lb
  d. 0.1036 Btu/°F
  e. 51.2 Btu given off
4-47. *a.* 24.5 per cent
  b. 0.479
  c. 0.545 lb/hp-hr
4-48. *a.* 174.8 psig
  b. 48.5 per cent methane
  51.5 per cent ethane
4-49. $x = 98.83$ per cent
4-50. 1106°F; 420 psia
4-51. $U = 0.836$ Btu/(sq ft)(hr)(°F)
4-52. 12 lb

4-53. *a.* 57 grains/lb
  b. 51.5°F
  c. 30 per cent relative humidity
4-54. 8.05 per cent
4-55. 187°F
4-56. *a.* 2,680 lb thrust
  b. 3,300 hp
  c. 13 per cent
4-57. 2.11 per cent
4-58. 21.4 cu ft
4-59. *a.* 2,510 fps
  b. 1,955 fps
4-60. *a.* 6.50 per cent hydrogen,
  93.50 per cent carbon
  (assuming complete com-
  bustion)
  b. 48.2 per cent
  c. 255 cu ft
4-61. 12 cu ft (assuming 45 psig)
4-62. *a.* 11.15 Btu
  b. 9.54 Btu
  c. 14.7 per cent
  d. 62 per cent
4-63. *a.* 82.2 lb/min
  b. 0.028 Btu/(lb)(°F)
4-64. *a.* 3.79
  b. 131 Btu/lb
  c. 497 Btu/lb
  d. 12.1 lb/min
  e. 1.24 hp/ton
  f. 498 lb/min
4-65. 0.192 cu ft

5-1. 261,000 lb-in.
5-2. $\dfrac{dy}{dx} = \dfrac{w}{EI} - \left(\dfrac{Lx^2}{4} - \dfrac{x^3}{6} - \dfrac{L^3}{24}\right)$
5-3. *a.* Each copper wire holds
  266 lb, steel wire 468 lb.
  b. 119.6°F
5-4. 50,000 psi
5-5. (Maximum shear stress)/
  (average shear stress) = $3\frac{1}{2}$.
  (See Fig. 5-P-105.)
5-6. *b.* $M_{max} = 363,000$ lb-in., 14 ft
  (See Fig. 5-P-106.)

FIG. 5-P-105

FIG. 5-P-111

5-12. *a.* 225 in.-lb
  b. 40 lb
5-13. *a.* See Fig. 5-P-113
  b. 0.96 cu in.

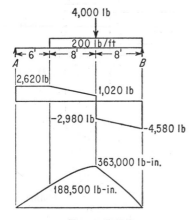

FIG. 5-P-106

5-7. 68,000 psi (disregarding stress
  due to deceleration of cable
  $E = 16 \times 10^6$ psi
5-8. 7.28 in.
5-9. *a.* 0.00216P
  b. 2.25P
5-10. 394,000 lb load permissible
5-11. See Fig. 5-P-111.

FIG. 5-P-113

Fig. 5-P-114

Fig. 5-P-120

5-14. Maximum shear $= -12,000$ lb; maximum moment $= -90,000$ lb-ft; both located 10.0 ft from left end of beam (see also Fig. 5-P-114)

5-15. $M_{max} = 10,230$ lb-ft at point 3.25 ft from left end; $S_{max} = -5,400$ lb

5-16. $M_{max} = 288,000$ lb-ft, $M_{min} = 192,000$ lb-ft; $S_{max} = 26,000$ lb, $S_{min} = 20,000$ lb

5-17. 2,000.778 ft

5-18. Use $2\frac{3}{4}$-in.-diameter shaft

5-19. 549 lb cement, 1,296 lb sand, 1,894 lb aggregate, 292 lb water

5-20. $M_{max} = 39,000$ ft-lb; 11.43 ft from left end.   (See also Fig. 5-P-120.)

5-21. 5,440 lb/ft

5-22. 8,400 psi shear stress and 12,600 psi crushing stress

5-23. 9,870 lb shear; 11,200 lb-ft bending moment

Fig. 5-P-124

5-24. See Fig. 5-P-124.
   c. 13,500 psi

5-25. 11 ft from left end of beam; 188,000 lb-ft

5-26. $-58°$F

5-27. See Fig. 5-P-127.

5-28. The deflections are approximately equal at $2.66 \times 10^{-4} \times F$.

5-29. Steel, 200 lb; copper, 100 lb

1,110 lb

4.69'

9,050 lb   −3,890 lb

FIG. 5-P-127

5-30. 7,500 psi
5-31. *a.* 750 psi
      b. 500 psi
5-32. 8,020 psi; 0.895°
5-33. 18,700 psi
5-34. *a.* No, 93.8 psi shear hori-
           zontally
      b. No, it is 1,685 psi bending
5-35. *a.* 2.34 in.
      b. Small shaft twist = 1.71 ×
           large shaft twist

6-1. *a.* 13,200 volts
     b. 112 watts
6-2. 10.4 ohms
6-3. 0.35
6-4. 15 ohm, 1.35 amp; 25 ohm,
     0.811 amp; 60 ohm, 1.66 amp;
     200 ohm, 0.50 amp
6-5. *a.* 4.0 amp
     b. 89.4 per cent
     c. 14.1 hp
6-6. Voltages equal at 53.3 volts
     Q_1 = 320 μcoulombs,
     Q_2 = 640 μcoulombs
6-7. *a.* 10.67 ohms
     b. 14.67 ohms

c. 0.728
d. 43.3°
e. current lags
f. 10.05 ohms
g. Inductive
6-8. 104.4 volts
6-9. 656 μf
6-10. 21.7 kvar
6-11. *a.* 245 amp
      b. 795 kvar
6-12. 45.3 watts
6-13. Open, V_L = 89.7 volts,
      V_{R_1} = 25.6 volts,
      V_{R_3} = 67.2 volts;
      closed, V_L = 83.8 volts,
      $V_{R_1} = V_{R_3}$ = 49.5 volts
6-14. *a.* 39.6 ohms
      b. 2.78 amp
      c. 72.3°
      d. 0.303
      e. 92.7 watts
6-15. *a.* 14,040 volts
      b. 14,800 volts
      c. 12,900 volts
6-16. 0.455 amp
6-17. 0.002 coulomb, 1.0 joule,
      20,000 volts/meter; 250 volts,
      0.250 joule
6-18. I_1 = 15.65 amp;
      I_2 = 7.5 amp; I_3 = 12.25 amp
6-19. *a.* 52.5 volts
      b. 63.475 volts
      c. 21.9 per cent
6-20. 1.0 volt; 2.5 ohms
6-21. *a.* 886 watts
      b. 0.943 leading
6-22. *a.* 0.192 volts per conductor
      b. E_avg = 0.637 E_max
          E_rms = 0.707 E_max
          for sine-wave voltages
6-23. *a.* Inductive reactance is
          greater.
      b. 24.0 amp

FIG. 6-P-131

Assuming drop of 150 volts across lamp

FIG. 6-P-133

6-24. *a.* 4.48 ohms
   b. 85.8 per cent
   c. 3,670 watts
6-25. 125 volts; 100 volts
6-26. *a.* 30.3 ohms
   b. 0.031 amp
   c. 0.089 amp
6-27. 257-kva transformers; 290 hp
   at 93 per cent efficiency and
   90 per cent power factor
6-28. *a.* 604 coulombs
   b. 120.8 amp
   c. 129.6 amp
6-29. $(\frac{5}{6})R$
6-30. 1.5 amp through 9-volt battery;
   0.5 amp through 6.5-volt battery
6-31. *a.* See Fig. 6-P-131.
   b. 118.15 kvar capacitance
6-32. *a.* 2,000 kw
   b. Same
6-33. *a.* 244 volts
   b. 0.606 lagging
   c. See Fig. 6-P-133.
6-34. $I_1 = 3.23$ amp, $I_2 = 3.66$ amp,
   $I_3 = 0.43$ amp
6-35. 20 amp
6-36. *a.* 25.4 ohms
   b. 61.7 volts

   c. 309 watts
   d. 0.786
6-37. 1.705 amp
6-38. *a.* 31 per cent full-load torque
   b. 196.6 volts
6-39. 14.2 ohms
6-40. 9.9 hp
6-41. *a.* 18 amp
   b. 13.7 amp at 39.8° lagging
6-42. 0.106 henry
6-43. *a.* 50 amp
   b. 5 volts
   c. 250 watts
   d. 25 amp
6-44. *a.* 1,746 rpm
   b. 602 lb-ft
   c. 253 amp
6-45. *a.* 2.13 volts
   b. 19.36 amp
6-46. 10 volts
6-47. *a.* See Fig. 6-P-147.
   b. 1,440.5 kw

FIG. 6-P-147

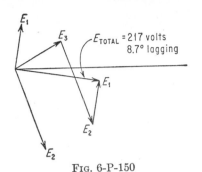

FIG. 6-P-150

6-48. 1,227 rpm (assuming full-load armature current of 58 amp)

6-49. 55 kva

6-50. *a.* 217 volts at 8.7° lagging
    b. See Fig. 6-P-150.

6-51. *a.* 53.4 amp
    b. 15.35 amp
    c. 3.68 kva
    d. 1.06 kw

6-52. *a.* 200 watts
    b. 141.4 volts
    c. 127.2 volts
    d. 1.11

6-53. 125.25 volts

6-54. 10 ohms, 2.21 amp; 30 ohms, 0.73 amp; 50 ohms, 1.96 amp; 100 ohms, 0.98 amp

6-55. 0.944

6-56. *a.* 55 volts
    b. 0.11 amp
    c. 0.055 amp

7-1. 93.2 per cent silver

7-2. *a.* $Ca_3(PO_4)_2 + 3SiO_2 + 5C \rightarrow 3CaSiO_3 + 2P + 5CO$
    b. 5.0

7-3. 2.48 lb

7-4. 50 per cent, $P_{N_2O_4} = 127$ mm, $P_{NO_2} = 253$ mm

7-5. *a.* 8.33 lb
    b. 5.83 lb

7-6. *a.* $Q_1 = 8.62$ gpm, $Q_2 = 41.38$ gpm
    b. 8.62 Btu/(gal)(°F)

7-7. 89.4 cu ft dry air

7-8. *a.* 1,082 lb
    b. 35,000 cu ft

7-9. 41.5 g

7-10. 5,460 lb

7-12. *a.* $3Ag + 4HNO_3 \rightarrow 3AgNO_3 + NO + 2H_2O$
    b. 88.7 lb

7-13. 1,990 g

7-14. 382 lb MgO; 8,160 cu ft

7-15. 0.0373 g of hydrogen

7-16. *a.* $C_3H_8 + 5O_2 \rightarrow 3CO_2 + 4H_2O$
    b. 250,000 cu ft

7-17. 51 tons

7-18. *a.* $Ca(HCO_3)_2 \rightarrow CaCO_3\downarrow + H_2CO_3$
    $\hookrightarrow H_2O + CO_2\uparrow$
    b. $Ca(HCO_3)_2 + Ca(OH)_2 \rightarrow 2CaCO_3\downarrow + 2H_2O$

7-19. *a.* 18.70 per cent CO_2, 0.28 per cent H_2, 2.82 per cent CH_4, 22.80 per cent CO, 55.40 per cent N_2
    b. $(CO_2) + H_2 + CH_4 + CO + (N_2) + 3O_2 \rightarrow 3H_2O + 2CO_2 + (N_2) + (CO_2)$
    c. 1.10 cu ft/cu ft

7-20. 60 per cent FeS, 18.1 per cent S, 21.9 per cent Fe

7-21. 10.6 per cent SO_2, 82.1 per cent N_2, 7.3 per cent O_2

7-22. *a.* 651 mm Hg
    b. 46.1 per cent

7-23. $Ca_3(PO_4)_2 + 3SiO_2 + 5C \rightarrow 3CaSiO_3 + 2P + 5CO$

7-24. *a.* 0.457 lb
    b. 1.235 lb $CaCO_3$, 0.222 lb H_2O

7-25. *a.* $2C_8H_{18} + 25O_2 \rightarrow 16CO_2 + 18H_2O$
    b. 3.51 lb O_2, 3.09 lb CO_2, 1.42 lb H_2O

7-26. *a.* 606 lb
    b. 3,060 cu ft
7-27. 19.8 per cent CO_2, 18.2 per cent H_2O, 62.0 per cent N_2
7-28. *a.* 9.60 lb air
    b. 10.490 lb flue gas (excluding ash) per lb fuel
    c. 17.1 per cent by volume
7-29. $CuO + H_2 \rightarrow Cu + H_2O$;
    7.98 g Cu, 2.27 g H_2O

8-1. 10 years, 2 months
8-2. *a.* $185,600
    b. $9,460
8-3. *a.* $3,770
    b. $16,000
    c. $9,000

8-4. *a.* $760
    b. $846
8-5. Reinforce old bridge. $2,078 per year vs. $3,038 per year
8-6. $834
8-7. *a.* $2,700
    b. $7,780
8-8. Purchased, $201,000 per year; power plant $131,900 per year
8-9. $2,490
8-10. $6,480
8-11. Repair old shovel; $3,528 vs. $4,030
8-12. $1,135
8-13. *a.* 7,720 miles
    b. $183 advantage to driving own car

Index

Page numbers in italics signify numerical examples